# MEDICAL
# EMBRYOLOGY

# MEDICAL EMBRYOLOGY

*Human Development—Normal and Abnormal*

## JAN LANGMAN, M.D., Ph.D.

Professor of Anatomy, University of Virginia, Charlottesville
(Formerly Professor of Anatomy, McGill University, Montreal)

Illustrations by JILL LELAND

SECOND EDITION

*The Williams & Wilkins Company* BALTIMORE 1969

Copyright ©, 1969
The Williams & Wilkins Company
428 E. Preston Street
Baltimore, Maryland 21202 U.S.A.

First edition
    Published: 1963
    Reprinted: February 1964; May 1964; July, 1965; September 1966; July 1967
    Spanish edition—1963
    French edition—1965
    Dutch edition—1966
    Portuguese edition—1966
    Italian edition—1967
    Japanese edition—1967
    Persian edition—in preparation
    Asian (English) edition—1966
    Indian (English) edition—1966
    Korean student edition—1966

Second edition
    Published: 1969
    Dutch edition—in preparation
    German edition—in preparation
    Asian (English) edition—1969
    Indian (English) edition—1969

*Made in the United States of America*

Library of Congress Catalog Card Number 69–16599

COVER ILLUSTRATION—"La Main de Dieu" (The Hand of God), by August Rodin, 1897. The hand is shaping a mass of formless matter, from which, as from a womb, emerge the bodies of Man and Woman. *Reproduced, with the permission of The Philadelphia Museum of Art, from a charcoal sketch of the bronze in its Rodin Museum.*

Composed and printed at the
Waverly Press, Inc.
Mt. Royal and Guilford Avenues
Baltimore, Maryland 21202 U.S.A.

To my wife
INA
in appreciation of her great support during
the writing of this book

# Preface to the Second Edition

The general acceptance of the first edition of *Medical Embryology* and the many foreign translations which have appeared since the original printing of the English text seem to indicate that the book fills a need among students preparing themselves for the medical profession. The concept of the new edition, therefore, has not been changed, although each chapter has been revised to a greater or lesser extent and has been brought up to date.

Realizing that a new edition usually means adding an extra hundred pages to the original text, I have tried to keep this edition as concise and short as the first one. Unfortunately, I have not been quite successful, mainly because a chapter on experimental embryology was added. I believe, however, that many students will enjoy and become fascinated by reading about the experiments undertaken to obtain an insight into the factors which regulate normal development.

Miss Jill Leland, who made the excellent drawings of the first edition, also made the great majority of the illustrations of the second edition. Many new drawings have been added, while others have been improved. I wish to express my sincere thanks to her for the great contribution she made to the success of this book.

I also wish to thank the many colleagues who wrote to me from all over the world. Many of their fine suggestions for improvement of the text and illustrations have been incorporated in this new edition.

# Preface to the First Edition

Recent advances in embryology, radioautography, and electron microscopy have been so overwhelming that the medical student often has difficulty in grasping the basic facts of development from the highly complicated picture presented to him. The aim of this book, therefore, is to give the future doctor a concise, well illustrated presentation of the essential facts of human development, clarifying the gross anatomical features without omitting the recent advances or changing concepts in the basic sciences. Furthermore, since embryology has become of great practical value because of the enormous progress made in surgery and teratology, each chapter on the development of the organ systems has been complemented by a description of those malformations important to the student in his further training. As a further reflection of the increased clinical importance of embryology an entire chapter has been devoted to the etiology of congenital defects.

Of the many colleagues who have been of help in the writing of this book, I particularly wish to thank Dr. C. P. Leblond for his continuous interest and encouragement; Dr. F. Clarke Fraser, for his help in discussing the various aspects of the congenital malformations; and my friends, Dr. Harry Maisel, Dr. Robert van Mierop, and Dr. Yves Clermont, who have spared no effort in assisting with the design of the drawings and the checking of the text.

I wish to express my sincere thanks to Miss Jill Leland, who prepared all the illustrations in this book, and to Mrs. E. Dawson, who has been of such excellent support to me in setting up the manuscript.

# Contents

PART ONE  GENERAL EMBRYOLOGY

1. **Gametogenesis** ........................................... 3
2. **Ovulation To Implantation** ........................ 23
   *First week of development*
3. **Formation Of The Bilaminar Germ Disc** ........... 37
   *Second week of development*
4. **Formation Of The Trilaminar Germ Disc** .......... 46
   *Third week of development*
5. **Differentiation Of The Germ Layers And Establish-
   ment Of Body Form** ............................... 54
   *Fourth to eighth weeks of development*
6. **Development Of The Fetus, Fetal Membranes, And
   Placenta** ......................................... 69
   *Third to tenth months of development*
7. **Congenital Malformations And Their Causes** ...... 84
8. **Experimental Embryology** ...................... 107

PART TWO  SPECIAL EMBRYOLOGY

9. **Skeletal System** ................................. 129
10. **Muscular System** ............................... 141
11. **Urogenital System** ............................. 148
    *Urinary system; genital system*
12. **Cardiovascular System** ......................... 183
    *Normal development of the heart; abnormal devel-
    opment of the heart; arterial system; venous system;
    circulatory changes at birth*

13. **Digestive Tube And Its Derivatives** ................ 237
    *Pharyngeal gut; caudal part of the foregut; midgut; hindgut*
14. **Coelomic Cavity And Mesenteries** ................ 276
15. **Central Nervous System** ........................ 290
    *Spinal cord; brain; autonomic nervous system*
16. **Eye** ............................................. 333
17. **Ear** ............................................. 343
18. **Face, Nose, And Palate** ........................ 354
19. **Integumentary System** ........................ 364
    **Index**

PART I

# GENERAL EMBRYOLOGY

# CHAPTER 1

# Gametogenesis

CHROMOSOMAL CHANGES DURING GERM CELL
MATURATION
- **DNA-DUPLICATION AND MITOSIS**
- **FIRST MIOTIC DIVISION**: *leptotene, zygotene, pachytene and diplotene stages; chiasma formation*
- **SECOND MIOTIC DIVISION**
- **ABNORMAL MIOTIC DIVISIONS**: *trisomy; monosomy; nondisjunction*

MORPHOLOGICAL CHANGES DURING GERM CELL
MATURATION
- **APPEARANCE AND MIGRATION OF PRIMORDIAL GERM CELLS**
- **OOGENESIS**: *oogonium; primary oocyte; secondary oocyte and polar body; primordial follicle; mature follicle; mature oocyte*
- **SPERMATOGENESIS**: *spermatogonium; primary spermatocyte; secondary spermatocyte; spermatid*
- **SPERMIOGENESIS**: *acrosomic head cap; middle piece, body and tail*
- **ABNORMAL GAMETES**: *multinucleated oocytes; abnormal spermatozoa*

The development of a human being begins with fertilization, a process by which two highly specialized cells, the *spermatozoon* from the male and the *oocyte* from the female, unite to give rise to a new organism, the *zygote*. In preparation for possible fertilization, both male and female germ cells undergo a number of changes involving the chromosomes as well as the cytoplasm. The purpose of these changes is twofold:

1. To reduce the number of chromosomes to half that in the normal somatic cell, *i.e.*, from 46 to 23. This is accomplished by two specialized divisions, known as *miotic* or *maturation* divisions. The reduction in the number of chromosomes is necessary, since otherwise fusion of a male and a female germ cell would result in an individual with twice the number of chromosomes of the parent cells.

2. To alter the shape of the germ cells in preparation for fertilization. The male germ cell, initially large and round, loses practically all of its cytoplasm and develops a head, neck and tail. The female germ cell, on the contrary, gradually becomes larger as the result of an increase in the amount of cytoplasm. At maturity the oocyte has a diameter of about 120 $\mu$.

Although the reduction in the number of chromosomes as well as the cytoplasmic changes are integral parts of the germ cell maturation, each process is discussed separately in the following paragraphs.

# *Chromosomal Changes During Germ Cell Maturation*

As a result of improved tissue culture techniques, it is now firmly established that the human somatic cell contains 46 chromosomes.[1-4] Forty-four of these are *autosomes* and two are *sex chromosomes*. In the female the latter are represented by two X-chromosomes; in the male by one X- and a much shorter Y-chromosome. Each autosome has among the other chromosomes a partner with the same morphological characteristics. Together they form the members of a *homologous pair*. Although the X- and Y-chromosomes in the male are not morphologically identical, the human somatic cell is said to contain 23 pairs, or a *diploid* (diploos—double) number of chromosomes. One chromosome of each pair is originally derived from the mother and the other from the father.

In 1960 the chromosomes were classified according to their total length, the position of the centromere, and the length of the arms on each side of the centromere (fig. 1-1*A*, *B*).[5, 6] When arranged in this manner, the X-chromosome resembles the autosomes of the 6–12 group, while the much smaller Y-chromosome resembles more closely those of the 21-22 group. Although the classification and arrangement in pairs is a convenient method for comparing chromosomal patterns, it must be realized that the members of a homologous pair are generally not in close proximity to each other either in the resting cell or during mitosis.

### DNA-Duplication and Mitosis

In a normal, non-dividing cell, the chromosomes are extremely long, diffusely spread out, and not recognizable with the light microscope. Just before mitosis begins, each chromosome duplicates its chemical components, among which the double-stranded DNA molecule is most important.[7] By assuming that chromosome duplication in man as in the bacterium E. coli is comparable with DNA

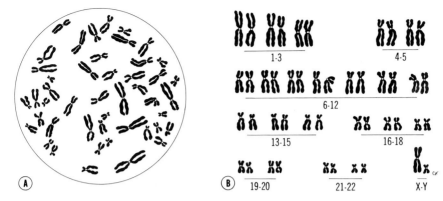

Figure 1-1. *A, Karyotype of a normal human cell. Chromosomal spreads are obtained by culturing cells in an artificial medium and subsequently exposing them to a colchicine solution to arrest the mitoses in the metaphase. After a brief treatment with a hypotonic salt solution, the cells are fixed, spread on a slide, stained and photographed. B, Diagrammatic representation (idiogram) of the chromosomes seen in A. The chromosomes are arranged and classified according to the Denver system.*

duplication, the events occurring during mitosis and miosis can be more easily explained and understood.[8]

The DNA molecule consists of a complementary pair of helices, linked together through side chains of purine and pyrimidine groups (fig. 1-2*A, B*). The duplication mechanism, postulated by Watson and Crick, involves the unzipping of the side chains and the production of two new strands by a template mechanism (fig. 1-2*C*).[9] The result of the replication is the formation of two identical DNA helices (fig. 1-2*C*). Hence, before a cell enters mitosis, each chromosome doubles its amount of DNA and each chromosome in fact has doubled (fig. 1-2*D, E*). The doubling of the chromosomes, however, cannot be observed until the prometaphase stage.

With the onset of mitosis, the chromosomes undergo coiling, contract and condense.[10] At *prophase* they are visible with the light microscope as slender threads, but the two paired subunits (*chromatids*) cannot yet be recognized as individual units (fig. 1-3*A*). During *prometaphase* the chromosomes form compact rods and the two chromatids become distinguishable (fig. 1-3*B, C*). During metaphase the chromosomes line up in the *equatorial plane* (fig. 1-3*D*). Soon afterwards, each chromosome undergoes a longitudinal division of the centromere and separates into two daughter chromosomes which migrate to opposite poles of the cell (fig. 1-3*E, F*). Each daughter cell receives one half of all the doubled chromosome material, and thus maintains the same number of chromosomes as the mother cell. Such a division is a typical *mitotic division*.

Gametogenesis

5

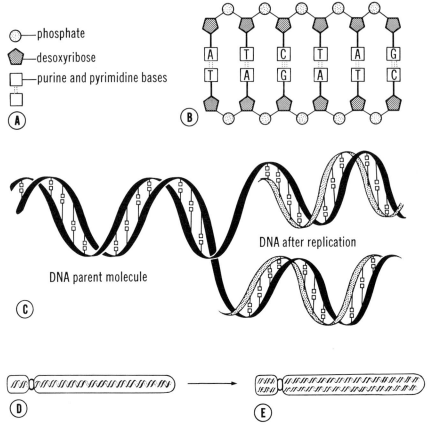

○—phosphate
⬠—desoxyribose
☐—purine and pyrimidine bases
☐

**A**

**B**

A T C T A G
T A G A T C

**C**

DNA after replication

DNA parent molecule

**D** ⟶ **E**

Figure 1-2. *A, Components essential for the synthesis of desoxyribonucleic acid (DNA): phosphate, desoxyribose and bases consisting of purines (adenine and guanine) and pyrimidines (thymine and cytosine). B, Schematic representation of the DNA molecule. Two polynucleotides are linked through base side chains in such a manner that adenine (A) links with thymine (T), and guanine (G) with cytosine (C). C, Diagram representing the replication of the DNA molecule. On the left is the parent molecule with the complementary helices linked through the base side chains; the right side shows the replication of the helices. After the hydrogen bonds between the base groups have opened, two new DNA strands are synthesized. The new strands have a complementary base composition with respect to the parent DNA strands. D and E, Schematic representation of a chromosome before and after DNA replication.*

**First Miotic Division**

The primitive germ cells undergo two special divisions, the *maturation* or *miotic divisions*, by which the number of chromosomes is reduced to half the normal number. The daughter cells contain 23 chromosomes, that is, the *haploid* (haploos—single) number.

General Embryology

Just before the first miotic division begins, the female as well as the male primitive germ cells (primary oocyte and primary spermatocyte) replicate their DNA in precisely the same manner as described for mitosis.[11] Hence, at the beginning of the division, the cells contain double the normal amount of DNA and each chromosome is a double structure.

The prophase of the first miotic division is considerably extended in comparison with that of mitosis and is subdivided into a number of stages. In the first or *leptotene stage*, the 46 chromosomes shorten by coiling and appear as single, slender threads (fig. 1-4A). The first fundamental difference between mitosis and miosis is observed in the second or *zygotene stage*. The homologous chromosomes, which in mitosis remain entirely separated, approach each other and begin to pair (fig. 1-4B). The pairing is exact and point for point, except for the X-Y combination, where this process is not well understood.[12] The centromere regions of the homologous chromosomes do not pair. As a result of the intimate pairing, the number of visible chromosomes is 23. Each pair forms a so-called *bivalent*. Since each individual chromosome contains two chromatids, the bivalent contains four chromatids (fig. 1-4C).

In the third, or *pachytene stage*, the chromosomes contract longitudinally, resulting in the appearance of shorter and thicker threads

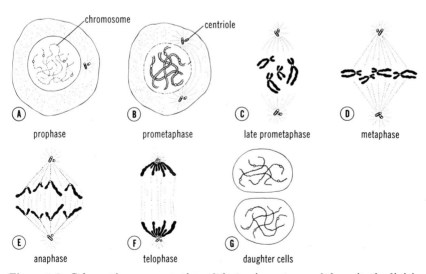

Figure 1-3. *Schematic representation of the various stages of the mitotic division. Note that in the prophase the chromosomes are visible as slender threads and that the paired chromatids cannot be recognized as individual units. In the prometaphase, however, the paired chromatids are clearly visible.*

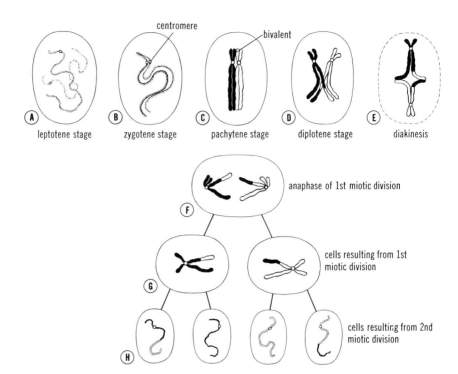

Figure 1-4. *Schematic representation showing the fate of two homologous chromosomes during the first and second miotic divisions. A, The chromosomes appear as individual, slender threads. B, In the zygotene stage the homologous chromosomes approach each other and begin to pair. Note that each chromosome consists of two chromatids. C, The homologous chromosomes are intimately paired and form a so-called bivalent. At this stage a longitudinal separation begins to appear in each member of the homologous pair. D, The intimately paired homologous chromosomes begin to separate. Note the chiasma. E, Diakinesis; note the exchange of chromosomal material. F, Anaphase of the first miotic division, in which each of the double-stranded homologous chromosomes moves to an opposite pole of the cell. G and H, During the second miotic division the double-stranded chromosomes split at the centromere. At completion of the division the chromosomes in each of the four daughter cells are different from each other.*

(fig. 1-4*C*). In the end of this stage a longitudinal separation becomes apparent in each member of the homologous pair. The centromeres, however, remain intact and do not split. During the longitudinal separation, one or more transverse breaks occur in the chromosomal strands and an interchange of chromatid segments between two homologous chromosomes occurs. In the next or *diplotene stage*, the intimately paired homologous chromosomes begin to separate, except for the points of interchange which temporarily remain united. The diplotene structure has then an X appearance, known as a *chiasma* (fig. 1-4*D*).[13, 14] The chiasma is the morphological expression of a genetic phenomenon, known as *crossing over*, during which blocks of genes are exchanged between homologous chromosomes. In the meantime the separation continues into *diakenesis*, a stage at which the coiled, and partially separated, chromosomes are clearly distinguishable (fig. 1-4*E*). In the metaphase the two members of each pair are oriented on the spindle, and in subsequent stages the members migrate to the opposite poles of the cell (fig. 1-4*F*).

After the first miotic division has been completed, each daughter cell contains one member of each chromosome pair (bivalent) and thus has a haploid number of chromosomes (fig. 1-4*G*). Each chromosome, however, is still double-structured except at the centromere, so that the amount of DNA in each daughter cell equals that of a normal somatic cell (2n).

## Second Miotic Division

During the second miotic division the 23 double-structured chromosomes divide at the centromere and each of the newly formed daughter cells receives 23 single chromosomes (fig. 1-4*H*). The amount of DNA in the newly formed cells is now half that of the normal somatic cell. Hence, the purpose of the two miotic or maturation divisions is twofold: (a) to enable the members of the homologous chromosome pair to exchange blocks of genetic material (first miotic division); and (b) to provide each germ cell with both a haploid number of chromosomes and half the amount of DNA of a normal somatic cell (second miotic division).

As a result of the miotic divisions, the primitive female germ cell (44 plus 2 X-chromosomes) gives rise to four daughter cells, each with 22 plus 1 X chromosomes. Only one of these develops into a mature oocyte; the other three, the *polar bodies*, receive hardly any cytoplasm and degenerate during subsequent development (fig. 1-5*A*). The primitive male germ cell gives rise to two daughter cells with 22 plus 1 X chromosomes and two with 22 plus 1 Y chromosomes (fig. 1-5*B*).

## Abnormal Miotic Divisions

The complicated events occurring during the miotic divisions apparently are not without hazards. No sooner was the normal chromosome pattern in man established than it became evident that some people possessed an abnormal number of chromosomes. These abnormalities involved either the autosomes (the absence of a chromosome or the presence of an extra one), or the sex chromosomes (usu-

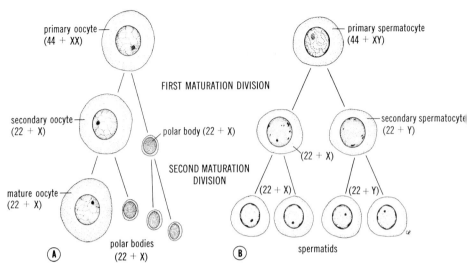

primary oocyte (44 + XX)

primary spermatocyte (44 + XY)

FIRST MATURATION DIVISION

secondary oocyte (22 + X)

polar body (22 + X)

secondary spermatocyte (22 + Y)

(22 + X)

SECOND MATURATION DIVISION

(22 + X)

(22 + X)

(22 + Y)

mature oocyte (22 + X)

polar bodies (22 + X)

**A**

**B**

spermatids

Figure 1-5. *Schematic drawing showing the events occurring during the first and second maturation divisions. A, The primitive female germ cell (primary oocyte) produces only one mature cell, the mature oocyte. B, The primitive male germ cell (primary spermatocyte) produces four spermatids, all of which develop into spermatozoa.*

ally the presence of an extra one). The presence of an extra chromosome makes the individual trisomic for the particular chromosome, and this condition is known as *trisomy*. If one of the partners of a chromosome pair is absent, the condition is known as *monosomy*.

Chromosomal abnormalities originate during the miotic divisions. Normally the two members of a homologous chromosome pair separate during the first miotic division so that each daughter cell receives one component of each pair (fig. 1-4). Sometimes, however, separation does not occur (*nondisjunction*), and both members of a pair then move into one cell. As a result of the nondisjunction of the chromosomes, one cell receives 24 chromosomes and the other 22, instead of the normal 23 chromosomes. When, at fertilization, a gamete having 23 chromosomes fuses with a gamete having 24 or 22 chromosomes, the result will be an individual with either 47 chromosomes (trisomy), or 45 chromosomes (monosomy). Nondisjunction is thought to occur during the miotic divisions of the female germ cells rather than during the divisions of the male germ cells.

Occasionally patients are found with 48 chromosomes, usually involving the presence of four sex chromosomes. It is believed that this abnormality is caused either by nondisjunction of the sex chromosomes in the gametes of both parents, or, more likely, by a nondisjunction of the X-chromosomes in the female gamete in both first

General Embryology

and second miotic divisions. (For further information about autosome and sex chromosome abnormalities, see Chapter 7.)

# Morphological Changes During Germ Cell Maturation

### Appearance and Migration of Primordial Germ Cells

The mature male and female germ cells are generally thought to be direct descendants of the primitive germ cells, which in human embryos appear at the end of the third week of development.[15] Large cells with a vesicular nucleus and abundant cytoplasm appear then in the wall of the yolk sac near the caudal end of the embryo (fig. 1-6).[16, 17] These cells, the *primordial germ cells*, migrate by ameboid movement from the yolk sac toward the developing gonads (primitive sex glands), where they arrive at the end of the fourth or the beginning of the fifth week.[18-20] Here the primordial germ cells exert an inductive influence on the gonadal tissues, which subsequently develop in either female or male direction. (For further details, see Chapter 11).

Initially, the primordial germ cells were thought to die soon after arrival in the primitive sex glands and to be replaced by new germ

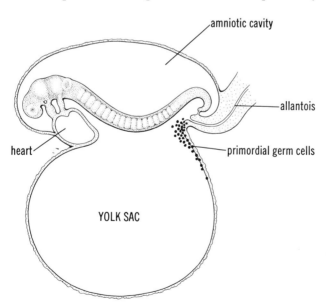

Figure 1-6. *Drawing of a three week old embryo, showing the position of the primordial germ cells in the wall of the yolk sac, close to the attachment of the allantois (after Witchi).*

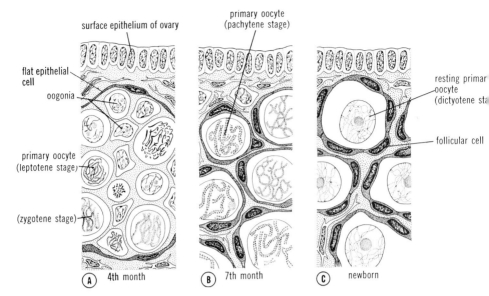

surface epithelium of ovary

primary oocyte
(pachytene stage)

flat epithelial
cell

oogonia

primary oocyte
(leptotene stage)

(zygotene stage)

resting primary
oocyte
(dictyotene sta

follicular cell

(A) 4th month   (B) 7th month   (C) newborn

Figure 1-7. *Schematic representation of a segment of the ovary at different stages of development. A, At four months. The oogonia are grouped in clusters in the cortical part of the ovary. Some show mitosis; others have already differentiated into primary oocytes and have entered the prophase of the first miotic division (leptotene and zygotene stages). B, At seven months. Almost all the oogonia are transformed into primary oocytes, which are in the pachytene stage of the first miotic division. C, At birth. Oogonia are absent. Each primary oocyte is surrounded by a single layer of follicular cells, thus forming the primordial follicle. The oocytes have entered the dictyotene stages in which they remain until just before ovulation. Only then do they enter the metaphase of the first miotic division (modified after Ohno et al.).*

cells originating from the surface epithelium of the glands. From a number of experimental studies in different mammalian species, however, it is now evident that the primordial germ cells do not die, but, on the contrary, are the direct predecessors of all germ cells.[21-25]

## Oogenesis

Once the primordial germ cells have arrived in the gonad of a genetic female, they differentiate into *oogonia*. These cells undergo a number of mitotic divisions, and by the end of the third month they become arranged in clusters which are surrounded by a layer of flat epithelial cells (fig. 1-7A). While all the oogonia in one cluster are probably derived from a single primordial germ cell, the flat epithelial cells are believed to originate from the surface epithelium covering the gland.

General Embryology

The majority of the oogonia continue to divide, but some of them differentiate into the much larger *primary oocytes*, which by the third month of development are found mainly in the deeper layers of the gonad.[26] Immediately after their formation, these cells enter the prophase of the first miotic division, and many leptotene and zygotene stages can be observed (fig. 1-7A).[27-30] During the next few months the oogonia increase rapidly and by the fifth month of development the total number of germ cells in the ovary reaches its maximum, estimated at 6,000,000.[26] At this time cell degeneration begins and many oogonia as well as primary oocytes become atretic.[26, 29] By the seventh month, the majority of the oogonia have degenerated, with the exception of a few near the surface. All surviving primary oocytes, however, have entered the first miotic division and most of them are now individually surrounded by a layer of flat epithelial cells (fig. 1-7B). A primary oocyte together with its surrounding epithelial cells, is known as a *primordial follicle*.

At birth the primary oocytes have finished the prophase of the first miotic division, but instead of proceeding into the metaphase, they enter the *dictyotene stage*, a resting stage between prophase and metaphase characterized by a lacy network of chromatin (fig. 1-7C).[28, 30] Primary oocytes have not been observed to finish their first miotic division before puberty is reached. The total number of primary oocytes at birth is estimated to vary from 700,000 to 2,000,000.[26, 31] Since during the following years of childhood the majority of the oocytes become atretic, only approximately 40,000 are present by the beginning of puberty.[19] Only then do the primordial follicles develop into mature Graafian follicles and the primary oocytes complete their first miotic division.

It is important to realize that some of the oocytes, reaching maturity late in life, have been dormant in the dictyotene stage of the first miotic division for forty years or more. Whether or not the dictyotene stage is the most suitable phase to protect the oocyte against environmental influences acting upon the ovary during life is presently unknown. Considering that the incidence of children with chromosomal abnormalities increases with maternal age, one questions whether or not the extended miotic division makes the primary oocyte vulnerable to damage.

With the onset of puberty, a number of primordial follicles begins to mature with each ovarian cycle. The primary oocyte (still in the dictyotene stage) begins to increase in size, while the surrounding epithelial cells, the *follicular cells*, become cuboidal (fig. 1-8A, B). Initially the follicular cells are in intimate contact with the oocyte, but soon a layer of acellular material consisting of glycoproteins is deposited on the surface of the oocyte.[32-34] This material gradually

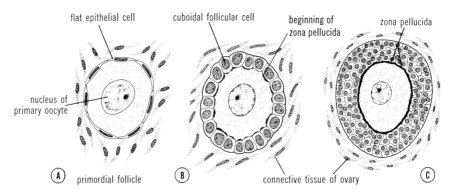

flat epithelial cell    cuboidal follicular cell    beginning of zona pellucida    zona pellucida

nucleus of primary oocyte

(A) primordial follicle    (B)    connective tissue of ovary    (C)

Figure 1-8. *A, Schematic drawing of a primordial follicle, consisting of a primary oocyte surrounded by a layer of flattened epithelial cells. B, As maturation of the follicle proceeds, the follicular cells become cuboidal. They now begin to secrete the zona pellucida, which is visible in irregular patches on the surface of the oocyte. C, With further maturation the follicular cells form an increasingly thick layer around the oocyte. The zona pellucida is well defined (modified after Shettles).*

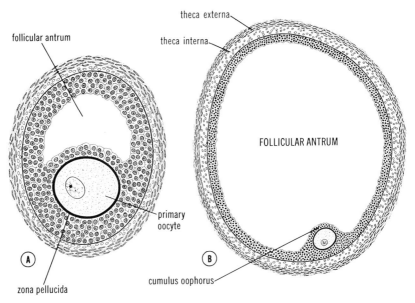

theca externa

follicular antrum    theca interna

FOLLICULAR ANTRUM

primary oocyte

(A)    (B)

zona pellucida    cumulus oophorus

Figure 1-9. *Schematic representation of a maturing follicle. A, The oocyte surrounded by the zona pellucida is eccentrically located; the follicular antrum has developed by coalescence of intercellular spaces. Note the arrangement of the cells of the theca interna and the theca externa. B, Mature Graafian follicle. The antrum has enlarged considerably, is filled with follicular fluid, and is surrounded by a stratified layer of follicular cells. The oocyte is embedded in a mound of follicular cells, known as the cumulus oophorus.*

increases in thickness, thus forming the *zona pellucida* (fig. 1-8C). Small finger-like processes of the follicular cells extend across the zona pellucida and remain in contact with the plasma membrane of the oocyte. These processes are thought to be important for the transport of materials from the follicular cells to the oocyte.[35, 36]

As development continues, the follicular cells begin to proliferate, thereby forming a thick cellular layer around the oocyte (fig. 1-8C). Subsequently, fluid-filled spaces appear between the follicular cells and when these spaces coalesce, the *follicular antrum* is formed. Initially the antrum is crescent-shaped, but with time it greatly enlarges (fig. 1-9A, B). The follicular cells surrounding the oocyte remain intact and form the *cumulus oophorus* or *cumulus ovaricus*. At maturity, the follicle is known as the *Graafian follicle*, and is surrounded by two layers of connective tissue: an inner cellular layer, the *theca interna*, which is rich in blood vessels, and an outer fibrous layer, the *theca externa*, which gradually merges with the ovarian stroma (fig. 1-9). The follicle then has a diameter varying from 6 to 12 mm.

Although with each ovarian cycle a number of follicles begins to develop, usually only one reaches full maturity. The others degenerate and become atretic. As soon as the follicle is mature, the primary oocyte leaves the dictyotene stage and resumes its first miotic division. The result of this division leads to the formation of two daughter cells of unequal size, but each with 23 chromosomes (fig. 1-10A, B). One, the *secondary oocyte*, receives all of the cytoplasm; the other, the *first polar body*, receives practically none. The

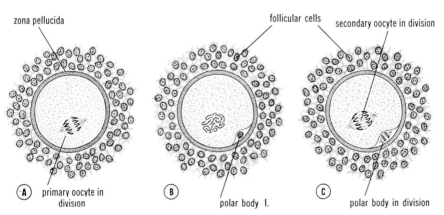

zona pellucida  follicular cells secondary oocyte in division

(A) primary oocyte in division (B) polar body I. (C) polar body in division

Figure 1-10. *Maturation of the oocyte. A, Primary oocyte showing the spindle of the first miotic division. B, Secondary oocyte and polar body I. Note that the nuclear membrane is absent. C, Secondary oocyte, showing the spindle of the second miotic division. Polar body I, likewise, is in division (adapted from several sources).*

Gametogenesis               15

latter is located between the zona pellucida and the cell membrane of the secondary oocyte (fig. 1-10*B*).

At completion of the first maturation division and before the nucleus of the secondary oocyte has returned to its resting stage, the cell enters the *second maturation division*. The moment the secondary oocyte shows the spindle formation, ovulation occurs and the oocyte is shed from the ovary (fig. 1-10*C*).[37] The second maturation division is completed only if the oocyte is fertilized; otherwise the cell degenerates approximately 24 hours after ovulation. Whether or not the first polar body always undergoes a second division is uncertain, but fertilized ova accompanied by three polar bodies have been observed.[36]

In recent experiments, human primary oocytes have been freed from their follicles and cultured in an artificial medium.[38, 39] In these conditions the oocyte moved from the dictyotene stage into diakinesis 25 to 28 hours after the beginning of the culture period. Extrusion of the first polar body and the metaphase of the second miotic division were observed 36 to 43 hours after the beginning of the experiment. In some cases the spindle of the second maturation division was seen within 30 minutes after the telophase of the first miotic division.

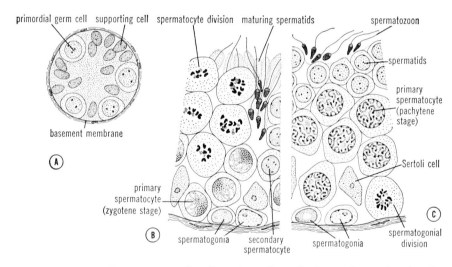

Figure 1-11. *A, Transverse section through testis cord of a newborn, showing the primordial germ cells and supporting cells surrounded by the basement membrane. B and C, Two different segments of the adult seminiferous tubule shown in transverse section. Each segment shows a different stage in the maturation of the male germ cells (derived from Clermont).*

General Embryology

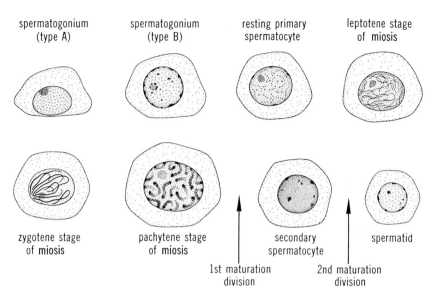

spermatogonium (type A)

spermatogonium (type B)

resting primary spermatocyte

leptotene stage of miosis

zygotene stage of miosis

pachytene stage of miosis

1st maturation division

secondary spermatocyte

2nd maturation division

spermatid

Figure 1-12. *Schematic representation of spermatogenesis in man. Note the leptotene, zygotene and pachytene stages during prophase of the first miotic division (derived from Clermont).*

## Spermatogenesis

During the fifth week of development, the primordial germ cells of the male embryo enter the gonad, where they are incorporated into the *primitive sex cords*. These cords are irregularly shaped and composed of cells derived from the surface epithelium of the gland.[40]

At birth the sex cords are solid and contain two types of cells (fig. 1-11A). The larger of the two is located along the basement membrane and has a large, lightly stained, spherical nucleus with one or more nucleoli. These cells have been identified as primordial germ cells.[41] The other, much smaller cell type is likewise found along the basement membrane and is characterized by nuclei with coarse chromatin granules. These cells proliferate actively and are known as the *supporting cells*.[42] After birth they cease to divide and become typical *Sertoli cells* (*sustentacular cells*), a nonspermatogenic cell type derived from the surface epithelium (fig. 1-11C).

Recently it has been shown that some of the primordial germ cells die in the course of development, while others develop into spermatogonia which later give rise to spermatozoa.[41]

In the course of postnatal development the sex cords acquire a lumen and become known as *seminiferous tubules*. The spermatogonia close to the basement membrane of the tubule begin to

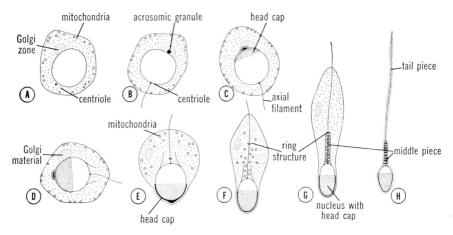

Figure 1-13. *Schematic drawings showing the successive stages in the transformation of the human spermatid into the spermatozoon (derived from Clermont and Leblond).*

divide and give rise either to new spermatogonia (the so-called type A spermatogonia which include the stem cells), or to a more differentiated type B which develops into *primary spermatocytes* (figs. 1-11 and 1-12).[43-46] The latter have a spherical nucleus with fine chromatin granules either free in the nucleoplasm or attached to the nuclear membrane. The primary spermatocytes then start with the prophase of the first miotic division (fig. 1-12). As in the case of the primary oocytes, they go through the leptotene, zygotene and pachytene phases, each of which is characterized by a special configuration of the chromosomes (fig. 1-12). After completion of the long-lasting prophase, the cells pass through the metaphase, anaphase and telophase and give rise to two *secondary spermatocytes* (fig. 1-5B). These cells have a very short life span and begin immediately with the *second maturation division*. This division gives rise to the *spermatids* (figs. 1-11 and 1-12). As a result of the two maturation divisions, each primary spermatocyte gives rise to four *spermatids*, each of which contains half the number of chromosomes found in the primary spermatocyte.

## Spermiogenesis

As soon as the spermatids are formed, they undergo a series of profound changes which result in the production of the spermatozoa. Initially the spermatid has a spherical nucleus, a clearly visible Golgi zone, and a large number of mitochondria (fig. 1-13A). The first noticeable change occurs in the Golgi zone, where a densely stained area, the *acrosomic granule*, becomes visible (fig. 1-13B).[47]

General Embryology

This granule subsequently gives rise to a thin membrane which spreads over the surface of the nucleus, forming the *head cap* (fig. 1-13*C*). With time, the head cap extends over half the nuclear surface, while the remaining portion of the Golgi zone moves to the other side of the cell (fig. 1-13*D, E, F*).[48]

Meanwhile, the centrioles migrate to the pole of the nucleus opposite the head cap and give rise to the *flagellum* or *axial filament*, which later forms the body and tail of the spermatozoon. The nucleus, displaced within the cytoplasm, becomes condensed and assumes a slightly flattened, elongated shape (fig. 1-13*E, F*).

Simultaneously, the mitochondria move toward the flagellum, where they become arranged in collar-like fashion around the filament (fig. 1-13*F, G, H*). Distally, this mitochondrial collar is bound by a ring-like structure. The portion of the flagellum covered with mitochondria is called the *middle piece*. At the end of spermiogenesis the cytoplasm not utilized in the formation of the spermatozoon is cast off, and eventually disintegrates.

When fully formed, the spermatozoa enter the lumen of the seminiferous tubules. From here, they are pushed toward the epididymis, possibly under the influence of contractile elements in the wall of the seminiferous tubules.[49] Though initially only slightly motile, the spermatozoa obtain full motility in the epididymis.[50]

## Abnormal Gametes

In man as well as in most mammals, one ovarian follicle occasionally contains two or three clearly distinguishable primary oocytes (fig. 1-14*A*).[51] Although these oocytes may give rise to twins or triplets, they usually degenerate before reaching maturity. In rare cases, one primary oocyte contains two or even three nuclei (fig. 1-14*B*). Such bi- or tri-nucleated oocytes, however, die before reaching maturity.

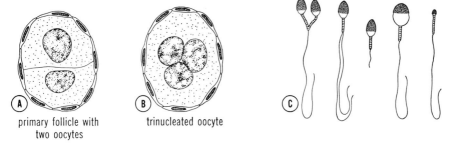

primary follicle with
two oocytes

trinucleated oocyte

Figure 1-14. *Drawings of abnormal germ cells in the female and male. A, Primordial follicle with two oocytes. B, Trinucleated oocyte. C, Various types of abnormal spermatozoa.*

Gametogenesis

Contrary to atypical oocytes, abnormal spermatozoa are seen frequently. The head as well as the tail may be abnormal; they may be giants or dwarfs; sometimes, they are joined (fig. 1-14C).[52] There is evidence suggesting that 10 per cent of the spermatozoa may be abnormal without any loss of fertility. When, however, a quarter or more of them are abnormal, fertility is usually impaired.

## References

1. YUNIS, J. J. *Human Chromosome Methodology*. Academic Press, New York, 1965.
2. TURPIN, R., AND LEJEUNE, J. *Les Chromosomes Humains*. Gauthier-Villars, Paris, 1965.
3. TIJO, J. H., AND LEVAN, A. A chromosome number in man. Hereditas, **42:** 1, 1956.
4. FORD, C. E., AND HAMERTON, J. L. The chromosomes in man. Nature, **178:** 1020, 1956.
5. PATAU, K. The identification of individual chromosomes, especially in man. Amer. J. Hum. Genet., **12:** 250, 1960.
6. Denver Conference. A proposed standard system of nomenclature of human mitotic chromosomes, Lancet, **1:** 1063, 1960
7. MAZIA, D. Mitosis and the physiology of cell division. In *The Cell*, edited by J. Brachet and A. E. Mirsky, Vol. 3, p. 80. Academic Press, New York, 1961.
8. CAIRNS, J. The bacterial chromosome and its manner of replication as seen by autoradiography. J. Molec. Biol., **6:** 208, 1963.
9. WATSON, J. D., AND CRICK, F. H. C. Molecular structure of nucleic acids: a structure for deoxyribose nucleic acids. Nature, **171:** 737, 1953.
10. SWANSON, C. P. *Cytology and Cytogenetics*. Macmillan, New York, 1958.
11. RHOADES, M. M. Meiosis. In *The Cell*, edited by J. Brachet and A. E. Mirsky, p. 1. Academic Press, New York, 1961.
12. EVANS, E. P., BRECKTON, G., AND FORD, C. E. An air-drying method for meiotic preparations from mammalian testes. Cytogenetics (Basel), **3:** 209, 1964.
13. WESTERGAARD, M. Studies on the mechanism of crossing over. I. Theoretical considerations. Comp. Rend. Trav. Lab. Carlsberg, **34:** 359, 1964.
14. WHITEHOUSE, H. L. K. *Towards an Understanding of the Mechanism of Heredity*. Arnold, London, 1965.
15. WITSCHI, E. Migration of the germ cells of the human embryos from the yolk sac to the primitive gonadal folds. Contrib. Embryol., **32:** 67, 1948.
16. McKAY, D. G., HERTIG, A. T., ADAMS, E. C., AND DANZIGER, S. Histochemical observations on the germ cells of human embryos. Anat. Rec., **117:** 201, 1953.
17. McKAY, D. G., ADAMS, E. C., AND HERTIG, A. T. Danziger's histochemical horizons in human embryos. I. 5 mm. embryos, Streeter Horizon XIII. Anat. Rec., **122:** 125, 1955.
18. BLANDAU, R. H., WHITE, B. J., AND RUMERY, R. E. Observations on the movements of the living primordial germ cells in the mouse. Fertil. and Steril., **14:** 482, 1963.
19. PINKERTON, H. M., McKAY, D. G., ADAMS, E. C., AND HERTIG, A. T. Development of the human ovary—a study using histochemical techniques. Obstet. and Gynec., **18:** 152, 1961.
20. FRANCHI, L. L., MANDL, A. M., AND ZUCKERMAN, S. The development of the ovary and the process of oogenesis. In *The Ovary*, edited by S. Zuckerman, A. M. Mandl, and P. Eckstein. Academic Press, New York, 1962.
21. EVERETT, N. B. Observational and experimental evidences relating to the origin and differentiation of the definitive germ cells in mice. J. Exp. Zool., **92:** 49, 1943.

22. CHIQUOINE, A. D. The identification, origin and migration of the primordial germ cells in the mouse embryo. Anat. Rec., **118**: 135, 1954.

23. MINTZ, B., AND RUSSELL, E. S. Gene induced embryological modifications of primordial germ cells in the mouse. J. Exp. Zool., **134**: 207, 1957.

24. MINTZ, B. Embryological development of primordial germ cells in the mouse: influence of a new mutation, W$\gamma^1$. J. Embryol. Exp. Morph., **5**: 396, 1957.

25. MINTZ, B. Embryological phases of mammalian gametogenesis. J. Cell. Comp. Physiol., **56**: 31, 1960.

26. BAKER, G. T. A quantitative and cytological study of germ cells in human ovaries. Proc. Royal Soc., B., **158**: 417, 1963.

27. OHNO, S., MAKINO, S., KAPLAN, W. D., AND KINOSITA, R. Female germ cells in man. Exp. Cell Res., **24**: 106, 1961.

28. OHNO, S., KLINGER, H. P., AND ATKIN, N. B. Human oogenesis. Cytogenetics, **1**: 42, 1962.

29. OHNO, S., AND SMITH, J. B. Role of fetal follicular cells in meiosis of mammalian oocytes. Cytogenetics, **3**: 324, 1964.

30. MANOTAYA, T., AND POTTER, E. L. Oocytes in prophase of meiosis from squash preparations of human fetal ovaries. Fert. and Steril., **14**: 378, 1963.

31. BLOCK, E. A quantitative morphological investigation of the follicular system in newborn female infants. Acta Anat., **17**: 201, 1953.

32. CHIQUOINE, A. D. The development of the zona pellucida of the mammalian ovum. Am. J. Anat., **106**: 149, 1960.

33. ODOR, D. L. The ultrastructure of unilaminar follicles of the hamster ovary. Amer. J. Anat., **16**: 493, 1965.

34. WEAKLEY, B. S. Electron microscopy of the oocyte and granulosa cells in the developing ovarian follicles of the golden hamster (Mesocricetus auratus). J. Anat., **100**: 503, 1966.

35. SHETTLES, L. G. The nourishment of the human ovum. Bull. Sloane Hosp. Women, **4**: 34, 1958.

36. SHETTLES, L. G. *Ovum Humanum*. Urban and Schwarzenberg, Munich and Berlin, 1960.

37. ALLEN, E., et al. Human tubal ova; related early corpora lutea and uterine tubes. Contrib. Embryol., **22**: 45, 1930.

38. EDWARDS, R. G. Meiosis in ovarian oocytes of adult mammals. Nature (London), **196**: 446, 1962.

39. EDWARDS, R. G. Cleavage of 1 and 2 celled rabbit eggs in vitro after removal of zona pellucida. J. Reprod. Fertil., **7**: 153, 1964.

40. CLERMONT, Y., AND HUCKINS, C. Microscopic anatomy of the sex glands and seminiferous tubules in growing and adult male albino rats. Amer. J. Anat., **108**: 79, 1961.

41. CLERMONT, Y., AND PEREY, B. Quantitative study of the cell population of the seminiferous tubules in immature rats. Amer. J. Anat., **100**: 241, 1957.

42. MANCINI, R. E., NARBAITZ R., AND LAVIERI, J. S. Origin and development of the germinative epithelium and Sertoli cells in the human testis; cytological, cytochemical and quantitative study. Anat. Rec., **136**: 477, 1960.

43. CLERMONT, Y., AND LEBLOND, C. P. Renewal of spermatogonia in the rat. Amer. J. Anat., **93**: 475, 1953.

44. CLERMONT, Y., AND LEBLOND, C. P. Differentiation and renewal of spermatogonia .1 the monkey. Amer. J. Anat., **104**: 237, 1959.

45. OAKBERG, E. F. Degeneration of spermatogonia of the mouse following exposure to x-rays, and stages in the mitotic cycle at which cell death occurs. J. Morph., **97**: 39, 1955.

46. OAKBERG, E. F. A description of spermiogenesis in the mouse and its use in

analysis of the cycle of the seminiferous epithelium and germ cell renewal. Amer. J. Anat., **99:** 391, 1956.

47. LEBLOND, C. P. Spermiogenesis of rat, mouse, hamster, and guinea pig as revealed by the "periodic acid-fuchsin sulfurous acid" technique. Amer. J. Anat., **90:** 167, 1952.

48. CLERMONT, Y., AND LEBLOND, C. P. Spermiogenesis of man, monkey, ram and other mammals as shown by periodic acid-Schiff technique. Amer. J. Anat., **96:** 229, 1955.

49. CLERMONT, Y. Contractile elements in the limiting membrane of the seminiferous tubules. Exp. Cell Res., **15:** 438, 1958.

50. BLANDAU, R. H., AND RUMERY, R. E. Fertilizing capacity of rat spermatozoa recovered from various segments of the epididymis. Anat. Rec., **139:** 209, 1961.

51. HAMILTON, W. J. Phases of maturation and fertilization in human ova. J. Anat., **78:** 1, 1944.

52. HOTCHKISS, R. S. *Fertility in Men.* J. B. Lippincott Co., Philadelphia, 1944.

# CHAPTER 2

# Ovulation to Implantation (First Week of Development)

NORMAL DEVELOPMENT
- OVULATION AND OVARIAN CYCLE: *corpus atreticum, corpus luteum, inhibition of ovulation*
- FERTILIZATION
- CLEAVAGE: *morula formation*
- BLASTOCYST FORMATION: *embryoblast, trophoblast, and blastocele*
- UTERUS AT TIME OF IMPLANTATION

ABNORMAL DEVELOPMENT
- ALTERNATIVES TO NORMAL FERTILIZATION
- ABNORMAL ZYGOTES
- ABNORMAL IMPLANTATION SITES

## *Normal Development*

### Ovulation and Ovarian Cycle

In the days immediately preceding ovulation, the Graafian follicle increases rapidly in size and expands to a diameter of 15 mm. The surface of the ovary then begins to bulge locally and at the apex an avascular spot appears, the so-called *stigma*. As a result of local weakening of the ovarian surface, follicular fluid oozes through the stigma, which gradually opens. Subsequently, when more fluid escapes, the tension in the follicle is released and the oocyte together with the surrounding cumulus oophorus cells breaks free and floats out of the ovary.[1-4] At the moment that the oocyte with its cumulus oophorus cells is discharged from the ovary—*ovulation*—the oocyte begins its second miotic division (fig. 2-1A).

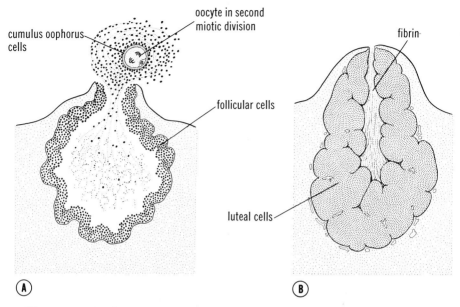

cumulus oophorus cells

oocyte in second miotic division

follicular cells

fibrin

luteal cells

(A)                                    (B)

Figure 2-1. *A, Ovulation. The oocyte, undergoing the second miotic division, is discharged from the ovary, together with a large number of cumulus oophorus cells. The follicular cells remaining inside the follicle differentiate into luteal cells. B, Corpus luteum. Note the massive accumulation of luteal cells. The remaining cavity of the follicle is now filled up with fibrin.*

The periodic shedding of an oocyte and the regular maturation of a group of primordial follicles constitute the cyclic changes in the ovary, referred to as the *ovarian cycle.* Ovulation takes place once in a cycle, approximately 14 days ± 1 day before the beginning of the following menstrual bleeding.[5, 6] Although the time between ovulation and the succeeding menstrual bleeding is constant, the time between ovulation and the preceding menstruation is highly variable and depends on the length of time the follicle needs to mature.

At the beginning of each ovarian cycle a number of primordial follicles begins to grow. Only one of these follicles, however, reaches full maturity and only one oocyte is discharged; the others degenerate and become atretic. In the next cycle another group of follicles begins to grow and again only one reaches maturity. Consequently, the majority of follicles degenerate without ever reaching full maturity. When a follicle becomes atretic, the oocyte and surrounding follicular cells degenerate and are replaced by connective tissue, thus forming a *corpus atreticum.*

When ovulation occurs, the follicular cells remaining in the wall of the ruptured follicle are vascularized by surrounding vessels and become polyhedral. Subsequently they develop a yellowish pigment and change into the *luteal cells* (fig. 2-1*B*). These cells form the *corpus luteum* and secrete *progesterone.* This hormone together with the estrogenic hormones produced by the theca cells and the surrounding ovarian tissue, cause the uterine mucosa to enter the *progestational* or *secretory stage* (fig. 2-6).

Shortly before ovulation, the fimbriae of the oviduct begin to cover the surface of the ovary and the tube itself begins to contract rhythmically. It is believed that the oocyte surrounded by the cumulus cells is carried into the tube by the sweeping movements of the fimbriae and by the motion of the cilia on the epithelial lining.[7-9] Once in the tube, the oocyte loses its cumulus cells. Though it was initially believed that these cells were dispersed by the action of the cilia on the epithelial lining of the tube, time lapse cinematography showed that they lose contact with the oocyte by withdrawing their cytoplasmic processes from the zona pellucida.[10] In artificial media the cumulus cells are dispersed in the same manner as *in vivo.*

Once the oocyte is in the Fallopian tube, it is pushed toward the uterine lumen by contractions of the muscular wall.[11, 12] The rate of transport is somewhat affected by the endocrine status during and after ovulation, but in man the fertilized oocyte reaches the uterine lumen in approximately three to four days.[9, 13]

If fertilization fails to occur, the corpus luteum reaches maximum development about nine days after ovulation. It can easily be recognized as a yellowish projection on the surface of the ovary.[14] Subsequently the corpus luteum decreases in size through degeneration of the luteal cells and forms a mass of fibrotic scar tissue, known as the *corpus albicans.* Simultaneously the progesterone production decreases, thus precipitating the menstrual bleeding (fig. 2-6).

If the oocyte is fertilized, degeneration of the corpus luteum is prevented by a gonadotropic hormone secreted by the developing zygote. The corpus luteum continues to grow, and forms the *corpus luteum of pregnancy* (*graviditatis*). By the end of the third month, this structure may be one-third to one-half of the total size of the ovary. The yellowish luteal cells continue to secrete progesterone until the end of the fourth month; thereafter they regress slowly. Removal of the corpus luteum of pregnancy before the fourth month usually leads to abortion.[15]

A thorough analysis of the relationship between the pituitary gland and the ovary has recently led to the discovery that ovulation can be inhibited by treatment with progestational compounds.[16, 17] This finding has led to the use of orally taken contraceptives. The progestin, 19-nortesterone, when given from day 5 to day 25 of the menstrual cycle, inhibits ovulation in almost 100 per cent of the cases.[18] Most of the presently used anti-ovulatory preparations (Enovid, Ortho-Novum) contain a small amount of estrogen (about 0.1 mg Mestranol), in addition to one of the progestin compounds.[19] Though both can prevent ovulation, the estrogenic component is thought to inhibit ovulation and the progestin component to ensure a normal menstrual bleeding upon withdrawal of the preparation on the 25th day of the cycle. Preliminary observations indicate that the maturation of the follicles is completely suppressed.

## Fertilization

Fertilization, the process by which the male and female gametes fuse, occurs in the ampullary region of the Fallopian tube.[20] Although it has been suggested that in some mammals the oocyte and spermatozoa are attracted to each other by chemical influences, solid proof for this concept is lacking.[21, 22] *In vitro* studies have shown that human spermatozoa, though swimming close to the oocyte, may pass by without any apparent attraction.[23]

Only one of the 200 to 300 million spermatozoa deposited in the female genital tract is needed for fertilization; the others have been thought to aid the fertilizing sperm in dispersing the corona radiata cells by the production of the enzyme *hyaluronidase*. However, since the treatment of spermatozoa with hyaluronidase inhibitors does not abolish the fertilizing capacity of sperms, the validity of the enzymatic action becomes doubtful.[24, 25] Once the spermatozoon touches the zona pellucida surrounding the oocyte, it becomes firmly attached and begins to penetrate the zona with the aid of an enzyme associated with the sperm head (fig. 2-2A, B).[26]

Once the spermatozoon begins to penetrate the oocyte, its plasma membrane fuses with that of the oocyte and is left behind on the oocyte surface.[27] In the human both the head and the tail enter the oocyte (fig. 2-2B). Other spermatozoa have been found embedded in the zona pellucida, but only one seems to be able to penetrate into the oocyte proper (fig. 2-2B).[28] The permeability of the zona pellucida changes immediately after entry of the first sperm. This change, the *zona reaction*, is probably evoked by contact of the sperm head with the oocyte surface, resulting in the release of a substance that causes an alteration in the properties of the zona pellucida.[29]

As soon as the spermatozoon has entered the oocyte, the latter finishes its second maturation division and the chromosomes (22 plus X) become arranged in a vesicular nucleus known as the

General Embryology

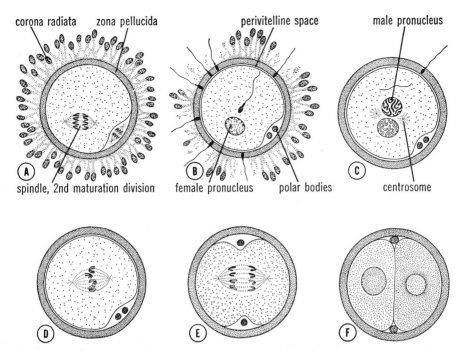

Figure 2-2. *A, Schematic drawing of the oocyte immediately after ovulation, showing the spindle of the second miotic division, the zona pellucida, and the cumulus oophorus cells forming the corona radiata (modified after Hamilton). B, A spermatozoon has penetrated the oocyte, which has finished its second miotic division and extruded its second polar body. The chromosomes of the oocyte are arranged in a vesicular nucleus, the female pronucleus. The cells of the corona radiata are partly detached and the heads of several spermatozoa are stuck in the zona pellucida. C, Stage of male and female pronuclei. Note the two centrosomes, derived from the anterior centriole of the spermatozoon. D and E, The chromosomes become arranged on the spindle, split longitudinally and move to opposites poles. F, The two-cell stage; the two blastomeres differ in the size of the nuclei.*

*female pronucleus* (fig. 2-2B).[30] The ooplasm shrinks and a *perivitelline space* becomes visible between the oocyte and the zona pellucida.

The spermatozoon meanwhile moves forward until it lies in close proximity to the female pronucleus. Its nucleus becomes swollen and forms the *male pronucleus* (fig. 2-2C). Morphologically the male and female pronuclei are indistinguishable.[31] The tail is detached from the head and degenerates. The origin of the *centrioles* is not clear, but they are thought to be derived from the anterior centriole of the spermatozoon (fig. 2-2C).[32]

Before fusion between the male and female pronuclei occurs,

each pronucleus duplicates its DNA.[33] Immediately thereafter the chromosomes become organized on the spindle, and the 23 maternal and 23 paternal chromosomes split longitudinally at the centromere as in a normal mitotic division. The resulting halves segregate at random and move to the opposite poles, thus providing each cell of the zygote with the normal number of chromosomes and the normal amount of DNA (2n) (fig. 2-2D, E). While the chromosomes move to the opposite poles, a deep furrow appears on the surface of the cell, gradually dividing the cytoplasm into two parts (fig. 2-2F).

The main results of fertilization are: (1) restoration of the diploid number of chromosomes; and (2) determination of the sex of the new individual (see Chapter 1).

## Cleavage

Once the zygote has reached the two-cell stage, it undergoes a series of mitotic divisions, resulting in a rapid increase in the number of cells. These cells, which become smaller with each cleavage division, are known as *blastomeres* (fig. 2-3). After a number of divisions the zygote, similar in appearance to a mulberry, is known as the *morula*.

Only a few human cleavage stages are known. Hertig and co-workers recovered a two-cell stage with two polar bodies and a zona pellucida from the Fallopian tube (fig. 2-2F).[34] Its age is unknown, but experiments *in vitro* have shown that the human zygote reaches the two-cell stage approximately 30 hours after fertilization.[23] This seems to be in accordance with the two-cell stage in the monkey which was recovered from the Fallopian tube 29½ hours after

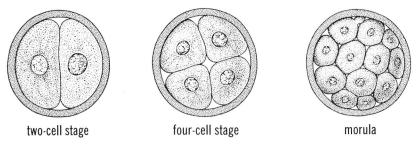

two-cell stage          four-cell stage          morula

Figure 2-3. *Schematic representation of the development of the zygote from the two-cell stage to the late morula stage. The two-cell stage is reached approximately 30 hours after fertilization; the four-cell stage at approximately 40 hours; the 12- and 16-cell stage at approximately 3 days; and the late morula stage at approximately 4 days. During this period the blastomeres are surrounded by the zona pellucida, which disappears when the zygote is ready for implantation at the end of the fourth day.*

General Embryology

ovulation.[35] At this stage one cell is usually larger and probably divides first, resulting in a three-cell stage. Subsequently, the small cell divides and the zygote then consists of two large and two small cells (fig. 2-3). *In vitro*, the four-cell stage is reached 40 to 50 hours after fertilization.[23]

As cleavage progresses, the zygote moves down the Fallopian tube and when the 12- to 16-cell stage is attained, it consists of a group of centrally located cells, the *inner cell mass*, and a surrounding layer, the *outer cell mass*. Although at this stage of development all the cells of the morula appear similar, from studies on further development it is known that the inner cell mass gives rise to the tissues of the embryo proper, while the outer cell mass forms the *trophoblast*, which later develops into the *placenta*. The morula is thought to reach the uterine cavity at about the 12- to 16-cell stage. *In vitro* this stage is reached approximately 60 hours after fertilization. Indeed, a human 12-cell morula, aged three days, has been recovered from the uterine cavity.[36]

## Blastocyst Formation

At about the time that the morula enters the uterine cavity, fluid begins to penetrate the zona pellucida into the intercellular spaces of the inner cell mass. Gradually the intercellular spaces become confluent and finally a single cavity, the *blastocele*, is formed (fig. 2-4A). At this time the zona pellucida disappears rapidly and the zygote is then known as the *blastocyst*. The cells of the inner cell mass, now referred to as the *embryoblast*, are located at one pole, while those of the outer cell mass, or *trophoblast*, flatten and form the epithelial wall of the blastocyst (fig. 2-4A). Although the cells of the blastocyst are greatly different from those in the early cleavage stages, differences between the trophoblast and the embryoblast cells are only minor.[37]

Two human blastocysts, consisting of 58 and 107 cells with an estimated age of 4 and 4½ days, respectively, have been recovered from the uterine cavity.[36] *In vitro*, a well advanced blastocyst has been found approximately 100 and 140 hours after fertilization. The 107-cell blastocyst contained an embryoblast with eight large vacuolated cells; the remaining 99 belonged to the trophoblast. Of the latter, 69 formed the wall of the blastocele, and 30 were grouped over the embryoblast. Although in the human the early attachment between the blastocyst and the uterine mucosa has not been observed, in all probability this occurs in man about 5½ to 6 days after ovulation.[36] It is thought that the implantation process is comparable to that in the Macaque monkey, in which the earliest attach-

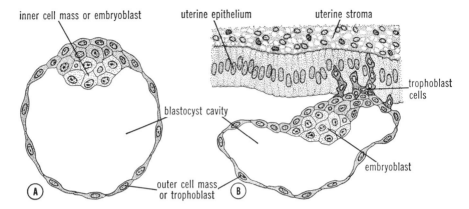

inner cell mass or embryoblast    uterine epithelium    uterine stroma

trophoblast
cells

blastocyst cavity

embryoblast

outer cell mass
or trophoblast

Ⓐ    Ⓑ

Figure 2-4. *A, Schematic representation of a section through a human blasto-cyst recovered from the uterine cavity at approximately 4½ days. The lightly dotted cells represent the inner cell mass or embryoblast, and the darkly dotted cells the outer cell mass or trophoblast (modified after Hertig and Rock). B, Schematic drawing of a section of a Macaque monkey blastocyst at the ninth day of development. The trophoblast cells, located at the embryonic pole of the blastocyst, begin to penetrate the uterine mucosa (modified after Wislocki and Streeter). The human blastocyst begins to penetrate the uterine mucosa proba-bly by the fifth or sixth day of development.*

ment occurs 9 days after ovulation.[38] At this time the trophoblastic cells over the embryoblast pole begin to penetrate between the epithelial cells of the uterine mucosa (fig. 2-4*B*). It is probable that the penetration and subsequent erosion of the epithelial cells of the mucosa results from proteolytic enzymes produced by the trophoblast. The uterine mucosa, however, promotes the tropho-blastic action of the blastocyst, so that implantation is the result of mutual action.[39] Hence, by the end of the first week of develop-ment, the human zygote has passed through the morula and blasto-cyst stages and has begun its implantation in the uterine mucosa (fig. 2-5).

**The Uterus at the Time of Implantation**

At the time of implantation the mucosa of the uterus is in the *secretory* or *progestational* phase (fig. 2-6). This phase is caused by the action of progesterone, which is produced by the corpus luteum. The first signs of progesterone action can be recognized two or three days after ovulation. At that time the uterine glands and arteries become coiled and the stroma becomes succulent. As a result of these changes, three distinct layers can be recognized: a superficial *compact layer*, an intermediate *spongy layer*, and a thin *basal layer* (fig. 2-6).

General Embryology

If the oocyte is fertilized, the glands in the endometrium show a steadily increasing secretory activity and discharge their products, including mucin and glycogen, into the lumen. The arteries which supply the spongy and compact layers become tortuous and form a dense capillary bed just beneath the uterine epithelium. The endometrium becomes highly edematous and is usually pale in color. The uterine mucosa is then ready to receive the blastocyst. Normally the human blastocyst implants in the endometrium along the posterior or anterior wall of the body of the uterus, where it becomes attached between the openings of the endometrial glands or occasionally in the mouth of one of the glandular ducts.

If the oocyte is not fertilized, the venules and sinusoidal spaces become gradually packed with blood cells. With impending menstruation, an extensive diapedesis of red and white blood cells into the stroma is seen. When the *menstrual phase* begins, probably as a

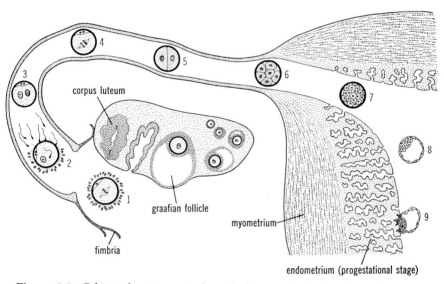

Figure 2-5. *Schematic representation of the events taking place during the first week of human development. (1) Oocyte immediately after ovulation. (2) Fertilization approximately 12 to 24 hours after ovulation. (3) Stage of the male and female pronuclei. (4) Spindle of the first mitotic division. (5) Two-cell stage (approximately 30 hours of age). (6) Morula containing 12 to 16 blastomeres (approximately 3 days of age). (7) Advanced morula stage reaching the uterine lumen (approximately 4 days of age). (8) Early blastocyst stage (approximately 4½ days of age). The zona pellucida has now disappeared. (9) Early phase of implantation (blastocyst approximately 6 days of age). The ovary shows the stages of the transformation between a primary follicle and a Graafian follicle as well as a corpus luteum. The uterine endometrium is depicted in the progestational stage.*

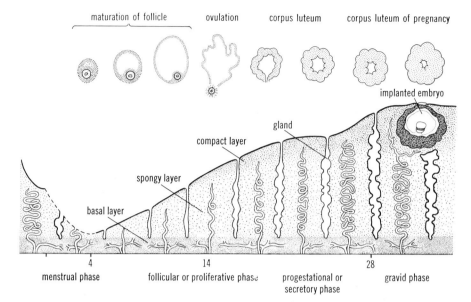

Figure 2-6. *Schematic representation of the changes taking place in the uterine mucosa correlated with those in the ovary. Note that the implantation of the blastocyst has caused the development of a large corpus luteum of pregnancy. The secretory activity of the endometrium increases gradually as a result of the large amounts of progesterone produced by the corpus luteum of pregnancy.*

result of a temporary constriction of the spiral arteries, blood escapes from the superficial arteries and small pieces of stroma and glands break away.[40] During the following three or four days the compact and spongy layers are expelled from the uterus and the basal layer is the only part of the endometrium which is retained. This layer, which is supplied by its own arteries, the *basal arteries*, functions as the regenerative layer in the rebuilding of glands and arteries in the *proliferative phase*.

# Abnormal Development

## Alternatives to Normal Fertilization

A female gamete cannot produce an embryo without participation of a male gamete. Occasionally, however, the oocyte is activated without sperm penetration and development may start. This form of reproduction is called *parthenogenesis*. Early parthenogenetic development of mammalian oocytes has been introduced by chilling, by the local application of heat, by hyperthermia and other means.[41-43] There is, however, no record of the birth of viable young originating in any of these ways. Sometimes cleaving oocytes are found in the ovary, where they may develop into an ovarian teratoma.[44]

## Abnormal Zygotes

Abnormal zygotes of a pre-implantation stage have been described by a number of authors.[23, 28] Of a total of eight zygotes recovered from the uterine tube by Hertig and coworkers, four appeared to be normal, whereas the other four were abnormal.[36] The abnormal zygotes, which varied from three to five days of age, showed multinucleated blastomeres and variable degrees of cellular degeneration. Although it is doubtful that any of these zygotes would have been able to implant, all four were recovered from patients of normal fertility.

## Abnormal Implantation Sites

The human blastocyst usually implants along the posterior or anterior wall of the body of the uterus. Occasionally implantation in the uterus itself may lead to serious complications. This is par-

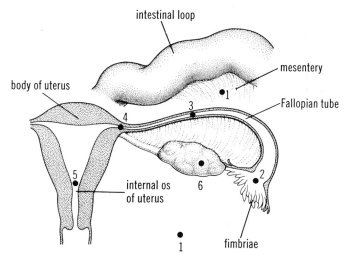

Figure 2-7. *Drawing to show the abnormal implantation sites of the blastocyst. (1) Implantation sites in the abdominal cavity. The ovum most frequently implants in the recto-uterine cavity (Douglas' pouch), but may implant at any place covered by peritoneum. (2) Implantation in the ampullary region of the tube. (3) Tubal implantation. (4) Interstitial implantation—that is, in the narrow portion of the uterine tube. (5) Implantation in the region of the internal os, frequently resulting in placenta praevia. (6) Ovarian implantation (modified after Hamilton, Boyd, and Mossman).*

ticularly so when the blastocyst implants close to the internal os. The placenta then overbridges the os (*placenta praevia*), and causes severe bleeding in the second part of pregnancy and during delivery.

Not infrequently implantation sites are found outside the uterus, resulting in *extra-uterine* or *ectopic pregnancy*. This may occur at any place in the abdominal cavity, ovary or Fallopian tube (fig. 2-7). Ectopic pregnancy usually leads to death of the embryo and severe hemorrhaging by the mother during the second month of pregnancy. In the abdominal cavity the blastocyst most frequently attaches itself to the peritoneal lining of the recto-uterine cavity (*Douglas' pouch*). The blastocyst also may attach itself to the peritoneal covering of the intestinal tract or to the omentum. Rarely does an extra-uterine embryo come to full term.

Sometimes the blastocyst develops in the ovary proper, causing a *primary ovarian pregnancy*. More commonly an ectopic pregnancy is lodged in the Fallopian tube (*tubal pregnancy*). In the latter case, the tube ruptures at about the second month of pregnancy, resulting in severe internal hemorrhaging by the mother.

## References

1. ELERT, R. Der Mechanismus der Eiabnahme im Laparoskop. Zbl. Bynaek., **69:** 38, 1947.
2. DOYLE, J. B. Ovulation and the effects of selective uterotubal denervation: direct observations by culdotomy. Fertil. and Steril., **5:** 105, 1954.
3. BLANDAU, R. J. Ovulation in the living albino rat. Fertil. and Steril., **6:** 391, 1955.
4. HARTMAN, D. G., AND LEATHEM, J. H. Oogenesis and ovulation. In *Mechanisms Concerned with Conception*, edited by C. G. Hartman, p. 205. The Macmillan Co., New York, 1963.
5. FARRIS, E. J. *Human Ovulation and Fertility*. J. B. Lippencott Co., Philadelphia, 1956.
6. SPECK, G. The determination of the time of ovulation. Obstet. Gynec. Survey, **14:** 798, 1959.
7. DECKER, A. Culdoscopic observations on the tubo-ovarian mechanism of ovum reception. Fertil. and Steril., **2:** 253, 1951.
8. DOYLE, J. B. Tubo-ovarian mechanism: observation at laparotomy. Obstet. Gynec., **8:** 686, 1956.
9. AUSTIN, C. R. Fertilization and transport of the ovum. In *Mechanisms Concerned with Conception*, edited by C. G. Hartman, p. 285. The Macmillan Co., New York, 1963.
10. BLANDAU, R. J. A teaching film of ovulation and egg transport in the rat. Anat. Rec., **130:** 468, 1958.
11. BLACK, D. L., AND ASDELL, S. A. Transport through the rabbit oviduct. Amer. J. Physiol., **192:** 63, 1958.
12. HARPER, M. J. K., BENNETT, J. P., BOURSNELL, J. C., AND ROWSON, L. E. A. An autoradiographic method for the study of egg transport in the rabbit Fallopian tube. J. Reprod. Fertil., **1:** 249, 1960.
13. NOYES, R. W., ADAMS, C. E., AND WALTON, A. The transport of ova in relation to the dosage of oestrogen in ovariectomized rabbits. J. Endocrinol., **18:** 108, 1959.

General Embryology

14. WHITE, R. F., HERTIG, A. T., ROCK, J., AND ADAMS, E. Histological and histochemical observations on the corpus luteum of human pregnancy, with special reference to corpora lutea associated with early normal and abnormal ova. Contrib. Embryol., **34:** 55, 1951.

15. AMOROSO, E. C. Comparative aspects of the hormonal functions. In *The Placenta and Fetal Membranes*, edited by C. A. Villee. The Williams & Wilkins Co., Baltimore, 1959.

16. ROCK, J., GARCIA, C. M., AND PINCUS, G. Synthetic progestins in the normal human menstrual cycle. Recent Prog. Horm. Res., **13:** 322, 1957.

17. PINCUS, G. Clinical effects of new progestational compounds. In *Clinical Endocrinology*, Vol. I, edited by E. B. Astwood, p. 526. Grune & Stratton, Inc., New York, 1960.

18. TYLER, E. T. Current status of oral contraception. J. Am. Med. Assoc., **187:** 562, 1964.

19. GOODMAN, L. S., AND GILMAN, A. In *The Pharmacological Basis of Therapeutics*. The Macmillan Co., New York, 1965.

20. HAMILTON, W. J. Phases of maturation and fertilization in human ova. J. Anat., **78:** 1, 1944.

21. SCHWARTZ, R., BROOKS, W., AND ZINSSER, H. H. Evidence of chemotaxis as a factor in sperm motility. Fertil. and Steril., **9:** 300, 1958.

22. TYLER, A., AND BISHOP, D. W. Immunological phenomena. In *Mechanisms Concerned with Conception*, edited by C. G. Hartman, p. 397. The Macmillan Co., New York, 1963.

23. SHETTLES, L. B. *Ovum Humanum*. Hafner Publishing Co., Inc., 1960.

24. BISHOP, D. W., AND TYLER, A. Fertilizing of mammalian eggs. J. Exp. Zool., **132:** 575, 1956.

25. CHANG, M. C., AND PINCUS, G. Does phosphorylated hisperidin effect fertility? Science, **117:** 274, 1953.

26. AUSTIN, C. R., AND BISHOP, M. W. H. Role of the rodent acrosome and perforatorium in fertilization. Proc. Roy. Soc. (b), **149:** 241, 1958.

27. SZOLLOSI, D. G., AND RIS, H. Observations on sperm penetration in the rat. J. Biophys. Biochem. Cytol., **10:** 275, 1961.

28. SHETTLES, L. B. The living human ovum. Obstet. Gynec. (N.Y.), **10:** 359, 1957.

29. AUSTIN, C. R., AND BRADEN, A. W. H. Early reactions of the rodent egg to spermatozoon penetration. J. Exp. Biol., **33:** 358, 1956.

30. HAMILTON, W. J. Early stages of human development. Ann. Roy. Coll. Surg. Eng., **4:** 281, 1949.

31. SZOLLOSI, D. Extrusion of nucleoli from pronuclei of the rat. J. Cell Biol., **25:** 545, 1965.

32. AUSTIN, C. R. Ultrastructural changes during fertilization. In *Preimplantation Stages of Pregnancy*, edited by G. E. W. Wolstenholme and M. O'Connor, p. 3. Little, Brown and Co., Boston, 1965.

33. MINTZ, B. Nucleic acid and protein synthesis in the developing mouse embryo. In *Preimplantation Stages of Pregnancy*, edited by G. E. W. Wolstenholme and M. O'Connor, p. 145. Little, Brown and Co., Boston, 1965.

34. HERTIG, A. T., ADAMS, E. C., AND MULLIGAN, W. J. On the pre-implantation stages of the human ovum: a description of four normal and four abnormal specimens ranging from the second to the fifth day of development. Contrib. Embryol., **35:** 199, 1954.

35. LEWIS, W. H., AND HARTMAN, C. G. Early cleavage stages of the egg of the monkey (Macacus rhesus). Contrib. Embryol., **24:** 187, 1933.

36. HERTIG, A. T., ROCK, J., AND ADAMS, E. C. A description of 34 human ova within the first 17 days of development. Amer. J. Anat., **98:** 435, 1956.

37. ENDERS, A. C., AND SCHLAFKE, S. J. Fine structure of the blastocyst. In *Preimplantation Stages of Pregnancy*, edited by G. E. W. Wolstenholme and M. O'Connor, p. 29. Little, Brown and Co., Boston, 1965.

38. HEUSER, C. H., AND STREETER, G. L. Development of the Macaque embryo. Contrib. Embryol., **29:** 15, 1941.

39. FAWCETT, D. W., WISLOCKI, G. B., AND WALDO, C. M. The development of the mouse ova in the anterior chamber of the eye and in the abdominal cavity. Amer. J. Anat., **81:** 413, 1947.

40. BARTELMEZ, G. W. Premenstrual and menstrual ischemia and the myth of endometrial arteriovenous anastomoses. Amer. J. Anat., **98:** 69, 1956.

41. CHANG, M. C. Development of parthenogenetic rabbit blastocysts induced by low temperature storage of unfertilized ova. J. Exp. Zool., **125:** 127, 1954.

42. BRADEN, A. W. H., AND AUSTIN, C. R. Reactions of unfertilized mouse eggs to some experimental stimuli. Exp. Cell Res., **7:** 277, 1954.

43. AUSTIN, C. R., AND BRADEN, A. W. H. Early reactions of the rodent egg to spermatozoon penetration. J. Exp. Biol., **33:** 358, 1956.

44. SIMARD, L. C. Polyembryonic embryos of the ovary of parthenogenic origin. Cancer, **10:** 215, 1957.

# CHAPTER 3

# Formation of the Bilaminar Germ Disc (Second Week of Development)

## NORMAL DEVELOPMENT
- EIGHTH DAY OF DEVELOPMENT: *trophoblast—cytotrophoblast and syncytio-trophoblast; embryoblast—entodermal and ectodermal germ layers; formation of amniotic cavity*
- NINTH DAY OF DEVELOPMENT: *lacunar stage of trophoblast development; primitive yolk sac or exocoelomic cavity*
- ELEVENTH TO TWELFTH DAY OF DEVELOPMENT: *trabecular stage of trophoblast development; uteroplacental circulation; extra-embryonic coelomic cavity; decidua reaction*
- THIRTEENTH DAY OF DEVELOPMENT: *primary stem villus; formation of definitive yolk sac*

## ABNORMAL DEVELOPMENT

During the second week of development, the human blastocyst becomes firmly embedded in the uterine mucosa, and the trophoblast and embryoblast begin their specific development. The *trophoblast* penetrates continuously deeper into the endometrium, thereby differentiating into the *syncytiotrophoblast* and the *cytotrophoblast;* the cells of the embryoblast form the *ectodermal* and *entodermal germ layers*, the two layers which constitute the *bilaminar germ disc.*

Though in the following paragraphs a day-by-day account is given of the major events occurring in the second week of development, it must be realized that embryos of the same fertilization age do not necessarily develop at the same rate. Indeed, considerable differences in the rate of growth have been found even at these early stages of development.[1]

# Normal Development

### Eighth Day of Development

At the eighth day of development the blastocyst is partially embedded in the endometrial stroma.[2] At the embryonic pole, that is, the area over the embryoblast, the trophoblast forms a solid disc composed of an inner layer of mononucleated cells, the *cytotrophoblast*, and an outer, multinucleated zone without distinct cell boundaries, the *syncytiotrophoblast* or *syncytium* (fig. 3-1). Mitotic figures are usually found in the cytotrophoblast but never in the syncytium, yet the thickness of the latter increases considerably, suggesting that the trophoblast cells divide in the cytotrophoblast and then migrate into the syncytiotrophoblast.[3] At the abembryonic pole the trophoblast remains temporarily undifferentiated, forming a thin layer of flattened cells (fig. 3-1).

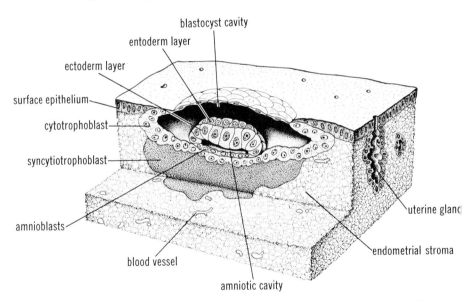

Figure 3-1. *Drawing representing a 7½ day human blastocyst, partially embedded in the endometrial stroma (modified after Hertig and Rock). The trophoblast consists of an inner layer with pale mononuclear cells, the cytotrophoblast, and an outer layer without distinct cell boundaries, the syncytiotrophoblast. The embryoblast is formed by the ectodermal and entodermal germ layers; the amniotic cavity appears as a small cleft. Note the mesothelial membrane forming the original lining of the blastocyst cavity.*

General Embryology

The cells of the inner cell mass or embryoblast differentiate into two distinct cell layers: (1) a layer of small, polyhedral cells, known as the *entodermal germ layer;* and (2) a layer of high columnar cells, the *ectodermal germ layer* (fig. 3-1). The cells of each of the germ layers form a disc and together they constitute the so-called *bilaminar germ disc.*

The cells of the ectodermal layer are initially firmly attached to the cytotrophoblast, but with further development small clefts appear between the two layers. These clefts subsequently coalesce, thus forming a cavity known as the *amniotic cavity* (fig. 3-1). Along the trophoblastic border of this newly formed cavity are found large, flattened cells, the *amnioblasts*, which are probably derived from the trophoblast. The junction between the amnioblasts and the ectodermal germ layer is known as the *amnio-ectodermal junction.*

The endometrial stroma adjacent to the implantation site is edematous and highly vascular and the large tortuous glands secrete abundant glycogen and mucus.

## Ninth Day of Development

The blastocyst is more deeply embedded in the endometrium, and the penetration defect in the surface epithelium is closed by a fibrin coagulum (fig. 3-2).[2] The trophoblast shows considerable progress in development, particularly at the embryonic pole, where isolated intracytoplasmic vacuoles appear in the syncytium. When these vacuoles fuse they form large lacunae, and this phase of the trophoblast development is therefore known as the *lacunar stage* (fig. 3-2). The endometrial stroma surrounding the trophoblast shows vascular congestion, and the cells are rich in glycogen.

At the abembryonic pole, meanwhile, flattened cells delaminate from the inner surface of the cytotrophoblast and form a thin membrane, known as *Heuser's membrane* (fig. 3-2). This membrane is continuous with the edges of the entoderm layer and together they form the lining of the *exocoelomic cavity* or *primitive yolk sac.* Although most investigators believe that the cells of Heuser's membrane are of cytotrophoblastic origin, others suggest that, as in the Macaque monkey, this membrane is formed by migration of the primitive entoderm cells along the inside of the blastocyst cavity.[4-6]

## Eleventh to Twelfth Days of Development

By the 11th to 12th day of development the blastocyst is completely embedded in the endometrial stroma, and the surrounding surface epithelium covers almost entirely the original defect in the

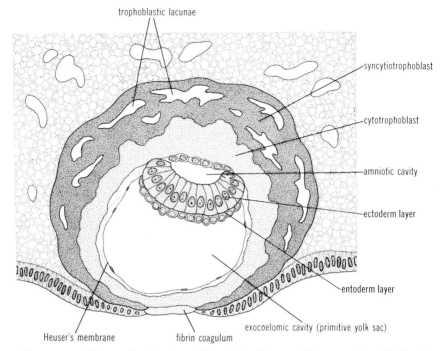

trophoblastic lacunae

syncytiotrophoblast

cytotrophoblast

amniotic cavity

ectoderm layer

entoderm layer

exocoelomic cavity (primitive yolk sac)

Heuser's membrane          fibrin coagulum

Figure 3-2. *Schematic drawing of a 9-day human blastocyst (modified after Hertig and Rock). The syncytiotrophoblast shows a large number of intracytoplasmic lacunae (lacunar stage in trophoblast formation). Note the flat mesothelial cells which have delaminated from the inner surface of the cytotrophoblast to form Heuser's membrane. The bilaminar germ disc consists of a layer of high columnar ectodermal cells and a layer of small polyhedral entodermal cells. The amniotic cavity is well delineated. The original surface defect is closed by a fibrin coagulum.*

epithelial lining of the mucosa (fig. 3-3). The blastocyst now produces a slight swelling on the inner surface of the uterus.

In comparison with the 9-day stage, the trophoblast has made considerable progress, and the lacunar spaces in the syncytium form an intercommunicating network. This is particularly evident at the embryonic pole, where the syncytium begins to assume a trabecular appearance (*trabecular stage*); at the abembryonic pole, however, the trophoblast consists mainly of cytotrophoblastic cells and only a few lacunar spaces are present (fig. 3-3).

The maternal capillaries around the implantation site are congested and dilated and form *sinusoids*. These sinusoids originate from anastomoses between the spiral arterioles and endometrial veins. It is thought that the trophoblast produces a substance capable of dilating blood vessels, thus aiding in the formation of the sinusoids.[7-9]

In the meantime the syncytial cells penetrate deeper into the stroma and erode the endothelial lining of the maternal sinusoids. The syncytium then becomes continuous with the endothelial cells of the vessels, and maternal blood enters the lacunar system (fig. 3-3). As the trophoblast continues to invade the stroma, more and more sinusoids are invaded and eventually the lacunae become continuous with the arterial and venous systems. As a result of the difference in pressure between the arterial and venous capillaries, maternal blood begins to flow through the trophoblastic lacunar system, thus establishing the *uteroplacental circulation*.

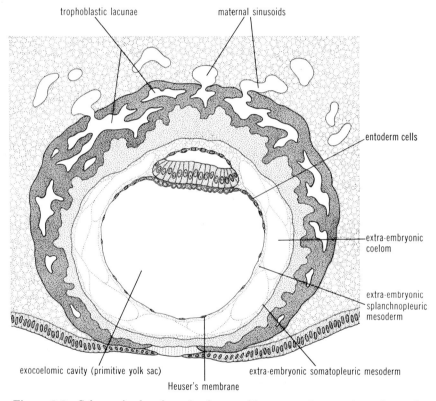

trophoblastic lacunae

maternal sinusoids

entoderm cells

extra-embryonic coelom

extra-embryonic splanchnopleuric mesoderm

exocoelomic cavity (primitive yolk sac)

Heuser's membrane

extra-embryonic somatopleuric mesoderm

Figure 3-3. *Schematic drawing of a human blastocyst of approximately 12 days (modified after Hertig and Rock). The trophoblastic lacunae at the embryonic pole are in open connection with the maternal sinusoids in the endometrial stroma. The trophoblast at the abembryonic pole shows little differentiation. Cells continue to delaminate from the cytotrophoblast to form the extra-embryonic mesoderm, which lines the inner aspect of the trophoblast (extra-embryonic somatopleuric mesoderm), and the outer surface of the primitive yolk sac (extra-embryonic splanchnopleuric mesoderm). Note the spread of entodermal cells over the inside of Heuser's membrane.*

Differentiation of the trophoblast is not restricted to the syncytial portion but also involves the cytotrophoblast. On the inner surface of this layer, cells continue to delaminate. In this manner a fine, loose tissue, known as the *extra-embryonic mesoderm*, is formed. It fills the expanding space between the trophoblast externally and the amnion and primitive yolk sac internally (fig. 3-3). Soon, large cavities develop in the extra-embryonic mesoderm and when these become confluent, a new space, known as the *extra-embryonic coelom*, is formed. This space surrounds the primitive yolk sac and amniotic cavity except where the extra-embryonic mesoderm forms the future connection between the germ disc and the trophoblast (figs. 3-3 and 3-4). The extra-embryonic mesoderm lining the cyto-trophoblast and amnion is called the *extra-embryonic somatopleuric mesoderm;* that covering the yolk sac is known as the *extra-embryonic splanchnopleuric mesoderm*.

The growth of the bilaminar germ disc is relatively slow compared to that of the trophoblast, but by about the end of the 12th day, cells originating from the entoderm begin to spread over the inside of Heuser's membrane (fig. 3-3).

The cells of the endometrium, meanwhile, become polyhedral and loaded with glycogen and lipids; the intercellular spaces are filled with extravasate and the tissue is edematous. These changes, known as the *decidua reaction*, are at first confined to the area immediately surrounding the implantation site, but soon spread throughout the endometrium.

**Thirteenth Day of Development**

By the 13th day of development the surface defect in the endometrium has usually healed. Occasionally, however, a bleeding may occur at the implantation site as a result of increased blood flow into the lacunar spaces at the abembryonic pole. Since this bleeding occurs at about the 28th day of the menstrual cycle, it may be confused with a normal menstrual bleeding and so cause an inaccuracy in determining the expected delivery date.

The trophoblast shows further organization, particularly at the embryonic pole. The syncytial trabeculae become arranged in such a manner that they radiate out from the cytotrophoblast (fig. 3-4). Cytotrophoblast cells, meanwhile, grow into the core of the syncytial trabeculae, which then become known as the *primary stem villi* (figs. 3-4 and 4-7A).

The entodermal germ layer, which in the 12-day embryo started to form a layer of flat epithelial cells along the inside of Heuser's membrane, continues to proliferate and the newly formed cells

General Embryology

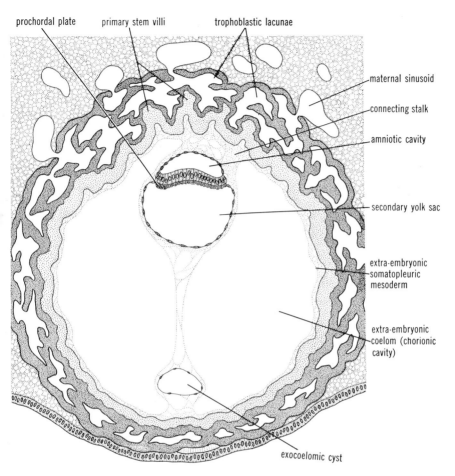

prochordal plate     primary stem villi     trophoblastic lacunae

maternal sinusoid

connecting stalk

amniotic cavity

secondary yolk sac

extra-embryonic somatopleuric mesoderm

extra-embryonic coelom (chorionic cavity)

exocoelomic cyst

Figure 3-4. *Schematic drawing of a 13-day human blastocyst completely embedded in the endometrium (modified after Hertig and Rock). The trophoblastic lacunae are now present at the embryonic as well as the abembryonic pole, and the uteroplacental circulation has begun. Note the formation of the primary stem villi and the extra-embryonic coelom. The secondary yolk sac is entirely lined with entoderm and the exocoelomic cyst in the extra-embryonic coelom forms a remnant of the primitive yolk sac or exocoelomic cavity.*

gradually line a new cavity known as the *secondary* or *definitive yolk sac* (fig. 3-4). This yolk sac is much smaller than the original exocoelomic cavity or primitive yolk sac and it is believed that during its formation large portions of the exocoelomic cavity are pinched off. These portions are thought to be represented by the so-called *exocoelomic cysts*, which are often found in the extra-embryonic coelom or *chorionic cavity* (fig. 3-4).[1] Other investigators, however, believe that the secondary yolk sac develops by dehiscence of the

Bilaminar Germ Disc                                                     43 entodermal germ disc and that the exocoelomic cavity is pinched off *in toto* and does not play any role in the formation of the secondary yolk sac.[10,11]

By the end of the second week, the germ disc is represented by two apposed cell discs: the ectodermal germ layer, which forms the floor of the continuously expanding amniotic cavity, and the entodermal germ layer which forms the roof of the secondary yolk sac. In its cephalic region the entodermal disc shows a slight thickening known as the *prochordal plate*. This is an area of columnar cells which are firmly attached to the overlying ectodermal disc (fig. 3-4).

# *Abnormal Development*

In 1956, Hertig, Rock and Adams described a series of 26 implanted blastocysts varying in age from 7½ to 17 days.[1] All these ova were recovered from patients of normal fertility. Surprisingly, nine (34.6 per cent) of the specimens appeared to be abnormal. Some consisted of syncytium only, whereas others showed variable degrees of trophoblastic hypoplasia. In two of them the embryoblast was absent and in some the germ disc showed an abnormal orientation.

It is likely that the most abnormal blastocysts would not have caused any sign of pregnancy, as their trophoblast was of such inferior quality that the corpus luteum could not have persisted. These ova probably would have been aborted with the following menstrual flow. Others, however, might have been able to survive for some time, presumably to be aborted at a later stage of pregnancy.

In some cases the trophoblast is characterized by a high proliferative activity. These cases result in the formation of noninvasive *hydatidiform moles*, or highly malignant tumors, known as *chorionepitheliomas*.

## References

1. HERTIG, A. T., ROCK, J., AND ADAMS, E. C. A description of 34 human ova within the first 17 days of development. Amer. J. Anat., **98:** 435, 1956.
2. HERTIG, A. T., AND ROCK, J. Two human ova of the previllous stage, having a developmental age of about seven and nine days respectively. Contrib. Embryol., **31:** 65, 1945.
3. WIMSATT, W. A. New histological observations on the placenta of the sheep. Amer. J. Anat., **87:** 391, 1950.
4. HERTIG, A. T., AND ROCK, J. Two human ova of the previllous stage, having an ovulation age of eleven and twelve days respectively. Contrib. Embryol., **29:** 127, 1941.
5. HEUSER, C. H., AND STREETER, G. L. Development of the Macaque embryo. Contrib. Embryol., **29:** 15, 1941.
6. WISLOCKI, G. B., AND STREETER, G. L. On the placentation of the Macaque (*Macaca*

*mulatta*) from the time of implantation until the formation of the definitive placenta. Contrib. Embryol., **27:** 1, 1938.

7. HAMILTON, W. J., AND BOYD, J. D. Development of the human placenta in the first three months of gestation. J. Anat., **94:** 297, 1960.
8. HAMILTON, W. J., AND BOYD, J. D. Phases of human development. In *Modern Trends in Obstetrics and Gynaecology*, edited by K. Bowes. Butterworth and Co., Ltd., London, 1950.
9. WISLOCKI, G. B., AND BENNETT, H. S. The histology and cytology of the human and monkey placenta with special reference to the trophoblast. Amer. J. Anat., **73:** 335, 1943.
10. STRAUSS, F. Gedanken zur Entwicklung des Amnions und des Dottersackes beim Menschen. Rev. Suisse Zool., **52:** 213, 1945.
11. STARCK, D. Die Frühphase der Menschlichen Embryonalentwicklung und ihre Bedeutung für die Beurteilung der Säugerontogenese. Ergebn. Anat. Entwicklungsgesch., **35:** 133, 1956.

# CHAPTER 4

# Formation of the Trilaminar Germ Disc (Third Week of Development)

---

### NORMAL DEVELOPMENT
- **TRILAMINAR GERM DISC**: *appearance of the primitive streak and node of Hensen; formation of the mesoderm layer; formation of the notochord*
- **FURTHER DEVELOPMENT OF THE TROPHOBLAST**: *secondary stem villus; cytotrophoblast shell; connecting stalk*

---

## *Normal Development*

### Trilaminar Germ Disc

At the end of the second week of development, when the germ disc consists of the apposed ectodermal and entodermal germ layers, a vaguely defined streak appears on the surface of the ectoderm facing the amniotic cavity (fig. 4-1). In a 15- to 16-day embryo this streak, known as the *primitive streak*, is clearly visible as a narrow groove with slightly bulging regions on either side (fig. 4-2*A*). The cephalic end of the streak, known as *Hensen's node*, consists of a small pit, surrounded by a slightly elevated area (fig. 4-2). When at this stage of development a transverse section is made through the caudal end of the embryonic disc (fig. 4-2*B*), the cells in the region of the primitive streak are found to be spherical; in addition, a new cell layer is visible on each side of the streak between the ectodermal and entodermal layers.

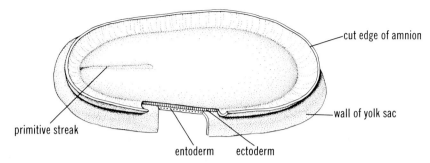

Figure 4-1. *Schematic view of the germ disc at the end of the second week of development. The amniotic cavity has been opened to permit a dorsal view of the ectodermal germ layer. In one area the amnion and the wall of the yolk sac have been removed to show the entodermal and ectodermal layers in contact with each other. Note that the primitive streak is being formed.*

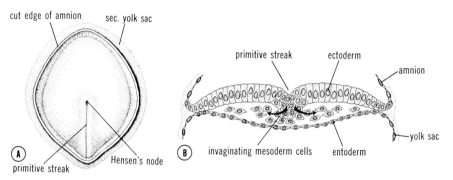

Figure 4-2. *A, Schematic drawing of the dorsal side of a 16-day presomite embryo (modified after Streeter). The primitive streak and Hensen's node are now clearly visible. B, Transverse section through the region of the primitive streak, showing the invagination of the mesoderm cells.*

In analogy with findings in the lower vertebrates, it is believed that in the human embryo also, cells of the ectodermal layer migrate along the surface of the disc in the direction of the primitive streak (fig. 4-3). In the region of the streak, the cells become spherical and move into the groove. This movement is known as *invagination*. Once the cells have invaginated, they migrate in lateral direction between the ectodermal and entodermal layers to form an intermediate cell layer, known as the *mesodermal germ layer* (fig. 4-2B).[1,2]

As more and more cells move in between the ectodermal and entodermal layers, they begin to migrate in lateral and cephalic directions (fig. 4-3). The cells invaginating in the region of the primitive pit move straight forward in cephalic direction until they reach the

Formation of the Trilaminar Germ Disc

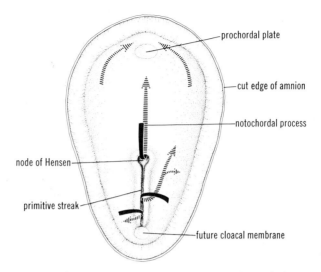

Figure 4-3. *Schematic representation of the dorsal side of the germ disc, indicating the movement of surface cells (solid black lines) toward the primitive streak and node of Hensen, and the subsequent migration of the mesoderm cells between the entodermal and ectodermal germ layers (broken lines). The notochordal process occupies the midline region extending from the prochordal plate to the node of Hensen.*

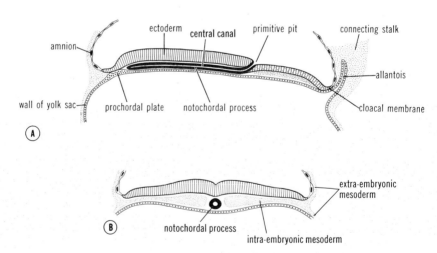

Figure 4-4. *A, Schematic drawing of a cephalo-caudal section through a 17-day embryo, showing the notochordal process and the central canal extending from the primitive pit in cephalic direction. Note the allantois. B, Transverse section through the cephalic part of a 17-day embryo. Note the notochordal process and the central canal; the intraembryonic mesoderm is in contact with the extra-embryonic mesoderm covering the yolk sac and the amnion.*

General Embryology

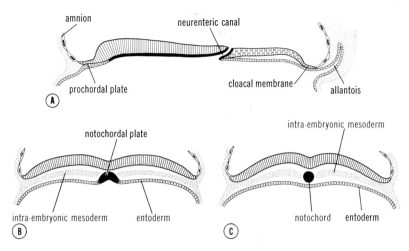

Figure 4-5. *A, Schematic drawing of a cephalo-caudal section through an 18-day embryo. The cells in the floor of the notochordal process which fused with the entoderm have disappeared and the neurenteric canal connects the amniotic cavity with the yolk sac. The remaining portion of the notochordal process is temporarily intercalated in the entodermal germ layer (B). C, Transverse section through the cephalic part of a 19-day embryo, showing the definitive notochord flanked by the intra-embryonic mesoderm.*

*prochordal plate,* a small area where the entodermal and ectodermal germ layers are firmly attached to each other (fig. 4-3). The mesoderm cells extending from the node of Hensen to the prochordal plate form a tube-like process, known as the *notochordal* or *head process* (fig. 4-4A). The small, central canal is considered as the forward extension of the primitive pit in the node of Hensen (fig. 4-4A). In the region of the prochordal plate the ectoderm and entoderm cells adhere so tightly to each other that the cells of the notochordal process are unable to separate them.

In the meantime the cells of the mesoderm layer migrate in lateral direction to such an extent that they establish contact with the extra-embryonic mesoderm covering the yolk sac and amniotic cavity (fig. 4-4B). In cephalic direction they pass on each side of the prochordal plate to meet each other in front of this area (figs. 4-3 and 4-4A). By the 17th day of development the mesoderm layer and the notochordal process separate the entoderm and ectoderm layers entirely with the exception of the prochordal plate in the cephalic region and the *cloacal plate* in the region caudal to the primitive streak (fig. 4-4A).

By the 18th day of development the floor of the notochordal process fuses with the underlying entoderm and in the merged areas

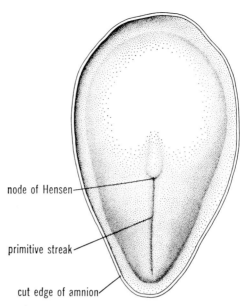

node of Hensen

primitive streak

cut edge of amnion

Figure 4-6. *Schematic drawing of the dorsal aspect of an 18-day presomite embryo (modified after Heuser). The embryo has a pear-shaped appearance and shows at its caudal end the primitive streak and node of Hensen.*

the two layers disintegrate (fig. 4-5A). Hence, the lumen of the notochordal process disappears and a small canal, the *neurenteric canal*, connects temporarily the yolk sac and the amniotic cavity (fig. 4-5A). The remaining portion of the notochordal process forms a narrow plate of cells, intercalated in the entodermal germ layer (fig. 4-5B). Subsequently, the notochordal cells proliferate and form a solid cord, known as the *definitive notochord*. This structure in turn becomes detached from the entoderm, which once again forms an uninterrupted layer in the roof of the yolk sac (fig. 4-5C).

Concomitantly with the formation of the cloacal membrane, the posterior wall of the yolk sac forms a small diverticulum which extends into the connecting stalk. This diverticulum, the *allanto-enteric diverticulum*, or *allantois*, appears at about the 16th day of development (figs. 4-4 and 4-5). Although in some lower vertebrates the allantois serves as a reservoir for the excretion products of the renal system, in man it remains rudimentary and plays no role in the development.

The embryonic disc, initially flat and round, gradually becomes elongated and by the 18th day has a broad cephalic and a narrow caudal end (fig. 4-6). In comparison to the younger stages it is evident that expansion of the embryonic disc occurs mainly in the cephalic region; the region of the primitive streak remains more or less the same size.

50

It must be realized, however, that much of the growth and elongation of the cephalic part of the disc is caused by a continuous migration of cells from the primitive streak region in cephalic direction. Although after the 19th day of development the primitive streak regresses caudally, invagination of surface cells and their subsequent migration in forward and lateral directions continue until the end of the fourth week. At that stage the primitive streak and node of Hensen show regressive changes and rapidly diminish in size. The fact that the caudal end of the disc continues to supply new cells until the end of the fourth week has an important bearing on the further development of the embryo. In the cephalic part the germ layers begin their specific differentiation by the middle of the third week, whereas in the caudal part this occurs by the end of the fourth week.

## Further Development of the Trophoblast

By the beginning of the third week the trophoblast is characterized by a great number of *primary stem villi* which consist of a cytotrophoblastic core covered by a syncytial layer (figs. 4-7A and 3-4). During further development mesodermal cells either originating from the extra-embryonic somatopleuric mesoderm or from the cytotrophoblast penetrate the core of the primary villi and grow in the direction of the decidua.[3,4] The newly formed structure, the *secondary stem villus*, is thus composed of a loose connective tissue core covered by a layer of cytotrophoblastic cells, which in turn is covered by a thin layer of syncytium (figs. 4-7B and 4-8).

By the end of the third week the mesodermal cells in the core of

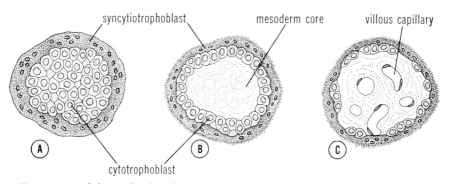

Figure 4-7. *Schematic drawings to show the development of the villus. A, Transverse section of a primary stem villus, showing a core of cytotrophoblastic cells covered by a layer of syncytium. B, Transverse section of a secondary stem villus with a core of mesoderm covered by a single layer of cytotrophoblastic cells, which in turn is covered by syncytium. C, The mesoderm of the secondary villus shows a number of capillaries.*

Formation of the Trilaminar Germ Disc 51

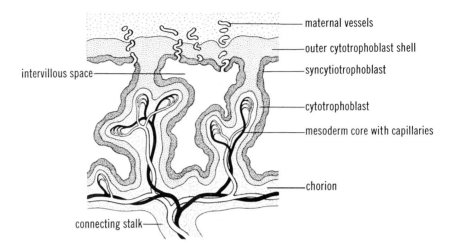

maternal vessels

outer cytotrophoblast shell

syncytiotrophoblast

intervillous space

cytotrophoblast

mesoderm core with capillaries

chorion

connecting stalk

Figure 4-8. *Schematic drawing of a villus at the end of the third week of development. Note that the maternal vessels penetrate the cytotrophoblast shell to enter the intervillous spaces, which surround the villi. The capillaries in the villi are in contact with the vessels in the connecting stalk, which in turn are connected to the intra-embryonic vessels.*

the villus begin to differentiate and small capillaries appear (fig. 4-7C). This villous capillary system soon makes contact with capillaries developing in the extra-embryonic mesoderm covering the inside of the trophoblast and in the connecting stalk (fig. 4-8). These vessels in turn establish contact with the intra-embryonic circulatory system during the fourth week of development, thus connecting the placenta and the embryo (see Chapters 5 and 12).

Meanwhile, the cytotrophoblastic cells in the villi penetrate progressively into the overlying syncytium until they reach the maternal endometrium. Here they establish contact with similar extensions of neighboring villous stems, thus forming a thin *outer cytotrophoblast shell* (fig. 4-8). This shell at first is localized on the embryonic pole only, but gradually it expands toward the abembryonic pole until it surrounds the trophoblast entirely (fig. 4-9).[5]

The extra-embryonic coelom or chorionic cavity meanwhile becomes larger, and by the 19th or 20th day the embryo is attached to its trophoblastic shell by a narrow *connecting stalk* only (fig. 4-9). This stalk is composed of extra-embryonic mesenchyme continuous with that lining the inner surface of the trophoblast and is attached to the embryo at its caudal end. The connecting stalk, also known as the *body stalk*, later develops into the *umbilical cord*, which forms the connection between the placenta and the embryo.

General Embryology

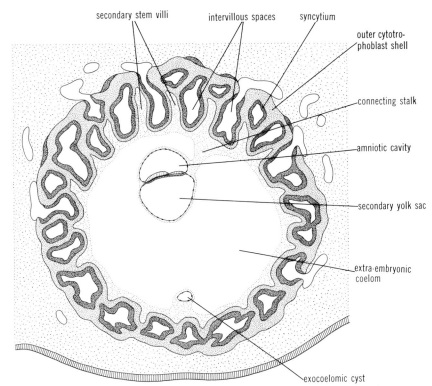

secondary stem villi | intervillous spaces | syncytium

outer cytotro-
phoblast shell

connecting stalk

amniotic cavity

secondary yolk sac

extra-embryonic
coelom

exocoelomic cyst

Figure 4-9. *Diagram showing a presomite embryo and the trophoblast at the end of the third week. The secondary stem villi give the trophoblast a characteristic radial appearance. The intervillous spaces are found throughout the trophoblast and are lined with syncytium. Note how the cytotrophoblastic cells surround the trophoblast entirely and are in direct contact with the endometrium. The embryo is suspended in the extra-embryonic coelom by means of the connecting stalk.*

## References

1. HOLTFRETER, J., AND HAMBURGER, V. Embryogenesis; progressive differentiation. In *Analysis of Development*, edited by B. H. Willier, P. A. Weiss, and V. Hamburger, p. 230. W. B. Saunders Co., Philadelphia, 1955.
2. MCCRADY, E. The evolution and significance of the germ layer. J. Tenn. Acad. Sci., **19:** 240, 1944.
3. HERTIG, A. T. Angiogenesis in the early human chorion and in the primary placenta of the Macaque monkey. Contrib. Embryol., **25:** 37, 1935.
4. WISLOCKI, J. B., AND STREETER, G. L. Placentation of the Macaque. Contrib. Embryol., **27:** 1, 1938.
5. HAMILTON, W. J., AND BOYD, J. D. Development of the human placenta in the first three months of gestation. J. Anat., **94:** 297, 1960.

CHAPTER **5**

# Differentiation of the Germ Layers and Establishment of Body Form (Fourth to Eighth Weeks of Development)

---

• ECTODERMAL GERM LAYER: *derivatives of the ectoderm*
• MESODERMAL GERM LAYER: *differentiation of the somite; intermediate mesoderm; somatic and visceral mesoderm layers; blood, blood vessels and hearttube*
• ENTODERMAL GERM LAYER: *derivatives of the entoderm*
• EXTERNAL APPEARANCE AT THE END OF THE SECOND MONTH: *crown-rump length*

---

During the fourth to eighth weeks of development, a period known as the *embryonic period*, each of the three germ layers gives rise to a number of specific tissues and organs. In general terms it can be said that by the end of the embryonic period the main organ systems have been laid down. As a result of the organ formation, the shape of the embryo changes greatly and the major features of the external body form are recognizable by the end of the second month.

In this chapter the main organs, developing from each of the three germ layers, are briefly described. In the second part of this book the development of each organ system will be discussed in detail. Since the external contours of the embryo are dependent on the development of the tissues and organs, it is not always possible to separate the development of body form from that of the germ layers.

## Ectodermal Germ Layer

At the beginning of the third week of development the ectodermal germ layer has the shape of a flat disc which in the cephalic region is somewhat broader than caudally (figs. 4-1 and 4-2A). Simultaneously with the formation of the notochord, however, and in all probability under its inductive influence, the ectodermal disc changes in form and gives rise to the *central nervous system*.

Initially the nervous system appears as a round to oval thickening of the ectoderm in the cephalic region of the embryo (fig. 5-1A). By the end of the third week, however, it has an elongated, slipper-shaped form, the *neural plate*, which gradually expands in the direction of the primitive streak (fig. 5-1B). During the next few days the lateral edges of the neural plate become more elevated to form the *neural folds*, while the depressed midregion forms a groove, the *neural groove* (figs. 5-1B and 5-2A, B). Gradually the neural folds approach each other in the midline, where they fuse (fig. 5-2C). This fusion begins in the region of the future neck (fourth somite) and proceeds in cephalic and caudal directions (fig. 5-3A, B). As a result of the fusion a tube-like structure, the *neural tube*, is formed. At the cephalic and caudal ends of the embryo this tube remains temporarily in open connection with the amniotic cavity by way of the *anterior* and *posterior neuropores*, respectively (figs. 5-3B and 5-4A). Closure of the anterior neuropore occurs approximately at day 25 (18- to 20-somite stage), whereas the posterior neuropore closes at day 27 (25-somite stage). The central nervous system then forms a closed tubular structure with a narrow caudal portion, the *spinal cord*, and a much broader cephalic portion characterized by a number of

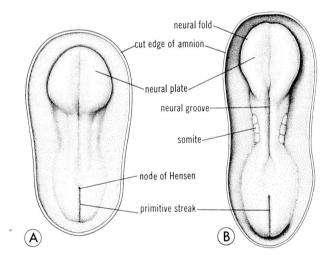

Figure 5-1. *A, Dorsal view of a late presomite embryo (approximately 1.4 mm.) (modified after Davis). The amnion has been removed. The neural plate is clearly visible. B, Dorsal view of a human embryo at approximately 20 days (modified after Ingalls). Note the appearance of the somites and the formation of the neural groove and the neural folds.*

Germ Layers and Body Form

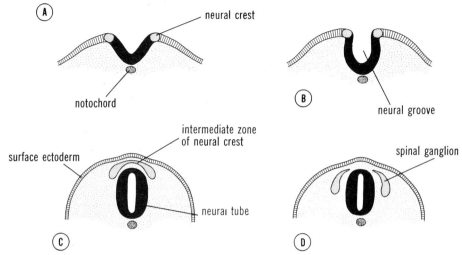

Figure 5-2. *Schematic drawing of a number of transverse sections through successively older embryos, showing the formation of the neural folds, neural groove, and neural tube. The cells of the neural crest, initially forming an intermediate zone between the neural tube and surface ectoderm (C) develop into the spinal and cranial sensory ganglia (D).*

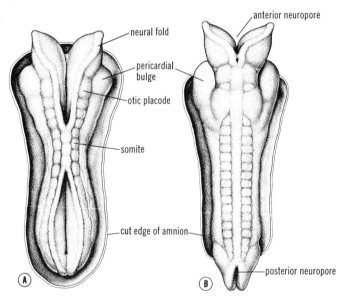

Figure 5-3. *A, Dorsal view of a human embryo at approximately day 22 (modified after Payne). Seven distinct somites are visible on each side of the neural tube. B, Dorsal view of a human embryo at approximately day 23 (modified after Corner). Note the pericardial bulge on each side of the midline in the cephalic part of the embryo.*

General Embryology

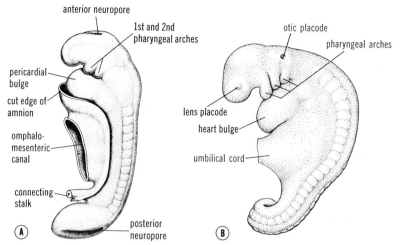

Figure 5-4. *Lateral view of a 14-somite embryo (approximately 25 days). Note the bulging pericardial area and the first and second pharyngeal arches separated by the first pharyngeal groove (modified after Heuser). B, Schematic drawing showing the left side of a 25-somite embryo approximately 28 days old. The first three pharyngeal arches and the lens and otic placodes are visible (modified after Streeter).*

dilatations, the *brain vesicles* (see "Central Nervous System," Chapter 15).

By the time the neural tube is closed, two other ectodermal derivatives, the *otic placode* and the *lens placode* become visible in the cephalic region of the embryo (fig. 5-4B). The otic placode is situated dorsal to the second pharyngeal cleft and forms a distinct ectodermal thickening on the lateral aspect of the embryo. During further development the otic placode invaginates and forms the *otic pit*. By the end of the fourth week this pit is closed over by the surface ectoderm, thus giving rise to the *otic vesicle* (see "The Ear," Chapter 17). At approximately the same time, the *lens placode* appears by induction of an outpocketing of the brain, the *optic vesicle*. This placode also invaginates and during the fifth week loses contact with the surface ectoderm to form the *lens vesicle* (see "The Eye," Chapter 16).

In summary, the ectodermal germ layer gives rise to: (1) the central nervous system; (2) the peripheral nervous system; and (3) the sensory epithelium of the sense organs. In addition the following structures are derived from the ectoderm: the epidermis including the hair, nails and subcutaneous glands; the hypophysis; the enamel layer of the teeth; and the epithelial lining of a number of other organs, which are described later.

Germ Layers and Body Form                                             57

## Mesodermal Germ Layer

Since the external contours of the embryo are greatly influenced by the formation of the *somites*, a series of mesodermal tissue blocks on each side of the midline, the development and differentiation of these structures will be discussed briefly.

Initially the cells of the mesodermal germ layer form a thin sheet of loosely woven tissue on each side of the midline (fig. 5-5A). By about the 17th day, however, some of the cells close to the midline proliferate and form a thickened plate of tissue, known as the *paraxial mesoderm* (fig. 5-5B). More laterally, the mesoderm layer remains thin and is known as the *lateral plate*. With the appearance and subsequent coalescence of numerous intercellular cavities in the lateral plate, this tissue is divided into two layers (fig. 5-5B, C): (1) a layer continuous with the extra-embryonic mesoderm covering the amnion, known as the *somatic* or *parietal mesoderm layer*; and (2) a layer continuous with the mesoderm covering the yolk sac, known as the *splanchnic* or *visceral mesoderm layer* (fig. 5-5C, D). Together, these layers line a newly formed cavity, the *intra-embryonic coelomic cavity*, which on each side of the embryo is continuous with the

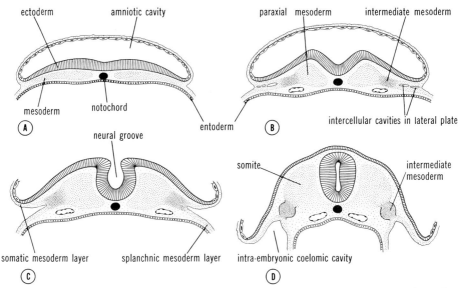

Figure 5-5. *Transverse sections showing the development of the mesodermal germ layer. A, At day 17; B, day 19; C, day 20; D, day 21. The thin mesodermal sheet gives rise to the paraxial mesoderm (the future somites), the intermediate mesoderm (the future excretory units), and the lateral plate, which is split into the somatic and splanchnic mesoderm layers lining the intra-embryonic coelomic cavity.*

General Embryology

extra-embryonic coelom. The tissue initially connecting the paraxial mesoderm and the lateral plate is known as the *intermediate mesoderm* (fig. 5-5B, D).

By the end of the third week the paraxial mesoderm on each side of the neural tube breaks up into segmented blocks of epithelioid cells, the *somites*. The first pair of somites arises in the cephalic part of the embryo, and from here new somites appear in craniocaudal sequence, until at the end of the fifth week approximately 42-44 pairs are present (figs. 5-3 and 5-4).[1] These are 4 occipital, 8 cervical, 12 thoracic, 5 lumbar, 5 sacral, and 8 to 10 coccygeal pairs. The first occipital and the last 5-7 coccygeal somites later disappear. During this period of development the age of the embryo is usually expressed in the number of somites, since they form one of its most characteristic external features. Based on embryos described by a number of authors, Table 5-1 represents the approximate age of the embryo correlated to the number of somites.[2-4]

DIFFERENTIATION OF THE SOMITE. By the beginning of the fourth week the epithelioid cells forming the ventral and medial walls of the somite are characterized by a high proliferative activity (fig. 5-6A, B). They gradually lose their epithelial shape, become polymorphous and migrate toward the notochord (fig. 5-6B). These cells, collectively known as the *sclerotome*, form a loosely woven tissue known as *mesenchyme* or *young connective tissue*. One of the main characteristics of the mesenchymal cells is their ability to differentiate in many different ways.[5-7] They may become *fibroblasts*, associated with the formation of the reticular, collagenous and elastic fibers as seen in connective tissue; *chondroblasts*, involved in the formation of cartilage; or *osteoblasts*, associated with bone formation (see "Skeletal System," Chapter 9).

After the sclerotome cells have migrated in ventro-medial direction, the remaining dorsal somite wall, now referred to as the *dermatome*, gives rise to a new layer of cells, which is directly in contact with its inner surface (fig. 5-6C).[8] The cells of this layer are characterized by pale nuclei and darkly stained nucleoli and fail to divide

Table 5-1. *Number of Somites Correlated to Approximate Age in Days*

| Approx. Age | No. of Somites | Approx. Age | No. of Somites |
|---|---|---|---|
| *days* | | *days* | |
| 20 | 1–4 | 25 | 17–20 |
| 21 | 4–7 | 26 | 20–23 |
| 22 | 7–10 | 27 | 23–26 |
| 23 | 10–13 | 28 | 26–29 |
| 24 | 13–17 | 30 | 34–35 |

Germ Layers and Body Form                                        59

once they are laid down. The tissue so composed is known as the *myotome*. Each myotome provides the musculature for its own segment
(see "Muscular System," Chapter 10).

After the cells of the dermatome have formed the myotome, they

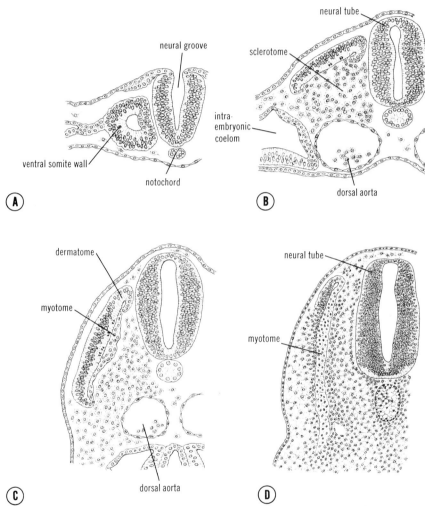

Figure 5-6. *Successive stages in the development of the somite. A, The mesoderm cells are arranged in epithelial fashion around a small cavity. B, As a result
of proliferation of the ventral and medial walls of the somite, the cells lose their
epithelial arrangement and migrate in the direction of the notochord. These cells
are referred to as the sclerotome. C, The dorsal somite wall gives rise to a new cell
layer, the myotome. D, After extension of the myotome in ventral direction, the
dermatome cells lose their epithelial configuration and spread out under the overlying ectoderm to form the dermis.*

lose their epithelial characteristics and spread out under the overlying ectoderm (fig. 5-6D). Here they form the *dermis* and subcutaneous tissue of the skin (see "Integumentary System," Chapter 19).

INTERMEDIATE MESODERM. This tissue, which temporarily connects the paraxial mesoderm with the lateral plate (fig. 5-5D), differentiates in a manner entirely different from that of the somites. In the cervical and upper thoracic regions it forms segmentally arranged cell clusters (the future *nephrotomes*), whereas more caudally it forms an unsegmented mass of tissue, known as the *nephrogenic cord*. From this partly segmented, partly unsegmented intermediate mesoderm develop the excretory units of the urinary system (see "Urinary System," Chapter 11).

SOMATIC AND VISCERAL MESODERM LAYERS. These layers, derived from the lateral plate and lining the intra-embryonic coelom (fig. 5-5C, D) form the *mesothelial* or *serous membranes* of the peritoneal, pleural and pericardial cavities (see "Coelomic Cavity and Mesenteries," Chapter 14).

BLOOD, BLOOD VESSELS AND HEART TUBE. At about the middle of the third week mesoderm cells located on each side of the midline and in front of the prochordal plate differentiate into blood- and vessel-forming cells. These cells, known as the *angioblasts*, form isolated clusters and cords (*angiogenetic cell clusters*), which gradually become canalized by confluence of intercellular clefts (fig. 5-7). The centrally located cells then give rise to the primitive blood cells, while those on the periphery flatten and form the *endothelial cells* lining the *blood islands* (fig. 5-7B, C). The blood islands approach each other rapidly by sprouting of the endothelial cells and after fusion give rise to small vessels.

The formation of blood cells and blood vessels is not restricted to the embryo proper, but also occurs in the extra-embryonic mesoderm of the villous stems, of the connecting stalk and in the wall

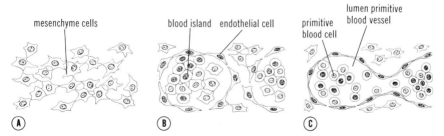

Figure 5-7. *Successive stages of blood vessel formation. A, Undifferentiated mesenchyme cells. B, Blood island formation. C, Primitive capillary. Note the differentiation of mesenchymal cells into the primitive blood cells and the endothelial cells.*

Germ Layers and Body Form                                                                 61

of the yolk sac (fig. 5-8). By continuous budding the extra-embryonic vessels establish contact with those inside the embryo, thus connecting the embryo and the placenta.

Although the vessels forming the *heart tube* are established in exactly the same manner as described for the other intra-embryonic vessels, the cephalo-caudal folding as well as the lateral folding of the embryonic disc make the formation and position of the heart somewhat more complicated to understand (see "Cardiovascular System," Chapter 12).

Besides the main derivatives of the mesodermal germ layer, briefly described above, the following tissues and organs are considered to be of mesodermal origin: (1) connective tissue, cartilage and bone; (2) striated and smooth musculature; (3) blood and lymph cells and

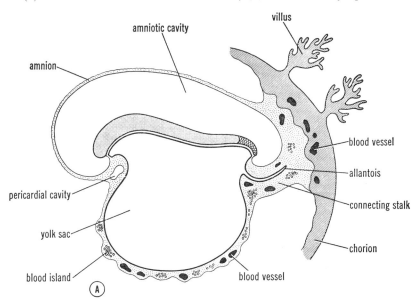

Figure 5-8. *Extra-embryonic blood vessel formation in the chorion, the connecting stalk, and the wall of the yolk sac in a presomite embryo of approximately 19 days (modified from Keibel and Elze).*

the walls of the heart, blood and lymph vessels; (4) kidneys, gonads and their corresponding ducts; (5) the cortical portion of the suprarenal gland; and (6) the spleen.

## Entodermal Germ Layer

The entodermal germ layer initially has the shape of a flat disc, closely apposed to the ectoderm (fig. 5-9A). With the development and the growth of the neural tube and particularly of the brain vesicles, however, the embryonic disc begins to bulge into the am-

General Embryology

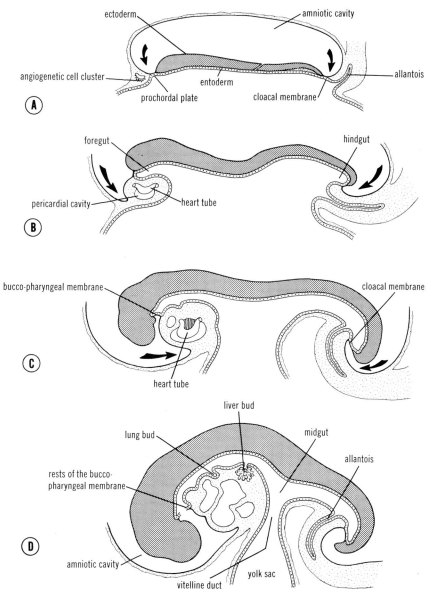

Figure 5-9. *Schematic drawings of sagittal sections through embryos at various stages of development to demonstrate the cephalocaudal flexion and its effect on the position of the entoderm lined cavity and the heart. A, Presomite embryo; B, seven-somite embryo; C, 14-somite embryo; D, at the end of the first month.*

niotic cavity and shows a marked folding in cephalocaudal direction. This folding is most pronounced in the regions of the head and tail, where the so-called *head fold* and *tail fold* are formed (fig. 5-9).

As a result of the cephalocaudal folding, a continuously larger ·

Germ Layers and Body Form 63

portion of the entodermal yolk sac is incorporated into the body of the embryo proper (fig. 5-9C). In the anterior part of the embryo the entoderm forms the *foregut*; in the tail region the *hindgut*. The intraembryonic part of the yolk sac located between the foregut and hindgut is known as the *midgut*. The ill-defined border between the midgut and foregut is the so-called *anterior intestinal portal*; that with the hindgut is the *posterior intestinal portal*. The midgut remains temporarily in open connection with the yolk sac by way of a broad stalk, the *omphalomesenteric* or *vitelline duct* (fig. 5-9D). This duct is initially wide, but with further growth of the embryo it becomes narrow and much longer.

Simultaneously with the cephalo-caudal folding, the embryonic disc folds in lateral direction (fig. 5-10A–C). As a result of this folding the initially flat embryonic disc obtains a round appearance and the ventral abdominal wall is formed. Similarly, the primitive gut becomes a tube-like structure, with only a narrow duct communicating with the yolk sac (fig. 5-10B).

At its cephalic end the foregut is temporarily bounded by the prochordal plate, an ectodermal-entodermal membrane, which is now called the *bucco-pharyngeal membrane* (fig. 5-9A, C). At the end of the third week the bucco-pharyngeal membrane ruptures, thus establishing an open connection between the amniotic cavity and the primitive gut (fig. 5-9D). The hindgut terminates at the *cloacal membrane* (fig. 5-9C). This membrane is later divided into the *urogenital* and *anal membranes*, which rupture at a much later stage of development.

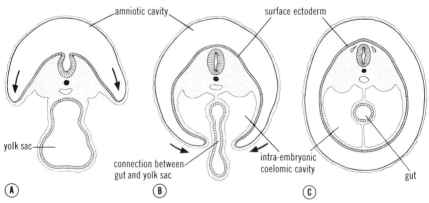

Figure 5-10. *Schematic drawings of transverse sections through embryos at various stages of development to show the effect of the lateral folding on the entoderm lined cavity. Note in B the connection between the gut and the yolk sac. At this stage of development the intra-embryonic coelomic cavity is in open communication with the extra-embryonic coelomic cavity.*

General Embryology

As a result of the formation of the tail fold, the *allantois* is partially incorporated into the body of the embryo, where it becomes attached to the ventral aspect of the hindgut. The distal portion of the allantois remains in the connecting stalk (fig. 5-9D).

In man, the yolk sac is vestigial and in all probability has a nutritive role only in the early stages of development. Its diameter is never more than 5 mm. In the second month of development it is usually found along the umbilical cord.

Hence, the entodermal germ layer initially forms the epithelial lining of the primitive gut and the intra-embryonic portions of the allantois and the vitelline duct (fig. 5-11A, B). During further development it gives rise to: (1) the epithelial lining of the respiratory tract; (2) the parenchyme of the tonsil, thyroid, parathyroids, thymus, liver and pancreas (see "Digestive Tube and Derivatives," Chapter 13); (3) the epithelial lining of part of the urinary bladder and urethra (see "Urogenital System," Chapter 11); and (4) the epithelial lining of the tympanic cavity and Eustachian tube (see "The Ear," Chapter 17).

## External Appearance at the End of the Second Month

The external appearance of the embryo is greatly influenced by the formation of the limbs, face, ear, nose and eyes. Although the

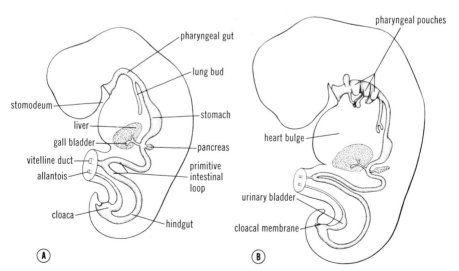

Figure 5-11. *Schematic drawings of sagittal sections through embryos at various stages of development to show the derivatives of the entodermal germ layer. The pharyngeal pouches give rise to the parenchyme of the tonsil, parathyroids and thymus; the epithelial lining of the tympanic cavity and Eustachian tube is formed by the lining of the first pharyngeal pouch.*

age of the embryo until the end of the sixth week is usually expressed in the number of somites, during subsequent development it is indicated as the crown-rump (C.R.) length and expressed in millimeters. The C.R. length is the measurement from the vertex of the skull to the midpoint between the apices of the buttocks. Owing to the considerable variation in the degree of flexure from one embryo to another, it is understandable that the measurements given in Table 5-2 can be only approximate indications of the real age of the embryo.[9]

By the beginning of the fifth week, the fore- and hindlimbs appear as paddle-shaped buds (fig. 5-12A). The former are located dorsal to the pericardial swelling at the level of the fourth cervical to the first thoracic somites, thus explaining the innervation by the brachial plexus. The hindlimb buds appear slightly later just caudal to the attachment of the umbilical stalk at the level of the lumbar and upper sacral somites. With further growth, the terminal portion

Table 5-2. *Crown-Rump (C.R.) Length Correlated to Approximate Age in Weeks*

| C.R. Length | Approx. Age | C.R. Length | Approx. Age |
|---|---|---|---|
| *mm.* | *weeks* | *mm.* | *weeks* |
| 5–8 | 5 | 17–22 | 7 |
| 10–14 | 6 | 28–30 | 8 |

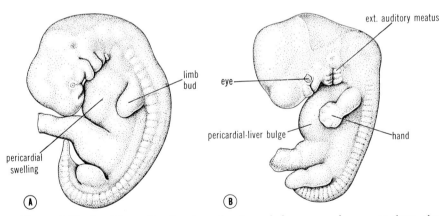

Figure 5-12. A, *Schematic drawing of a 5-week human embryo seen from the left. Crown-rump length is approximately 7 mm. Note the paddle-shaped limb buds and the pharyngeal arches (modified after Streeter). B, Schematic drawing of a 6-week human embryo seen from the left. Crown-rump length is approximately 13 mm. The upper limb buds show a flattened terminal portion with four radial grooves. Note the formation of the eye and the external auditory meatus flanked on each side by three hillocks derived from the mandibular and hyoid arches (modified after Streeter).*

General Embryology

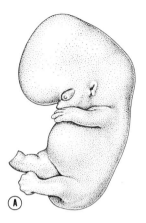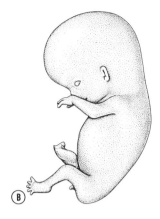

Figure 5-13. *A, Schematic drawing of a 7-week human embryo seen from the left. Crown-rump length is approximately 18 mm. The upper extremities are more advanced in development than the lower ones (modified after Streeter). B, Drawing of an 8-week human embryo seen from the left. Crown-rump length is approximately 30 mm. Note the size of the head in comparison with the remaining part of the body. The eye lids are not present and the eyes are wide open (modified after Streeter).*

of the buds flattens and becomes separated from the proximal, more cylindrically shaped segment by a circular constriction. Soon four radial grooves separating five slightly thicker areas appear on the distal portion of the buds, foreshadowing the formation of the digits (fig. 5-12B). While the fingers and toes are being formed a second constriction divides the proximal portion of the buds into two segments, and the three parts characteristic of the adult extremities can be recognized (figs. 5-13A, B). During their formation the limb buds undergo a profound change in orientation. Initially they project at right angles to the body, but with the development of the elbow and knee joints the distal portions bend ventrally. Finally, the upper and lower extremities undergo a 90° torsion along their longitudinal axis, but in opposite directions so that the elbow points dorsally and the knee ventrally.

## References

1. AREY, L. B. The history of the first somite in human embryos. Contrib. Embryol., **27**: 233, 1938.
2. STREETER, G. L. Developmental horizons in human embryos: age group XI, 13-20 somites, and age group XII, 21-29 somites. Contrib. Embryol., **30**: 211, 1942.
3. STREETER, G. L. Developmental horizons in human embryos: age group XIII, embryos 4 or 5 mm. long, and age group XIV, indentation of lens vesicle. Contrib. Embryol., **31**: 26, 1945.
4. DAVIS, C. L. Description of a human embryo having 20 paired somites. Contrib. Embryol., **15**: 1, 1923.

5. BLOOM, W. Cellular differentiation and tissue culture. Physiol. Rev., **17:** 589, 1937.
6. FISHER, F. *Biology of Tissue Cells.* Cambridge University Press, London, 1946.
7. WILLIER, B. H., WEISS, P. A., AND HAMBURGER,V. *Analysis of Development.* W. B. Saunders Co., Philadelphia, 1955.
8. LANGMAN, J., AND NELSON, G. R. A radioautographic study of the development of the somite in the chick embryo. J. Embryol. exp. Morph., **19:** 217, 1968.
9. STREETER, G. L. Developmental horizons in human embryos: age groups XV, XVI, XVII, and XVIII (the third issue of a survey of the Carnegie Collection). Contrib. Embryol., **32:** 133, 1948.

# CHAPTER 6

# Development of the Fetus, Fetal Membranes, and Placenta (Third to Tenth Months of Development)

---

- •DEVELOPMENT OF THE FETUS
- •DEVELOPMENT OF THE FETAL MEMBRANES AND THE PLACENTA: *chorion frondosum, chorion laeve, decidua basalis, decidua capsularis, decidual septa, cotyledons*
- •FUNCTION OF THE PLACENTA: *placental barrier; transmission of antibodies; hormone production*
- •AMNION AND UMBILICAL CORD: *physiological umbilical hernia; hydramnios*
- •FETAL MEMBRANES IN TWINS: *dizygotic twins; monozygotic twins; conjoined twins*

---

### Development of the Fetus

The period from the beginning of the third month to the end of intra-uterine life is known as the *fetal period*. It is characterized by rapid growth of the body, while further differentiation of the tissues is of minor importance.[1] During this time the age of the fetus is usually expressed as the crown-rump (C.R.) length (sitting height), or the crown-heel (C.H.) length, the measurement from the vertex of the skull to the heel (standing height). Based on measurements derived from various sources, Table 6-1 shows the age of the fetus in lunar months correlated to the C.R. and C.H. lengths. In addition, the average weight is given.

One of the most striking changes taking place during fetal life is

Table 6-1. *Growth in Length and Weight During the Fetal Period*

| Age | Crown-Rump Length | Crown-Heel Length | Weight |
|---|---|---|---|
| *lunar months* | *cm.* | *cm.* | *gm.* |
| 3 | 5–6 | 7 | 20 |
| 4 | 10 | 15 | 120 |
| 5 | 15 | 23 | 300 |
| 6 | 20 | 30 | 640 |
| 7 | 23 | 35 | 1230 |
| 8 | 27 | 40 | 1700 |
| 9 | 30 | 45 | 2300 |
| 10 | 34 | 50 | 3250 |

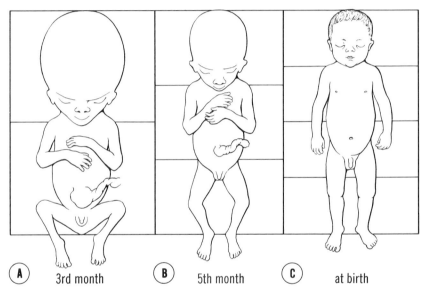

(A) 3rd month   (B) 5th month   (C) at birth

Figure 6-1. *Schematic drawing showing the size of the head in relation to the rest of the body at various stages of development. A, Note the swelling of the umbilical cord at its attachment to the abdominal wall. This is caused by herniation of the intestinal loops into the extra-coelomic cavity in the umbilical cord (see fig. 6-7).*

the relative slowdown in the growth of the head compared to the rest of the body. At the beginning of the third month, the head constitutes approximately one-half of the C.R. length; by the beginning of the fifth month about one-third and at birth approximately one-fourth of the C.H. length (fig. 6-1).

During the third month the face becomes more human-looking. The eyes, initially directed laterally, become located on the ventral aspect of the face; the ears come to lie close to their definitive posi-

General Embryology

tion at the side of the head; the limbs reach their relative length in comparison to the rest of the body, although the lower limbs are still a little shorter and less developed than the upper extremities; and the external genitalia develop to such a degree that the sex of the fetus can be determined by external examination.

During the fourth and fifth months the fetus lengthens rapidly and at the end of the first half of intra-uterine life its standing height (C.H. length) is approximately 23 cm. (C.R. length, 15 cm.), that is, about half the total length of the newborn. The weight of the fetus, however, increases little during this period and by the end of the fifth month is still less than 500 gm. During the second half of intra-uterine life the weight increases considerably, particularly during the last 2½ months, when 50 per cent of its full term

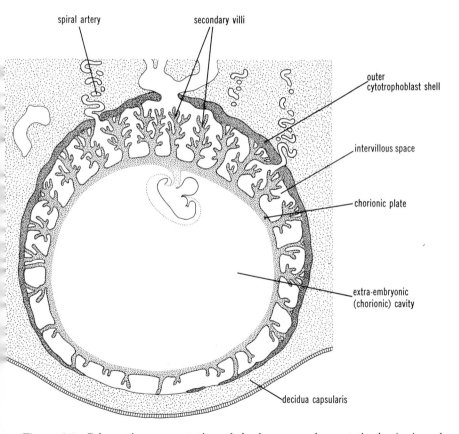

Figure 6-2. *Schematic representation of the human embryo at the beginning of the second month of development. At the embryonic pole the villi are numerous and well formed; at the abembryonic pole they are few in number and poorly developed (modified after von Ortmann).*

Development of the Fetus, Fetal Membranes and Placenta 71

weight (approximately 3200 gm.) is added. The fetus has at first a wrinkled appearance, because of the lack of underlying connective tissue; during the last couple of months, however, it obtains well-rounded contours as the result of the deposition of subcutaneous fat. By the end of intra-uterine life the skin is covered by a whitish, fatty substance, the *vernix caseosa*, which is composed of the secretory products of the sebaceous glands.

At the end of the 10th lunar month, the skull has the largest circumference of all parts of the body, an important fact with regard to its passage through the birth canal.

### Development of the Fetal Membranes and the Placenta

By the beginning of the second month, the *trophoblast* is characterized by a great number of secondary villi which give it a strikingly radial appearance (fig. 6-2). The villi are anchored in the mesoderm of the *chorionic plate* and are attached peripherally to the maternal decidua by way of the outer *cytotrophoblast shell*. The surface of the villi is formed by the syncytium, resting on a layer of cytotrophoblastic cells which in turn cover a core of vascular mesoderm (fig. 6-3A). This mesoderm is at first found on the chorionic side of the villi but gradually penetrates toward the decidual side.

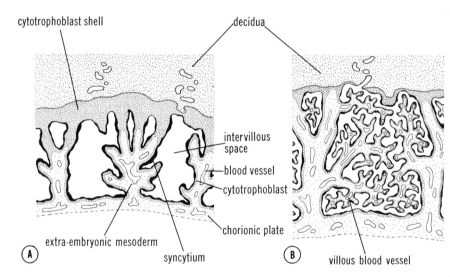

Figure 6-3. *Schematic drawing of the structure of the villi at various stages of development. A, During the fourth week. Note how the extra-embryonic mesoderm penetrates the secondary stem villi in the direction of the decidual plate. B, During the fourth month. In many small villi the wall of the capillaries is in direct contact with the syncytium (modified after Starck).*

General Embryology

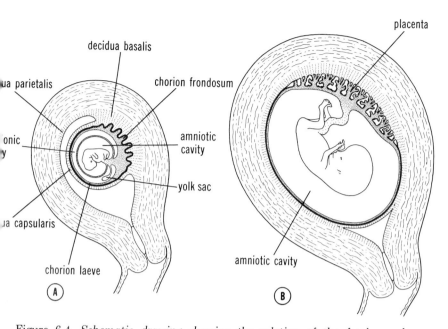

decidua basalis

ua parietalis

chorion frondosum

onic
y

amniotic
cavity

yolk sac

ua capsularis

chorion laeve

(A)

placenta

amniotic cavity

(B)

Figure 6-4. *Schematic drawing showing the relation of the fetal membranes and the wall of the uterus. A, End of the second month. Note the yolk sac in the chorionic cavity between the amnion and chorion. At the abembryonic pole the villi have disappeared (chorion laeve). B, End of the third month. The amnion and chorion have fused and the uterine cavity is obliterated by fusion of the chorion laeve and the decidua parietalis.*

The capillary system in the core of the villous stems soon comes in contact with the capillaries of the chorion and connecting stalk, thus giving rise to the extra-embryonic vascular system (fig. 5-8). This system in turn establishes contact with the intra-embryonic vessels.

During the following months, numerous small extensions sprout from the existing villous stems into the surrounding *lacunar* or *intervillous spaces*. These newly formed villi initially have the same layers as the the stem villi, but by the beginning of the fourth month the cytotrophoblastic cells as well as some of the connective tissue cells disappear. The syncytium and the endothelial wall of the blood vessels are then the only layers which separate the maternal and fetal circulations (fig. 6-3B). The disappearance of the cytotrophoblastic cells progresses from the smaller to the larger villi, although some always persist in the stem villi. In the latter, however, the blood vessels in the center of the villous core do not participate in the exchange between the two circulations (fig. 6-3B).

Although in the early weeks of development the villi cover the entire surface of the chorion (fig. 6-2), as pregnancy advances this situation changes. The villi on the embryonic pole continue to grow and expand, thus giving rise to the *chorion frondosum* (bushy chorion); those on the abembryonic pole degenerate, and by the third month this side of the chorion is smooth and known as the *chorion laeve* (fig. 6-4A).

The difference in the embryonic and abembryonic poles of the chorion is also reflected in the structure of the decidua. The decidua over the chorion frondosum, the *decidua basalis*, consists of a compact layer which is tightly connected to the chorion. This layer is often referred to as the *decidual plate*. The decidual layer over the abembryonic pole is known as the *decidua capsularis* (fig. 6-4A). At first it is similar to the decidua basalis but with increase in the size of the chorionic vesicle, this layer becomes stretched, and begins to degenerate. Subsequently, the chorion laeve comes into contact with the epithelium of the *decidua parietalis* on the opposite side of the uterus and the two fuse (fig. 6-4B). The lumen of the uterus is then obliterated. Hence, the only functional portion of the chorion is the chorion frondosum and together with the decidua basalis, the two make up the *placenta*.

By the beginning of the fourth month, the placenta has two components: (1) a *fetal portion* formed by the chorion frondosum, and (2) a *maternal portion* formed by the decidua basalis (fig. 6-4B). On

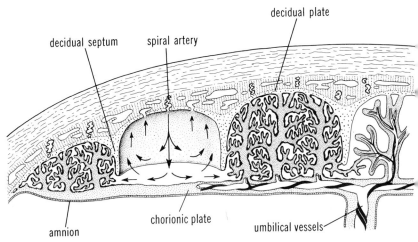

Figure 6-5. *Composite drawing of the placenta in the second half of pregnancy. The cotyledons are partially separated from each other by the decidual (maternal) septa. Note that most of the intervillous blood returns to the maternal circulation by way of the endometrial veins in the decidual plate. A small portion enters neighboring cotyledons. The intervillous spaces are lined by syncytium (modified after Ramsey; and Hamilton and Boyd).*

General Embryology

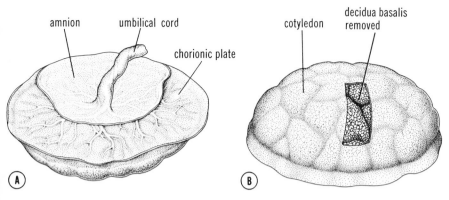

Figure 6-6. *Drawing of a full term placenta. A, As seen from the fetal side. Note that this side is covered by the amnion. B, As seen from the maternal side. Note the cotyledons. In one area the decidua has been removed.*

the fetal side the placenta is bordered by the *chorionic plate*; on its maternal side by the decidua basalis, of which the compact layer or *decidual plate* is most intimately incorporated into the placenta. In the so-called *junctional zone* the trophoblast and decidua cells intermingle. This zone, which represents the zone of invasion of the trophoblastic cells into the uterine tissues, is characterized by decidual and syncytial giant cells and is rich in amorphous mucopolysaccharide material. Between the chorionic and decidual plates are the intervillous spaces which are filled with maternal blood and lined with syncytium of fetal origin. The villous trees grow into the intervillous blood lakes (fig. 6-3).

During the fourth and fifth months the decidua forms a number of septa, the *decidual septa*, which project into the intervillous spaces but do not reach the chorionic plate (fig. 6-5). These septa have a core of maternal tissue, but their surface is covered by a layer of syncytial cells.[2] As a result of this septum formation, the placenta is divided into a number of compartments or *cotyledons* (fig. 6-6).

The manner in which the cotyledons receive their blood supply has long been a subject of discussion. Originally it was thought that the spiral arteries of the decidua entered the intervillous spaces of a cotyledon by way of the maternal septa and that the venous blood passed from one intervillous space to another and finally drained into a marginal sinus at the periphery of the placenta.[3, 4] It is now generally accepted that the spiral arteries pierce the decidual plate and enter the intervillous spaces at more or less regular intervals.[5, 6] The lumen of the spiral artery is narrow when it pierces the decidual plate, resulting in an increased blood pressure when entering the intervillous space. The pressure in the arteries forces the blood into the intervillous spaces and bathes the numerous small villi of the villous tree in oxygenated blood.[7-9] The venous openings draining the intervillous spaces are found over the entire surface of the decidual plate, and the blood from the intervillous lakes drains back into the maternal circulation through these openings (fig. 6-5).

As a result of the continuous growth of the fetus and expansion of the uterus, the placenta also enlarges. Its increase in surface area roughly parallels that of the expanding uterus and throughout pregnancy covers approximately 25 to 30 per cent of the internal surface of the uterus. The increase in thickness of the placenta results from the arborization of existing villi and is not caused by further penetration in the maternal tissues.[10]

Under normal conditions, the intervillous spaces of the full-grown placenta contain approximately 150 cc. of blood, which is replenished about three or four times per minute.[11] This blood moves along the chorionic villi which have a surface area varying from 4 to 14 square meters. It must be remembered, however, that placental exchange does not take place in all villi, but only in those in which the fetal vessels are in intimate contact with the covering syncytial membrane. In these villi the syncytium often has a brush border consisting of numerous microvilli, thus greatly increasing the exchange rate between the maternal and fetal circulations.[12]

At full term, the placenta has a discoid shape, a diameter of 15 to 25 cm., and is approximately 3 cm. thick. At birth it is torn from the uterine wall, and approximately 30 minutes after birth of the child, expelled from the uterine cavity. When, after birth, the placenta is viewed from the decidual side, 15 to 20 slightly bulging areas, the *cotyledons*, covered by a thin layer of decidua basalis and cytotrophoblastic shell, are clearly recognizable (fig. 6-6B). The grooves between the cotyledons are formed by the decidual septa.

The fetal surface of the placenta does not show a cotyledon structure, and is covered entirely by the chorionic plate. A number of large arteries and veins, the *chorionic vessels*, are seen to converge toward the umbilical cord (fig. 6-6A). The chorion in turn is covered by the amnion. The attachment of the umbilical cord is usually eccentric and occasionally even marginal. Rarely, however, does it insert into the chorionic membrane outside the placenta (*velamentous insertion*).

## Function of the Placenta

The main functions of the placenta are: (1) the exchange of metabolic and gaseous products between the maternal and fetal blood streams, with no mixing of the two, and (2) the production of hormones. The dividing membrane between the two circulations, often referred to as the *placental barrier*, is composed exclusively of fetal tissue. In the early stages it consists of four layers: (1) the endothelial lining of the fetal vessels; (2) the connective tissue in the core of the villus; (3) the cytotrophoblastic layer; and (4) the covering syncytium (fig. 6-3).

From the fourth month on, however, the placental barrier becomes much thinner, since most of the villi lose their cytotrophoblastic layer as well as the connective tissue surrounding the fetal capillaries. The endothelial lining of the vessels comes then in intimate contact with the syncytial membrane, thus greatly increasing the rate of exchange.[13] In the final stages of pregnancy, the small villi show an extremely thin, double-layered membrane separating the maternal and fetal circulations. These layers, however, persist at all times.

Although in most areas the syncytial membrane becomes extremely thin, occasionally a thickened *syncytial knot* with many nuclei may be observed. These knots sometimes get detached, fall into the intervillous spaces, and move then into the maternal circulation. Large, multinucleated syncytial masses have been found in the maternal blood stream and may form emboli in the lungs and other organs.

Since the maternal blood in the intervillous spaces is separated from the fetal blood by the placental barrier, a chorionic derivative, the human placenta is considered to be of the *hemochorial* type.

In addition to the exchange of gaseous products, electrolytes, amino-acids, carbohydrates, fats and other metabolic products, the placenta is also important for the *transmission of antibodies*. It was initially thought that large macromolecules such as maternal gamma globulins could pass through the placental barrier only in the case of actual breaks. Though the passage of antibodies from the maternal blood stream to the fetus has been repeatedly demonstrated, the precise transport mechanism remains unknown.[14, 15] In all probability the antibodies are taken up by pinocytosis of the syncytiotrophoblast and subsequently transported to the fetal capillaries. In this manner the fetus acquires maternal antibodies against infectious diseases such as diphtheria, smallpox, measles and others.

Of great importance is the so-called Rh-incompatibility. Fetal red blood cell antigens invade the maternal blood stream and elicit an antibody response in the mother. The maternal antibodies against the fetal antigens then return to the fetus and cause a breakdown of the red blood cells of the fetus. Small bleedings at the surface of the villi are probably responsible for this antigen-antibody interaction between fetus and mother.

At the end of pregnancy a number of changes occur in the placenta which may be an indication of a reduced exchange between the two circulations. These changes include: (1) an increase of the fibrous tissue in the core of the villus; (2) an increase in the thickness of the basement membrane of the fetal capillaries; (3) obliterative changes in the small capillaries in the villi; and (4) the deposition of fibrinoid on the surface of the villi in the junctional zone and in the chorionic plate. Excessive fibrinoid formation frequently causes infarction of an intervillous lake or sometimes of an entire cotyledon. The cotyledon then obtains a whitish appearance.

By the end of the fourth month, the placenta produces *progesterone* in sufficient amounts to maintain pregnancy in case the corpus luteum is removed or fails to function properly. In all probability the steroid hormone is synthesized in the syncytial cytoplasm. In addition to progesterone, the placenta produces increasing amounts of *estrogenic hormones* until just before the end of pregnancy, when a maximum level is reached. The sudden drop in estrogenic hormone production is presumably one of the factors responsible for the beginning of parturition.

The syncytiotrophoblast also produces *gonadotropins*, which have an effect similar to that of the luteinizing hormones of the anterior lobe of the pituitary. These hormones are excreted by the mother in the urine and in the early stages of gestation their presence is used as an indicator of pregnancy.

### Amnion and Umbilical Cord

As a result of the cephalocaudal folding of the embryo the junction between the amnion and the ectodermal surface layer becomes located on the ventral aspect of the embryo (fig. 5-9C, D). The line of reflexion between the amnion and the ectoderm, the *amnio-ectodermal junction*, is oval-shaped, and known as the *primitive umbilical ring*. At about the middle of the second month the following structures pass through the ring (fig. 6-7A, C): (1) the connecting stalk containing the allantois and the umbilical vessels consisting of two arteries and one vein; (2) the yolk sac stalk (vitelline duct) accompanied by the omphalomesenteric or vitelline vessels; and (3) the canal, connecting the intra- and extra-embryonic coelomic cavities (fig. 6-7C). The yolk sac proper occupies a space in the exocoelomic or *chorionic cavity*, that is the space between the amnion and chorion.

During further development the primitive umbilical ring constricts, thereby crowding its contents together. Simultaneously the amniotic cavity enlarges rapidly at the expense of the chorionic cavity, and the amnion comes in contact with the chorion, thereby

General Embryology

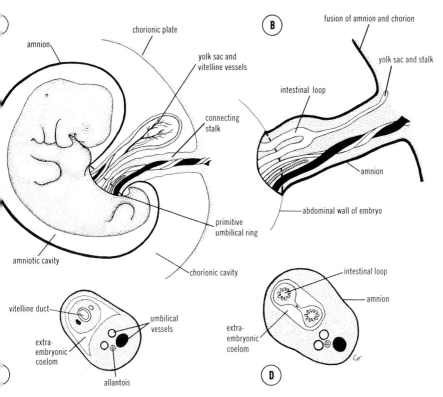

Figure 6-7. *A, Schematic drawing of a five-week embryo to show the structures passing through the primitive umbilical ring. C, Transverse section through the structures contained by the umbilical ring. Note the extra-embryonic coelomic cavity. B, Schematic drawing of the primitive umbilical cord. Note that the cord is completely surrounded by the amnion· and that the amnion has fused with the chorionic plate, thereby obliterating the chorionic cavity. D, Transverse section through the primitive umbilical cord, showing the intestinal loops protruding in the extra-embryonic coelom of the cord.*

obliterating the chorionic cavity (figs. 6-4*B* and 6-7*B*). The amnion also envelopes the connecting and yolk sac stalks, thus causing the formation of the *primitive umbilical cord* (fig. 6-7*B*). The cord contains then the yolk sac and its stalk, the umbilical vessels and the remnant of the allantois. In addition, it contains some intestinal loops (fig. 6-7*B, D*).

The abdominal cavity is temporarily too small for the rapidly developing intestinal loops and some of them are pushed into the extra-embryonic coelomic space in the umbilical cord. These extruding intestinal loops form the so-called *physiological umbilical hernia* (see Chapter 13, Digestive Tube and Derivatives). At about the end of the third month, the loops are withdrawn into the body of the embryo and the coelomic cavity in the cord is obliterated. When in addition the allantois, the vitelline duct and the vitelline vessels are obliterated, all that remains in the cord are the umbilical vessels surrounded by the *jelly of Wharton*. This tissue, which has a mesenchymal appearance, is rich in mucopolysaccharides and functions as a protective layer for the blood vessels. The walls of the arteries are muscular and contain many elastic fibers. These structures together with spiral thickenings of the endothelial lining probably contribute to a rapid constriction and contraction of the vessels after the cord is tied off.

At birth the umbilical cord is approximately 2 cm. in diameter and 50 to 60 cm. long. It is tortuous, causing the so-called *false knots*. An extremely long cord may encircle the neck of the fetus, whereas a short one may cause difficulties during delivery by pulling the placenta from its attachment in the uterus.

The amniotic cavity is filled with a clear, watery fluid produced by the amniotic cells. During the early months of pregnancy, the embryo is suspended by its umbilical cord in this fluid, which serves as a protective cushion. The fluid absorbs jolts, prevents the adherence of the embryo to the amnion, and allows for fetal movements. Probably from the beginning of the fifth month, the fetus swallows its own amniotic fluid. Fetuses unable to swallow, either because of esophageal atresia or through lack of nervous control of the swallowing mechanism, as in anencephaly, are usually surrounded by large amounts of amniotic fluid (*hydramnios*). Under normal conditions the amniotic fluid is absorbed through the gut of the fetus into the blood stream and passes into the maternal blood by way of the placenta. At the end of pregnancy and during childbirth, the amnion and chorion combined form a hydrostatic wedge which helps to dilate the cervical canal.

## Fetal Membranes in Twins

The arrangement of the fetal membranes in twins varies considerably and is dependent on the type of twins as well as on the time of separation in the case of monozygotic twins.

The most common type of twins is formed by the *dizygotic or fraternal twins*. They result from the shedding of two oocytes at the same time and the fertilization by two different spermatozoa. Since both zygotes have a totally different genetic constitution the individual members have no more resemblance then brothers or sisters of different ages. They may or may not have a different sex. Both zygotes implant individually in the uterus and each of them develops its own placenta, its own amnion and its own chorionic sac. Sometimes, however, the two placentas are located so close together that fusion occurs. Similarly the walls of the chorionic sacs may also come into close apposition and fuse. Occasionally the members of dizygotic twins possess red blood cells of two different types (*erythrocyte mosaicism*), indicating that the fusion of the two placentas was so intimate that red cells between the two circulations were exchanged. Though in cattle the fusion of the chorionic circulations of two partners with different sex may disturb the sexual development of the female (freemartin), such abnormalities are unknown in man.

The second type of twins develops from one single fertilized ovum and is known as *monozygotic* or *identical twins*. They result from the splitting of the zygote at various stages of development. The earliest separation is believed to occur at the two-cell stage, in which case two separate zygotes develop within the zona pellucida. After disappearance of the zona both blastocysts implant separately and each embryo has its own placenta and chorionic sac (fig. 6-8A). Although the arrangement of the membranes of these twins resembles that of the dizygotic twins, the two can be recognized as partners of a monozygotic pair by their strong resemblance in blood groups, fingerprints, sex and external appearance such as eye and hair color.[16]

In most cases the splitting of the zygote occurs at the early blastocyst stage. The inner cell mass splits then into two separate groups of cells within the same blastocyst cavity (fig. 6-8B). The two embryos have a common placenta and a common chorionic cavity, but separate amniotic cavities (fig. 6-8B). In rare cases, the separation occurs at the stage of the bilaminar germ disc just before the appearance of the primitive streak (fig. 6-8C). This method of splitting results in the formation of two partners with a single placenta and a common chorionic and amnion sac.

The frequency of twinning differs considerably from country to country and has been recorded to vary from 0.65% of all births in Japan to 1.45% in Norway. In the United States, the incidence of twins is 1.08% in the white population and 1.36% in the colored group. Approximately 70% belong to the dizygotic type and 30% to the monozygotic type. Though the incidence of monozygotic twins is independent of maternal age, the frequency of dizygotic twins increases with the age of the mother. If twins are born after the first pregnancy, the chance that the next pregnancies will result in twins is three to five times greater than in the normal population.

The splitting of the zygote during later stages of development may result in an abnormal or incomplete splitting of the axial area of the germ disc. Such incompletely separated discs lead to the forma-

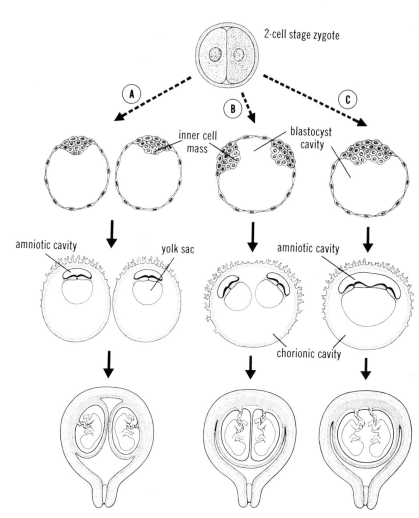

Figure 6-8. *Schematic diagrams showing the possible relations of the fetal membranes in monozygotic twins. A, Splitting occurs at the two-cell stage and each embryo has its own placenta, amniotic cavity and chorionic cavity. B, Splitting of the inner cell mass in two completely separated groups. The two embryos have a common placenta, a common chorionic sac, but separate amniotic cavities. C, Splitting of the inner cell mass at a late stage of development. The embryos have a common placenta, a common amniotic cavity and a common chorionic cavity.*

tion of *conjoined twins* or *double monsters*. According to the nature and degree of the union, they are classified as *thoracopagus* (pagus—fastened), *pygopagus* and *craniopagus*. Occasionally the partners of monozygotic twins are connected to each other only by a common skin bridge or by a common liver bridge (*Siamese twins*). Several

General Embryology

of such conjoined twins have successfully been separated by surgical procedures.

# References

1. Scammon, R. E., and Calkins, H. A. *Development and Growth of the External Dimensions of the Human Body in the Foetal Period*. University of Minnesota Press, Minneapolis, 1929.
2. Serr, D. M., Sadowsky, A., and Kohn, G. The placental septa. J. Obstet. Gynaec. Brit. Emp., **65:** 774, 1958.
3. Bumm, E. Über die Entwicklung des mutterlichen Blutkreislaufes in der menschlichen Placenta. Arch. Gynaek., **43:** 181, 1893.
4. Spanner, R. Mutterlicher und kindlicher Kreislauf der menschlichen Placenta und seine Strombahnen. Z. Anat. Entwicklungsgesch., **105:** 163, 1935.
5. Hamilton, W. J., and Boyd, J. D. Development of the human placenta in the first three months of gestation. J. Anat., **94:** 297, 1960.
6. Ramsey, E. M. Distribution of arteries and veins in the mammalian placenta. In *Gestation* (Transactions of the Second Conference on Gestation), edited by C. A. Villee, p. 299. Josiah Macy, Jr., Foundation, New York, 1956.
7. Ramsey, E. M. Vascular patterns in the endometrium and the placenta. Angiology, **6:** 321, 1955.
8. Ramsey, E. M. Vascular adaptions of the uterus to pregnancy. Ann. N. Y. Acad. Sci., **75:** 726, 1959.
9. Borell, U., Fernstrom, I., and Westman, A. Eine arteriographische Studie des Plazentarkreislaufs. Geburtsch. Frauenheilk., **18:** 1, 1958.
10. Stieve, H. Die Entwicklung und der Bau der menschlichen Plazenta, Zotten, Trophoblastinseln und der Scheidewand in der ersten Hälfte der Schwangerschaft. Z. Mikroskopischanat. Forsch., **48:** 287, 1940.
11. Assali, N. S., Rauramo, L., and Peltonen, T. Measurement of uterine blood flow and uterine metabolism. VIII. Uterine and foetal blood flow and oxygen consumption in early human pregnancy. Amer. J. Obstet. Gynec., **79:** 86, 1960.
12. Wislocki, G. B., and Dempsey, G. W. Electron microscopy of the human placenta. Anat. Rec., **123:** 133, 1955.
13. Flexner, L. B., Cowie, D. G., Hellman, L. M., Wilde, W. S., and Vosburgh, G. J. Permeability of human placenta to sodium in normal and abnormal pregnancies and supply of sodium to human fetus as determined with radioactive sodium. Amer. J. Obstet. Gynec., **55:** 469, 1948.
14. Malmnäs, C. *Immunity in Pregnancy*. Almquist and Wiksells, Stockholm, 1958.
15. Hagerman, D. C., and Villee, C. A. Transport functions of the placenta. Physiol. Rev., **40:** 313, 1960.
16. Smith, S. M., and Penrose, L. S. Monozygotic and dizygotic twin diagnosis. Ann. Hum. Gen., **19:** 273, 1955.

# CHAPTER 7

# Congenital Malformations and Their Causes

INCIDENCE

ETIOLOGY OF MALFORMATIONS

•ENVIRONMENTAL FACTORS

*Infectious agents:* rubella, cytomegalovirus; Asian influenza and other viral infections; toxoplasmosis; syphilis

*Radiation*

*Chemical agents:* drugs

*Hormones:* progestins; cortisone; maternal diabetes

*Antibodies*

*Nutritional deficiencies*

*Hypoxia*

•CHROMOSOMAL AND GENETIC FACTORS

*Autosome abnormalities:* trisomy 21; trisomy 17-18 and 13-15

*Abnormal chromosomes in abortions*

*Sex chromosome abnormalities:* Klinefelter's syndrome; Turner's syndrome; triple-X syndrome

*Abnormalities of the genes:* autosomal dominant inheritance; sex-linked inheritance; autosomal recessive inheritance; sporadic cases

GENERAL CONSIDERATIONS ON THE ACTION OF TERATOGENS

---

Congenital malformations are defined as "gross structural defects" present at birth.[1] Although several abnormalities at the cellular and the molecular level are also known to be congenital in nature, they are not usually included in the above definition but rather referred to as "congenital anomalies."

## *Incidence*

The figures on the incidence of congenital malformations vary greatly. In studies of official records and birth certificates, the percentage of children with abnormalities varied from 0.75 to 1.98 per cent.[2-6] These estimates were found to be rather low when compared with data from hospital and clinic birth records in which a variation of 1.43 to 3.3 per cent was noted.[7-9] Although the latter figures are probably the more accurate, they differ considerably among themselves. This may be due to actual differences in frequency in different countries or to the types of malformations considered. The racial make-up of the sample may also influence the incidence figures, since the frequency and types of malformations vary from race to race.[9]

In a recent worldwide survey on the incidence of congenital malformations comprising approximately 20 million births, it was found that based on birth certificates the percentage of congenital malformations was 0.83; according to hospital and clinic records it was 1.26; based on more intensive examinations by groups of pediatricians the percentage was found to be 4.50.[10] In the latter group the incidence for the United States was the highest (8.76 per cent) and that for Germany the lowest (2.20 per cent). When the figure is based on examination of infants at 6 and 12 months of age, the percentage often doubles, and an incidence of 7.5 per cent has been reported.[11]

Summarizing, it is probable that 2 to 3 per cent of all liveborn infants show one or more significant congenital malformations at birth, and that at the end of 1 year this figure is doubled by discovery of malformations indiscernible at birth.

## Etiology of Malformations

The human embryo is well protected from outside mechanical injury by the uterus, fetal membranes, and amniotic fluid, and from damaging agents present inside the maternal organism by the placenta, long considered an almost impregnable barrier. Hence, until the early 1940's it was assumed that congenital defects were caused mainly by hereditary factors. With the discovery by Gregg[12] that German measles affecting a mother during early pregnancy caused abnormalities in the embryo, it suddenly became evident that congenital malformations in humans could also be caused by environmental factors. The pioneering work of Warkany and Kalter[1, 13] who showed that a specific maternal dietary deficiency during pregnancy was teratogenic in rats, has since stimulated a great many investigations and led to the discovery of a large number of environmental factors teratogenic for the developing mammalian embryo. (For significant contributions in this field, see Warkany and Kalter,[1, 13] Wilson,[14] Fraser,[15, 16] and Giroud and Tuchmann-Duplessis.[17])

Despite the rapid development of the field of teratology, our knowledge of congenital malformations in humans has increased relatively little. At present it is estimated that approximately 10 per cent of all known human malformations are caused by environmental factors and another 10 per cent by genetic and chromosomal factors; the remaining 80 per cent are presumably caused by the intricate interplay of several genetic and environmental factors.

## Environmental Factors

### Infectious Agents

RUBELLA OR GERMAN MEASLES. Gregg[12] was the first to suggest that German measles affecting pregnant women in the early stages of gestation could lead to congenital malformations in the offspring. At present it is well established that rubella virus can cause malformations of the eye (cataract and microphthalmia); internal ear (congenital deafness due to destruction of the organ of Corti); heart (persistence of the ductus arteriosus as well as atrial and ventricular septal defects); and occasionally of the teeth (enamel layer).[18-20] The virus may also be responsible for some cases of brain abnormalities and mental retardation.[21, 22] More recently it has become evident that the virus also causes intrauterine growth retardation, myocardial damage and vascular abnormalities.[23, 24]

The type of malformation is determined by the stage of embryonic development at which infection occurs. For example, cataracts result from infection during the sixth week of pregnancy, and deafness from infection during the ninth week. Cardiac defects follow infection in the fifth to 10th weeks, and dental deformities between the sixth and ninth weeks.[25-28]

It is extremely difficult to determine the exact incidence of malformations in the offspring of infected mothers, since German measles may be mild and thus escape detection, or may be accompanied by unusual clinical features and remain unrecognized. Furthermore, as pointed out above, some birth defects are not recognized until the child is 2 to 4 years of age. On the other hand, rashes caused by other viruses may be incorrectly attributed to rubella. Initial figures indicated a malformation risk of about 75 per cent when the disease occurred during the first 4 months of pregnancy. These figures have since been found to be greatly exaggerated.[29-31] In a prospective study, the risk of malformations in infants examined immediately after birth was estimated at 47 per cent when the infection occurred during the first 4 weeks of pregnancy; 22 per cent following infection in the fifth to eighth weeks; 7 per cent in the ninth to 12th weeks; and 6 per cent in the

13th to 16th weeks.[32] Prematurity and fetal death may also follow infection in the first 8 weeks.[33]

If abnormalities such as mental retardation and dental defects, which do not become evident until later in life, were to be considered it is likely that the above percentages would be higher (65 per cent of congenital deafness due to rubella is not discovered until the fourth year).[34]

In the last five years two important advances have been made with regard to the problems of rubella-caused malformations. Laboratory tests are now available which permit the detection of the virus in specimens from patients and the determination of antibody levels in the serum of patients. An important application of this test is to determine if a patient is immune and therefore need not fear the occurrence of rubella during pregnancy. An epidemiological study of 600 women has shown that 85 per cent was immune. A second important advance was the discovery that the virus penetrates into the fetus by way of the placenta and that the infection of the child may persist in the child after birth for a number of months or years. These children, usually showing no sign of infection, can transmit the virus to hospital personnel, such as nurses, doctors and other hospital attendants.[35, 36] The development of safe and effective vaccines for rubella now appears only a few years away.[24]

CYTOMEGALOVIRUS. Although about a dozen viruses have been implicated as causing congenital malformations, only two of these, rubella and cytomegalovirus, have been positively identified as causing malformations and chronic fetal infection which persists after birth. The congenital cytomegalic inclusion disease is in all probability the result of a human cytomegalovirus infection acquired *in utero* from an asymptomatically infected mother.[37, 38] The principal findings of the infection are microcephaly, cerebral calcifications, blindness and chorioretinitis, and hepato-splenomegaly. Some infants have kernicterus and multiple petechiae of the skin. Initially the disease was recognized only at autopsy and was based on the presence of enlarged cells, with large nuclei containing giant inclusion bodies. The inclusion bodies are most common in cells lining the renal tubules. The disease is often fatal when affecting the embryo or fetus, but in case of survival the destructive meningoencephalitis may cause severe mental retardation.[39] Since the disease is usually unrecognized in pregnant women, it is not known what the difference is between an early or late infection during development. It seems not unlikely that when the embryo is affected at an early stage of development, the damage is so severe that it is unable to survive. Those cases which come to our attention are probably only fetuses which have been infected late in pregnancy.

ASIAN INFLUENZA. Reports on the possible teratogenic effects of Asian influenza have been rather controversial.[40, 41] Some investigators find no indication of such effects, others report that the frequency of anencephaly is higher in offspring of mothers infected with the virus during early pregnancy than in the control population.[42] It has been concluded, therefore, that anencephaly may occur occasionally as a result of maternal infection but the risk appears low.[43]

OTHER VIRAL INFECTIONS. Malformations following maternal infection with measles, mumps, hepatitis, poliomyelitis, chickenpox, and ECHO viruses have been described.[44] Recent prospective studies, however, indicate that probably none of them causes malformations.[45] With regard to measles, some results were negative and some suggestive.[46]

TOXOPLASMOSIS. Maternal infection with the protozoon parasite, *Toxoplasma gondii*, has been shown to produce congenital malformations. The affected child may have cerebral calcification, hydrocephalus, or mental retardation; chorioretinitis, microphthalmus, and other ocular defects have been reported as well.[47, 48] It is impossible to give precise figures on the incidence of malformations caused by toxoplasmosis since, as in the case of cytomegalovirus, the disease is usually unrecognized in pregnant women.

SYPHILIS. Formerly it was thought that syphilis was a major cause of malformations. This has since proved to be ill-founded. When syphilis was widespread, congenital malformations such as cleft lip and palate, spina bifida, and others were often attributed to this disease. However, when the disease became rarer, the association of the disease with congenital malformations also became rarer. Yet, there is no doubt that syphilis may lead to congenital deafness and mental retardation in the offspring. In addition, many other organs such as the lungs and liver are characterized by diffuse fibrosis.[49]

*Radiation*

The teratogenic effect of x-irradiation has been known for many years, and it is well recognized that microcephaly, skull defects, spina bifida, blindness, cleft palate, and defects of the extremities may result from treating pregnant women with large doses of roentgen rays or radium.[50] Although the maximum safe dose for humans is not known, in mice the fetus probably can be damaged with a dose as small as 5 r.[51] It must be realized that the nature of the malformation depends on the dose of radiation and the stage of development at which the radiation is given.[52, 53]

General Embryology

Studies of the offspring of Japanese women pregnant at the time of the atomic bomb explosions over Hiroshima and Nagasaki revealed that among the survivors, 28 per cent aborted, 25 per cent gave birth to children who died in their first year of life, and 25 per cent of the surviving children had abnormalities of the central nervous system, such as microcephaly and mental retardation.[54, 55]

In addition to the effect of direct radiation on the embryo, indirect effects on the germ cells must be considered. Indeed, relatively small doses of radiation in mice have been shown to cause mutations which subsequently led to the occurrence of congenital malformations in succeeding generations.[56]

Although some investigations have shown that radiation caused no abnormalities in children of exposed parents,[57] others have suggested that an accumulated dose of radiation of between 30 to 80 r per generation may double the spontaneous incidence of mutation in man.[58-60] Despite the fragmentary and often controversial findings, one must be aware of the possible dangers of radiation in man.

## Chemical Agents

DRUGS. The role of drugs in the production of developmental abnormalities in man is difficult to assess, because most studies carried out in this field are of necessity retrospective. Few of the many drugs used during pregnancy have been positively identified as being teratogenic for the child. The best example is *thalidomide*, an anti-nauseant and sleeping pill. About ten years ago it was noted in West Germany that the frequency of *amelia* and *phocomelia* (total or partial absence of the extremities), heretofore considered a rare hereditary abnormality, had suddenly increased. This led to the examination of the prenatal histories of the affected children, resulting in the discovery that many of the mothers had taken thalidomide early in pregnancy. In the case of some women who could not recall having taken the drug, pharmacy records revealed that it had been prescribed. The causal relationship between thalidomide and phocomelia was discovered only because the drug produced such an unusual type of abnormality. If the defect had been of a more common type, such as harelip or heart malformations, the association with the drug might easily have been overlooked.

The defects produced by thalidomide are: absence or gross deformities of the long bones, intestinal atresia, and cardiac abnormalities.[61-63] As a result of the discovery that thalidomide was directly related to phocomelia, the drug was immediately removed from the market. The incidence of phocomelia has since been reduced dramatically.

An older drug, long suspected as being teratogenic, is *quinine*. In high doses it has frequently been used as a means of abortion and, as such, is believed to produce congenital deafness.[64] Although animal experiments seem to support this belief, there is no positive evidence for it as far as humans are concerned.[65]

A more dangerous drug, likewise used to cause abortion, is *aminopterin*. This compound belongs to the antimetabolites and is an antagonist of folic acid. Since, in doses somewhat higher than the teratogenic level, the drug will terminate pregnancy, it has been used during early pregnancy to induce therapeutic abortion in women suffering from tuberculosis.[66, 67] In four cases in which abortion did not occur, malformed offspring were found. The defects noted were anencephaly, meningocele, hydrocephalus, and cleft lip and palate. Since the drug has been used in a number of cases during pregnancy without producing teratogenic effects, its teratogenicity in man cannot yet be considered to have been demonstrated satisfactorily.

Though only a few drugs have been positively proven to cause congenital malformations in man, caution has been expressed with regard to a number of other compounds, which might be damaging to the embryo or fetus.[68-71] The most prominent among these are: propylthiouracil and potassium iodide (goiter and mental retardation); streptomycin (possible deafness); sulfonamides (kernicterus); tetracyclines (inhibition of bone growth); smoking (birth of small babies); sulphonurea derivatives (multiple malformations?); meprobamate (retarded development?); and antihistamines (infertility? abnormalities?). Considerable more information, however, is required before these compounds may be considered positively as teratogenic.

*Hormones*

PROGESTINS. Synthetic progestins are frequently used during pregnancy to avert abortion. Occasionally, however, progestin treatment has been associated with the production of congenital malformations, and many cases of masculinization of the genitalia in female embryos have been reported.[72] The abnormalities produced consisted of an enlarged clitoris associated with varying degrees of fusion of the labioscrotal folds. Comparable results have been obtained experimentally by treating pregnant rats with progestins.[73]

CORTISONE. Experimental work has repeatedly shown that cortisone injected into mice and rabbits at certain stages of pregnancy may cause a high percentage of cleft palates in the offspring.[74, 75] Although some investigations indicate that cortisone given to pregnant women during early gestation may cause cleft palate in the child, a number of cases have been reported in which the mother received cortisone throughout pregnancy, yet the baby was normal.[76, 77] So far, it has been impossible to implicate cortisone as an environmental factor causing cleft palate in man.

MATERNAL DIABETES. Disturbances in carbohydrate metabolism due to maternal diabetes or prediabetic stages in pregnancy cause a high incidence of stillbirths, neonatal deaths, and abnormally large infants. According to some workers, an increased incidence of congenital malformations of the skeletal components of the pelvis and lower extremities has been noted.[78-80] Critical analysis of the data available, however, shows that the incidence of congenital malformations in diabetic and prediabetic women is approximately the same as in the general population.[81-84]

It has been reported that when women with previous histories of congenital defects and an indication of a disturbed carbohydrate metabolism were treated with insulin or thyroid, or both, subsequent pregnancies resulted in fewer miscarriages, stillbirths, and infants with congenital malformations.[85] Unfortunately, however, there is no proof that these women would not have produced normal children without treatment.

*Antibodies*

A new teratogenic mechanism is presently under consideration as a possible cause of congenital malformations. It was found that the serum of several mothers who had given birth to athyrotic cretins contained antithyroid antibodies and a thyrotoxic factor. This suggested a causal relationship between cretinism and maternal autoimmunization to thyroid tissue.[86, 87] Some support for this theory can be found in recent experimental work in which pregnant animals were immunized against kidney and placenta extracts. The newborn showed a great number of congenital malformations.[88] Much work remains to be done in this field, however, particularly as to the manner in which antibodies pass through the placenta, how they enter the fetal circulation, and how an antigen-antibody reaction inside the embryo occurs.

*Nutritional Deficiencies*

Although many nutritional deficiencies, particularly vitamin deficiencies, have been proved to be teratogenic in experimental work, there is no definite evidence that they are teratogenic in humans. With the exception of endemic cretinism, which is related to maternal iodine deficiency, no analogies to the animal experiments have been found in humans. (For an extensive review on nutritional deficiencies and their effect on the production of congenital malformations in experimental animals, see Kalter and Warkany,[13] and Giroud and Tuchmann-Duplessis.[17])

*Hypoxia*

Hypoxia induces congenital malformations in a great variety of experimental animals.[89] Whether the same is valid for humans remains to be seen. Although children born at relatively high altitudes are usually lighter in weight and smaller than those born near or at sea level, an increase in the incidence of congenital malformations has not been noted.[90] In addition, women with cyanotic cardiovascular disease often give birth to small infants, but usually without gross congenital malformations.

## Chromosomal and Genetic Factors

As a result of advances in tissue culture techniques, it is now possible to analyze the chromosomal pattern of the human cell in almost every hospital in the country. By culturing cells in an artificial medium and subsequently exposing them to a colchicine solution to arrest the mitoses in the metaphase, the chromosomes can easily be counted (fig. 1-1). The normal human somatic cell contains 46 chromosomes, which can be arranged in 23 pairs. In the normal female cell the sex chromosomes are represented by two X-chromosomes, which resemble the autosomes of the 6-12 group (fig. 1-1*B*); in the male cell they are represented by an X-chromosome and a much shorter Y-chromosome, which resembles somewhat the autosomes of the 21-22 group.

Once the normal chromosomal pattern was firmly established, it soon became evident that some patients had an abnormal number of chromosomes.[91] Some of these abnormalities involved the autosomes, usually an extra chromosome; others, the sex chromosomes, usually the X chromosome. If an additional chromosome is present, making three chromosomes instead of the usual pair, the individual is said to be trisomic for this chromosome and the condition is known as *trisomy*. Four such conditions are now well established: (1) trisomy 21; (2) trisomy 17-18; (3) trisomy 13-15; and (4) trisomy X. If one of the chromosomes is absent the condition is known as *monosomy*. This abnormality, however, is rare.

*Autosome Abnormalities*

TRISOMY 21. This condition is found in the somatic cells of patients with Down's syndrome (mongoloid defectives).[92, 93] During

General Embryology

miosis the members of the chromosome pairs separate so that each daughter cell receives only half as many chromosomes as the mother cell (see Chapter 1). If instead of separating, both members of a pair move into the same cell (*nondisjunction*), this cell will contain 24 instead of the normal 23 chromosomes. When at fertilization another set of 23 chromosomes is added to the abnormal gamete, the result will be 47 chromosomes, of which three will be identical (trisomy). Since the frequency of Down's syndrome increases with advancing maternal age, it is thought that nondisjunction occurs during oogenesis rather than during spermatogenesis.[94, 95]

In a few cases of Down's syndrome, the extra chromosome 21 is not free but is found attached to another chromosome, usually to one of the 13–15 or 21–22 group. This is the result of a phenomenon known as *translocation*.[96-98] The cells have then 46 chromosomes, but one of them is unusually large, since in effect it consists of two chromosomes.

In some cases a translocation of chromosome 21 can be seen in the parent of a child with trisomy 21. This parent then has 45 chromosomes, but is clinically normal since all the normal chromosomal material is present. The bearers of this chromosomal pattern are referred to as *carriers*.[96, 99] The pairing and separation of the translocated chromosome and the two single normal homologs (21 and 13–15) during miosis determines the chromosomal complement of the germ cells.[100] Although many of the possible combinations are thought to be lethal to the developing embryo, it is known that when a normal gamete with a chromosomal combination 13–15 plus 21 combines with a translocated chromosome 13–15–21, plus a free 21, the result will be trisomy 21, a pattern characteristic of Down's syndrome.

The chromosomal studies have been of considerable importance. If the parents of a mongoloid defective child have normal chromosomes, the chance of a second child with Down's syndrome is 1 to 2 per cent. If, however, one of the parents is a carrier of a translocated chromosome 21, the chances of a second mongoloid defective child being born to them are greatly increased and are thought to be about one in three.[101]

TRISOMY 17–18. Patients with this chromosomal arrangement show the following features suggesting a distinct clinical entity: mental retardation, congenital heart defects, low-set ears, and flexion of fingers and hands.[102, 103] In addition, the patients frequently show micrognathia, renal anomalies, syndactyly, and malformations of the skeletal system. The incidence of this condition is about 0.3 per 1000 births. The infants usually die by the age of 2 months.

TRISOMY 13–15. The main abnormalities of this syndrome are mental retardation, congenital heart defects, deafness, cleft lip and palate, and eye defects such as microphthalmia, anophthalmia, and coloboma.[104] The incidence of this abnormality is about 0.2 per 1000 newborns. Most of the infants die by the age of 3 months.

## Abnormal Chromosomes in Abortions

In recent years a number of cytogenetic studies have been performed in spontaneous abortions to determine whether a relationship exists between chromosomal abnormalities and abortions.[105] The incidence of chromosomal abnormalities in abortions is reported to range from 10 to 64 per cent. Whatever the precise incidence may be, the percentage of chromosomal abnormalities in abortions is certainly 50 times that at full term. The chromosomal abnormalities involve the autosomes as well as the sex chromosomes. Monosomy for the X chromosome seems to be one of the most frequently seen abnormalities.

## Sex Chromosome Abnormalities

An important stimulus to the study of sex chromosome abnormalities was provided by Barr, Bertram and Moore,[106-108] who observed a difference in the morphology of the cell nuclei. In approximately 40–80 per cent of the cells of a normal female, a small, darkly stained body located almost always against the nuclear membrane was found. This body, initially called the *paranuclear body* or *nucleolar satellite* was rarely, if ever, found in normal male cells. Though the nature of the chromatin body was initially unknown, it soon became apparent that it represented one of the two X-chromosomes of the female cell.[109] The body is now referred to as the *sex chromatin body* and the female cells are called chromatin-positive, and the male ones chromatin-negative.

Application of the nuclear sexing technique together with chromosome analysis has shown that some cases of infertility are characterized by an abnormal sex chromosome complement. As in the case of autosomal abnormalities, it is likely that these are also caused by nondisjunction of the chromosomes. If, during miosis, the two members of the X chromosome pair fail to separate and move into one daughter cell, the oocyte will have either two X chromosomes or none. If an oocyte with two X chromosomes combines with a Y-containing sperm, the result will be a zygote with an XXY sex chromosomal complement. In case the XX oocyte combines with an X-containing sperm, the result is an XXX zygote. Similarly, if the oocyte without sex chromosomes is fertilized with an X sperm, the zygote will be characterized by an XO sex chromosomal make-up. Fertilization with a Y sperm will produce a YO zygote. Alternatively, nondisjunction during spermatogenesis can give rise to sperms without a sex chromosome, with both an X and Y, or even with two Y. Fertilization of a normal oocyte will result in an XO, XXY or YYX sex chromosomal complement. A number of patients with these abnormal sex chromosomal complements have been observed.

KLINEFELTER'S SYNDROME. The clinical features of this syndrome found only in males are sterility, testicular atrophy, hyalinization of the seminiferous tubules, and usually gynecomastia.[110] The cells have 47 chromosomes with a sex chromosomal complement of the XXY type, and a sex chromatin body is found in 80 per cent of cases.[111] The patients with Klinefelter's syndrome, based on testicular morphology, are now separated into three classes. The incidence is about 1 in 500 males in the normal population.[112-114] Among mentally defective subjects the incidence is as high as 1 in 100 males.[115] On the basis of statistical evidence it is believed that nondisjunction of the XX homologs is the most common causative event.

Occasionally patients with Klinefelter's syndrome have 48 chromosomes, that is, 44 autosomes and 4 sex chromosomes (XXXY).[116] This sex chromosome complement is thought to be caused either by nondisjunction of the sex chromosomes in the gametes of both parents or, and this is more likely, by a nondisjunction of the X chromosomes in the female gamete in both the first and second miotic divisions.

In some patients it was found that the tissues contained cells with a variety of abnormal chromosome configurations.[117] This phenomenon, known as *mosaicism*, is thought to be caused by nondisjunction of the sex chromosomes during the miotic cleavage divisions.

TURNER'S SYNDROME. This condition, found in women with an unmistakably female appearance, is characterized by the absence of the ovaries (*gonadal dysgenesis*). Other abnormalities frequently found are webbed neck, lymphedema of the extremities, skeletal deformities and mental retardation. Despite the female appearance of these patients, almost all of their cells are sex chromatin-negative.[118] In addition the cells have only 45 chromosomes with an XO chromosomal complement.[119] Genetic analysis has shown that this syndrome is usually caused by nondisjunction in the male gamete during miosis. As in patients with Klinefelter's syndrome, patients with Turner's syndrome occasionally show mosaicism (XO/XX; XO/XY; or XO/XYY combinations are seen). The incidence of XO females is presently estimated at about one in 3000 in the normal population. The incidence of chromatin-negative females in mental institutions is not significantly different.

TRIPLE-X SYNDROME. Patients with triple-X syndrome are infantile, with scanty menses and some degree of mental retardation.[120] They have two sex chromatin bodies in their cells and are therefore sometimes called "superfemale." The triple-X syndrome results from fertilization of an XX oocyte and an X-containing sperm. Some of the patients are of proven fertility and surprisingly, the offspring has been uniformly normal. On theoretical grounds the triple-X patients should produce equal numbers of oocytes containing one or two X-chromosomes. Fertilization of the abnormal XX oocytes should give rise to XXX and XXY zygotes.

## Abnormalities of the Genes

It has long been known that many congenital malformations in man are inherited and that some show a clear Mendelian pattern of inheritance. In many cases the abnormality is directly attributable to a change in a single gene, hence the name *single gene mutation*. It is estimated that this type of defect makes up approximately 10 per cent of all human malformations.[121-123]

In addition to causing congenital malformations, defined as structural defects present at birth, a large number of inborn errors of metabolism attributable to defective gene action have recently been described. These diseases, among which phenylketonuria,[124] homocystinuria, and galactosemia are the best known, are frequently accompanied by or cause various degrees of mental retardation. A detailed discussion of the affected metabolic pathways and enzymatic disorders, however, would lead beyond the scope of this book. Hence, in the following paragraphs mention is made only of the gross congenital malformations.

AUTOSOMAL DOMINANT INHERITANCE. In such conditions the affected gene will cause malformations whether the gene comes from only one parent (heterozygous) or from both (homozygous). Usually, the abnormality is of heterozygous origin, since it would be rare, indeed, if both parents were to carry similarly affected genes.

In malformations with autosomal dominant inheritance the child of the affected (heterozygous) individual has a 50 per cent chance of being affected. The following malformations are examples of such conditions: achondroplasia; cleidocranial dysostosis; lobster claw defects of hands and feet; osteogenesis imperfecta.

SEX-LINKED INHERITANCE. In these conditions the abnormal genes are carried by the X chromosome (diseases caused by genes carried by the Y chromosome have not yet been found).[125, 126] Congenital malformations showing sex-linked dominant inheritance have not been reported in man. If the affected gene on the X chromosome is recessive it will not express itself in heterozygous females but only in males. In such cases the abnormality is transmitted through the female and appears in half the sons. Such conditions include: one form of hydrocephalus, one form of gargoylism, and the testicular feminization syndrome.

AUTOSOMAL RECESSIVE INHERITANCE. A recessive gene expresses itself only when homozygous, that is, when inherited from both father and mother. Malformations caused by recessive genes are seen infrequently, and affected children almost always come from unaffected heterozygous parents. Each sibling of an affected child has one chance in four of being affected. Parents of children with recessive diseases have a higher frequency of consanguinity than is found in the general population. Examples of recessively inherited malformations include: chondro-ectodermal dystrophy; some cases of microcephaly; chondrodystrophia calcificans congenita.

SPORADIC CASES. Malformations which suddenly appear in families in which there are no other affected relatives with congenital defects are usually regarded as sporadic cases. As these patients are often referred to the physician for genetic advice, a brief summary of the possibilities to be considered is given:

*Recessive genes.* As discussed above, a child of a parent carrying a recessive gene has one chance in four of being affected. This, combined with the relatively small size of the modern family, means that most cases of recessively inherited malformations often appear to be sporadic. In the case of achondroplasia this may produce difficulties since both a dominant and a recessive type of this malformation exist.

*Mutation.* A mutation is a sudden and persistent change in the expression of a gene. If this mutation is dominant, the offspring of the affected person will have a 50 per cent chance of being affected.

*Reduced penetrance.* Normally, a dominant gene expresses itself similarly in individuals who are either homozygous or heterozygous for that gene. If, however, the effects of a dominant gene do not appear in some individuals, the gene is said to have reduced penetrance. Similarly a recessive gene shows reduced penetrance when it fails to manifest itself in the homozygous individual. In the case of dominant genes with reduced penetrance, the disease appears to "skip" generations. Reduced penetrance can sometimes be explained by the fact that one of the individuals affected died before the disease became apparent.

*Phenocopies.* If a genetically normal individual is exposed to a specific environmental change at a particular stage of development it may acquire an abnormal phenotype. For example, a cataract resulting from a prenatal infection with rubella may be regarded as a phenocopy of a clinically similar cataract caused by an abnormal gene action. If in a sporadically occurring abnormality a genetic change is involved, the probability of recurrence of the malformation within the same family may be quite high; if, however, the malformation is a phenocopy, the chance of recurrence is low. Unless a prenatal factor such as rubella can be identified, it is often impossible to distinguish this from other reasons for a negative family history. (For a discussion of the genetic factors in human malformations, see Stern.[126])

# General Considerations on the Actions of Teratogens

From data available on the action of teratogenic factors in mammals, a few basic principles have emerged.[127] Although it is too early to list these as "laws," they must be kept in mind when considering the probability of children being affected by specific teratogenic factors.

1. *The stage of embryonic development determines the susceptibility to teratogenic factors.* Mammalian development starts with a rapid multiplication of cells which show little, if any, differentiation. This period, which lasts from fertilization to the formation of the germ layers, is referred to as the *pre-germ layer stage* or *pre-differentiation stage*. The next stage is known as the *embryonic period*, during which the cells begin to show distinct morphological differences resulting from changes at the chemical level. The final stage, or *fetal period*, is characterized by growth of the organ system.

It is generally accepted that when a teratogen acts during the pre-differentiation stage, it either damages all or a majority of the cells of the embryo, resulting in its death; or it injures only a few cells, in which case the regulative potentialities of the embryo will compensate for the loss and no abnormalities will be apparent. Several teratogenic factors, such as hypervitaminosis A and radiation, which in later stages of development are known to be highly teratogenic, were found to have no effect on the embryo in the first phase of development.[128-130] At present only a few scattered examples are known in which teratogens given during the first phase of development have caused malformations. It may well be, however, that these teratogens remain in the maternal tissue and become active only when the susceptibility of the embryo increases during the second stage of development.

During the embryonic period, that is, the stage of intensive differentiation, most teratogenic agents are highly effective and produce numerous malformations. The type of malformation produced, however, depends on which organ is most susceptible at the time of the

General Embryology

teratogenic action. Each organ seems to go through its most susceptible stage early in its differentiation, and the various body organs become susceptible one after the other. This was clearly demonstrated by giving rats a pteroylglutamic acid-deficient diet.[131, 132] It was thus found that abnormalities of the central nervous system and heart can be produced from day 7 to day 9; skeletal, urinary and other cardiovascular abnormalities from day 9 to day 11; and skeletal defects from day 11 to day 14. The same seems to be true for the action of the rubella virus in the human embryo. Depending on the day of development the virus will affect one organ after the other, each at its own critical stage.[20]

During the third or fetal period of development, which is characterized by growth of the organs, susceptibility to teratogenic agents rapidly decreases. A small number of organs such as the cerebellum, cerebral cortex and some urogenital structures, however, continue with their differentiation. It is not impossible, therefore, that some of these structures remain susceptible to the action of teratogenic factors until late in pregnancy. Indeed, when mice were treated with high doses of vitamin A during the later stages of pregnancy, the cerebral cortex was seriously affected.[133] It is not unlikely that also in the human environmental factors may damage the developing brain in the second half of pregnancy and thus cause mental retardation.

2. *The effect of a teratogenic factor depends on the genotype.* A number of experiments seem to indicate that a teratogenic agent accentuates the incidence of those defects which occur sporadically without treatment and that the malformations appear as they do because of underlying genetic instabilities. When a strain of mice that regularly produces approximately 2 per cent of offspring with skeletal abnormalities was starved for 24 hours, the result was a 22 per cent increase in skeletal defects.[134]

Another example of the importance of the genotype is seen in the fact that not only different species but also different strains and substrains react differently to similar teratogenic agents.[135] These differences were mainly quantitative with variations of up to 70 per cent.

When an appropriate dose of cortisone was injected into pregnant mice of strains A and C57, it caused cleft palate in all the offspring of strain A and in 19 per cent of strain C57. When a strain C57 male was bred with a strain A female, 43 per cent of the young had cleft palate. When a strain C57 mother was crossed with a strain A father, however, the incidence dropped to 4 per cent; this showed that the genes of the mother as well as those of the embryo may influence the susceptibility to a teratogen.[136]

3. *A teratogenic agent acts in a specific way on a particular aspect of cell metabolism.* Many teratogenic agents produce a characteristic pattern of malformations when applied to a certain species at a specific stage of development. If the malformations produced by two teratogenic factors are completely different, they most likely act on entirely different biochemical phases of the embryonic metabolic pattern. When malformations caused by two different agents overlap, it is likely that both factors act partially on similar phases of development and differ in others. When the pattern produced by two agents is the same or similar, their action is likely to be the same, though not necessarily so.

A teratogenic agent does not necessarily act on one specific metabolic process but may interfere with different biochemical processes at completely different times of development. For example, the teratogenic action of insulin on the chick embryo early in development was counteracted by pyruvic acid. At a later stage of development, however, only nicotinamide could prevent the teratogenic effects produced by the insulin.[137]

## References

1. WARKANY, J., AND KALTER, H. Congenital malformations. New Engl. J. Med., **265**: 993, 1961.
2. GENTRY, J. T., PARKHURST, E., AND BULIN, G. V. Epidemiological study on congenital malformations in New York State. Amer. J. Public Health, **49**: 497, 1959.
3. IVY, R. H. Congenital anomalies, as recorded on birth certificates in Division of Vital Statistics of Pennsylvania Department of Health for period 1951–1955, inclusive. Plast. Reconstr. Surg., **20**: 400, 1957.
4. WALLACE, H. M., AND BAUMGARTNER, L. Congenital malformations and birth injuries in New York City. Pediatrics, **12**: 525, 1953.
5. NEEL, J. V. Study on major congenital defects in Japanese infants. Amer. J. Hum. Genet., **10**: 398, 1958.
6. McKEOWN, T., AND RECORD, R. G. Malformations in population observed for five years after birth. In *Ciba Foundation Symposium on Congenital Malformations*, edited by G. E. W. Wolstenholme and E. M. O'Connor, p. 2. Little, Brown and Co., Boston, 1960.
7. SCHENK, H. Über die Missbildungen in den Jahren 1938–41 an der Universitäts-Frauenklinik, Berlin. Zbl. Gynaek., **46**: 2078, 1942.
8. BÖÖK, J. A., AND FRACCARO, M. Research on congenital malformations. Études néo-natales, **5**: 39, 1956.
9. STEVENSON, S. S., WORCESTER, J., AND RICE, R. G. Six hundred and seventy-seven congenitally malformed infants and associated gestational characteristics. I. General considerations. Pediatrics, **6**: 37, 1950.
10. KENNEDY, W. P. Epidemiologic aspects of the problem of congenital malformations, in *Birth Defects Original Article Series*, edited by D. Bergsma, **3**: 1, 1967.
11. McINTOSH, R., *et al.* Incidence of congenital malformations; a study of 5964 pregnancies. Pediatrics, **14**: 505, 1954.
12. GREGG, N. M. Congenital cataract following German measles in mothers. Trans. Ophthal. Soc. Aust., **3**: 35, 1941.

13. KALTER, H., AND WARKANY, J. Experimental production of congenital malformations in mammals by metabolic procedure. Physiol. Rev., **39**: 69, 1959.
14. WILSON, J. G. General principles in experimental teratology. In *Proceedings of the First International Conference on Congenital Malformations*, p. 187. J. B. Lippincott Co., Philadelphia, 1961.
15. FRASER, F. C. The use of teratogens in the analysis of abnormal developmental mechanisms. In *Proceedings of the First International Conference on Congenital Malformations*, p. 179. J. B. Lippincott Co., Philadelphia, 1961.
16. FRASER, F. C. Methodology of experimental mammalian teratology. In *Methodology in Mammalian Genetics*, edited by W. J. Bundette, p. 233. Hold and Day, San Francisco, 1962.
17. GIROUD, A., AND TUCHMANN-DUPLESSIS, H. Malformations congénitales. Role des facteurs exogènes. Path. Biol. (Par.), **10**: 119, 1962.
18. LOGAN, W. P. D. Effects of virus infections in pregnancy. Medicine (Illus.), **8**: 502, 1954.
19. RHODES, A. J. Virus infections and congenital malformations. In *Proceedings of the First International Conference on Congenital Malformations*. J. B. Lippincott Co., Philadelphia, 1961.
20. TÖNDURY, G. Zur Kenntnis der Embryopathica rubeolica, nebst Bemerkungen über die Wirkung anderer Viren auf den Keimling. Geburtsh. Frauenheilk., **12**: 865, 1952.
21. ARIENS KAPPERS, J. Developmental disturbance of the brain induced by German measles in an embryo of the 7th week. Acta Anat., **31**: 1, 1957.
22. LACOMME, M. Le point de vue de l'obstétricien sur les malformations congénitales. Maternité, **6**: 231, 1954.
23. TÖNDURY, G., AND SMITH, D. W. Fetal rubella pathology. J. Pediat., **68**: 867, 1966.
24. DUDGEON, J. A. Maternal rubella and its effect on the foetus. Arch. Dis. Child., **42**: 110, 1967.
25. BASS, M. H. Diseases of pregnant women affecting the offspring. Advance. Intern. Med., **5**: 15, 1952.
26. TEDESCHI, C. G., HELFERN, M. M., AND INGALLS, T. H. Pathological manifestations in an infant after maternal rubella in the sixteenth week of gestation. New Engl. J. Med., **249**: 439, 1953.
27. JACKSON, H. D. M., AND FISH, L. Deafness following maternal rubella; results of a prospective investigation. Lancet, **2**: 1241, 1958.
28. KEITH, J. K., ROWE, R. D., AND VLAD, P. *Heart Disease in Infancy and Childhood*. The Macmillan Co., New York, 1958.
29. AYCOCK, L. W., AND INGALLS, T. H. Maternal disease as principle in epidemiology of congenital anomalies; with review of rubella. Amer. J. Med. Sci., **212**: 366, 1946.
30. INGALLS, T. H., AND PURSHOTTOM, N. Fetal risks from rubella during pregnancy. New Engl. J. Med., **249**: 454, 1953.
31. OXORN, H. Rubella and pregnancy. Amer. J. Obstet. Gynec., **77**: 628, 1959.
32. MICHAELS, R. H., AND MELLIN, G. W. Prospective experience with maternal rubella and associated congenital malformations. Pediatrics, **26**: 200, 1960.
33. SIEGEL, M., AND GRÜNBERG, M. Fetal death, malformation and prematurity after maternal rubella; results of a prospective study, 1949–1958. New Engl. J. Med., **262**: 389, 1960.
34. JACKSON, A. D. M., AND FISH, L. Deafness following maternal rubella; results of a prospective study. Lancet, **2**: 1241, 1958.
35. KORONES, S. B., AINGER, L. E., MONIF, G. R., ROANE, J., SEVER, J. L., AND

FUSTE, F. Congenital rubella syndrome: new clinical aspects with recovery of virus from affected infants. J. Pediat., **67**: 166, 1965.
36. SEVER, J. L., NELSON, K. B., AND GILKESON, M. R. Rubella epidemic 1964. Effect on 6000 pregnancies. Amer. J. Dis. Child., **110**: 395, 1965.
37. MEDEARIS, D. N., JR. Cytomegalic inclusion disease: an analysis of the clinical features based on the literature and six additional cases. Pediatrics, **19**: 467, 1957.
38. WELLER, T. H., AND HANSHAW, J. B. Virologic and clinical observations on cytomegalic inclusion disease. New Engl. J. Med., **266**: 1233, 1962.
39. MEDEARIS, D. N. Observations concerning human cytomegalovirus infection and disease. Bull. Johns Hopkins Hosp., **114**: 181, 1964.
40. WALKER, W. M., AND MCKEE, A. P. Asian influenza in pregnancy. Obstet. Gynec. (N.Y.), **13**: 394, 1959.
41. WILSON, M. G., HEINS, H. L., IMAGAWA, D. T., AND ADAMS, J. M. Teratogenic effects of Asian influenza. J. A. M. A., **171**: 638, 1959.
42. COFFEY, V. P., AND JESSOP, W. J. E. Maternal influenza and congenital deformities. Lancet, **2**: 935, 1959.
43. DOLL, R., HILL, A. B., AND SAKULA, J. Asian influenza in pregnancy and congenital defects. Brit. J. Prev. Soc. Med., **14**: 167, 1960.
44. WESSELHOEFT, C. Acute infectious diseases in pregnancy. Ann. Intern. Med., **42**: 555, 1955.
45. MANSON, M. M., LOGAN, W. P. D., AND LOY, R. M. *Rubella and Other Virus Infections during Pregnancy* (Great Britain Ministry of Health Reports on Public Health and Medical Subjects, Publication No. 101). Her Majesty's Stationery Office, London, 1960.
46. DUMONT, M. Viroses inapparentes et malformations foetales. Presse Med., **68**: 1087, 1960.
47. FELDMAN, H. A. Toxoplasmosis. Pediatrics, **22**: 559, 1958.
48. LELONG, M. Rapport sur la prophylaxie de la toxoplasmose du nouveau-né et de la femma enceinte. Rev. Hyg. Med. Soc., **7**: 71, 1959.
49. RASMUSSEN, D. M. Syphilis and the fetus. In *Intrauterine Development*, edited by A. C. Barnes, p. 419. Lea and Febiger, Philadelphia, 1968.
50. CUSHER, I. M. Irradiation of the fetus. In *Intrauterine Development*, edited by A. C. Barnes, p. 378. Lea and Febiger, Philadelphia, 1968.
51. RUGH, R., AND GRUPP, E. Congenital defects following low level X-irradiation. Anat. Rec., **138**: 380, 1960.
52. WILSON, J. G. Differentiation and the reaction of rat embryos to radiation. J. Cell. Comp. Physiol., **43**: 11, 1954.
53. HICKS, S. P. The effects of ionizing radiation, certain hormones and radiometric drugs on the developing nervous system. J. Cell. Comp. Physiol., **43**: 151, 1954.
54. PLUMMER, G. Anomalies occurring in children exposed in utero to atomic bomb in Hiroshima. Pediatrics, **10**: 687, 1952.
55. YAMASAKI, J. N., WRIGHT, S. W., AND WRIGHT, P. M. Outcome of pregnancy in women exposed to atomic bomb in Nagasaki. A. M. A. J. Dis. Child., **87**: 448, 1954.
56. CARTER, T. C., LYON, M. F., AND PHILLIPS, R. J. S. Genetic hazard of ionizing radiations. Nature (Lond.), **182**: 409, 1958.
57. NEEL, J. V. *Genetic Effects of Radiation*. A. H. Thomas Co., Springfield, Ill., 1963.
58. CROW, J. F. Comparison of fetal and infant death rates in progeny of radiologists and pathologists. Amer. J. Roentgenol., **73**: 467, 1955.
59. SCHULL, W. J., AND NEEL, J. V. Radiation and sex ratio in man. Science, **128**: 343, 1958.

60. Biological Effects of Atomic Radiation (summary of reports from a study by the National Academy of Sciences, National Research Council). U. S. Government Printing Office, Washington, D. C., 1956.
61. LENZ, W. Thalidomide and congenital abnormalities. Lancet, 1: 1219, 1962.
62. SOMERS, G. F. Thalidomide and congenital abnormalities. Lancet, 1: 912, 1962.
63. WEICKER, H., AND HUNGERLAND, H. Thalidomid-embryopathie. I. Vorkommen inner und ausserhalb Deutschlands. Deutsch. Med. Wschr., 87: 992, 1962.
64. WHITEHOUSE, D. B., AND McKEOWN, T. Note on significance of attempted abortion in aetiology of congenital abnormalities. J. Obstet. Gynaec. Brit. Emp., 63: 224, 1956.
65. WINKEL, C. F. W. Quinine and congenital injuries of ear and eye of foetus. J. Trop. Med., 51: 2, 1948.
66. THIERSCH, J. B. The effects of antimetabolites on the fetus and litter of the rat in utero. In Proceedings of the Sixth International Conference on Planned Parenthood, p. 156. International Planned Parenthood Federation, New Delhi, India, 1959.
67. WARKANY, J., BEAUDRY, P. H., AND HORNSTEIN, S. Attempted abortion with aminopterin: malformations of the child. A. M. A. J. Dis. Child., 97: 274, 1959.
68. COHLAN, S. Q. Fetal and neonatal hazards from drugs administered during pregnancy. New York J. Med., 64: 493, 1964.
69. FRASER, F. C. Experimental teratogens in relation to congenital malformations in man. Proc. Second Internat. Congr. Congenital Malformations, 1963.
70. APGAR, V. Drugs in pregnancy. J. Amer. Med. Assoc., 190: 840, 1964.
71. BARNES, A. C. The fetal environment: drugs and chemicals. In Intrauterine Development, edited by A. C. Barnes, p. 362. Lea and Febiger, Philadelphia, 1968.
72. WILKINS, L., JONES, H. W., JR., HOLMAN, G. H., AND STEMPFEL, R. S., JR. Masculinization of the female fetus associated with administration of oral and intramuscular progestins during gestation; nonadrenal female pseudohermaphroditism. J. Clin. Endocr., 18: 559, 1958.
73. REVESZ, C., CHAPPEL, C. I., AND GANDRY, R. Masculinization of female fetuses in rat by progestational compounds. Endocrinol., 66: 140, 1960.
74. FRASER, F. C., KALTER, H., WALKER, B. E., AND FAINSTAT, T. D. Experimental production of cleft palate with cortisone and other hormones. J. Cell. Comp. Physiol. (Suppl. 1), 43: 237, 1954.
75. FAINSTAT, T. D. Cortisone-induced congenital cleft palate in rabbits. Endocrinol., 55: 502, 1954.
76. HARRIS, J. W. S., AND ROSS, I. P. Cortisone therapy in early pregnancy; relation to cleft palate. Lancet, 1: 1045, 1956.
77. PREISLER, O. Is prolonged cortisone treatment in pregnancy damaging to the infant? Zbl. Gynaek., 18: 675, 1960.
78. KUÇERA, J., LENZ, W., AND MAIER, W. Missbildungen der Beine und der kaudalen Wirbelsäule. Deutsch. Med. Wschr., 90: 901, 1965.
79. PASSARGE, E., AND LENZ, W. Syndrome of caudal regression in infants of diabetic mothers. Pediat., 37: 672, 1966.
80. WILSON, J. S. P., AND VALLANCE-OWEN, J. Congenital deformities and insulin antagonism. Lancet, 2: 940, 1966.
81. RUBIN, A., AND MURPHY, D. P. Studies in human reproduction. III. Frequency of congenital malformations in offspring of non-diabetic and diabetic individuals. J. Pediat., 53: 579, 1958.
82. KOLLER, O. Diabetes and pregnancy. Acta Obstet. Gynec. Scand., 32: 80, 1953.
83. GELLIS, S. S., AND HSIA, D. Y. The impact of the diabetic mother. Amer. J. Dis. Childh., 97: 1, 1959.
84. LONG, N. L., AND HOLTZMAN, G. B. Hazards to the fetus from maternal diabetes.

Congenital Malformations

In *Intrauterine Development*, p. 427. Edited by A. C. Barnes. Lea and Febiger, Philadelphia, 1968.

85. HOET, J. P., GOMMERS, A., AND HOET, J. J. Causes of congenital malformations; role of prediabetes and hyperthyroidism. In *Ciba Foundation Symposium on Congenital Malformations*. Little, Brown & Co., Boston, 1960.

86. BLIZZARD, R. M., CHANDLER, R. W., LANDING, B. H., PETTIT, H. D., AND WEST, C. D. Maternal auto-immunization to thyroid as a probable cause of athyrotic cretinism. New Engl. J. Med., **263**: 327, 1960.

87. SUTHERLAND, J. M., ESSELBORN, V. M., BURKET, R. L., SKILLMAN, T. B., AND BENSON, J. T. Familial nongoitrous cretinism apparently due to maternal antithyroid antibody. New Engl. J. Med., **263**: 336, 1960.

88. BRENT, R. L. Production of congenital malformations using tissue antisera. Proc. Soc. Exp. Biol. Med., **125**: 1024, 1967.

89. INGALLS, T. H., CURLEY, F. J., AND PRINDLE, R. A. Experimental production of congenital abnormalities; timing and degree of anoxia as factors causing fetal deaths and congenital abnormalities in mouse. New Engl. J. Med., **247**: 758, 1952.

90. LICHTY, J. A., TING, R. Y., BRUNS, P. D., AND DYAR, E. Studies on babies born at high altitudes. I. Relation of altitude to birth and weight. A. M. A. J. Dis. Childh., **93**: 666, 1957.

91. HIRSCHORN, K., AND COOPER, M. L. Chromosomal aberrations in human disease. Amer. J. Med., **31**: 442, 1961.

92. LEJEUNE, J., GAUTIER, M., AND TURPIN, R. Les chromosomes humaines en culture de tissus. C. R. Acad. Sci. (Par.), **248**: 602, 1959.

93. JACOBS, P. A., BAIKIE, A. G., COURT BROWN, W. M., AND STRONG, J. A. The somatic chromosomes in mongolism. Lancet, **1**: 710, 1959.

94. PENROSE, L. S. Relative aetiological importance of birth order and maternal age in mongolism. Proc. Roy. Soc. (Biol.), **115**: 431, 1934.

95. PENROSE, L. S. Mongolism. Brit. Med. Bull., **17**: 184, 1961.

96. CARR, D. M. The chromosome abnormality in mongolism. Canad. Med. Assn. J., **87**: 490, 1962.

97. CARTER, C. O., *et al.* Chromosome translocation as a cause of familial mongolism. Lancet, **2**: 678. 1960.

98. FRACCARO, M., KAIJSER, K., AND LINDSTEN, J. Chromosomal abnormalities in father and Mongol child. Lancet, **1**: 724, 1960.

99. SERGOVICH, F. R., SOLTAN, H. C., AND CARR, D. H. A 13–15/21 translocation chromosome in carrier father and mongol son. Canad. Med. Assn. J., **87**: 852, 1962.

100. GERMAN, J. L., DEMAYO, A. P., AND BEARN, A. G. Inheritance of an abnormal chromosome in Down's syndrome (mongolism) with leukemia. Amer. J. Hum. Genet., **14**: 31, 1962.

101. HAMERTON, J. L., *et al.* Differential transmission of Down's syndrome (mongolism) through male and female translocation. Lancet, **2**: 956, 1961.

102. KOENIG, E., LUBS, M., AND BRANDT, T. Congenital malformations and autosomal abnormalities. Yale J. Biol. Med., **35**: 189, 1962.

103. EDWARDS, J. H., HARNDEN, D. G., CAMERON, A. H., CROSSE, J. M., AND WOLFF, O. W. A new trisomic syndrome. Lancet, **1**: 787, 1960.

104. PATAU, K., SMITH, W. D., THERMAN, E., AND INHORN, S. L. Multiple congenital anomalies caused by an extra autosome. Lancet, **1**: 790, 1960.

105. CARR, D. H. Chromosome studies in spontaneous abortions. Obstet. Gynec., **26**: 308, 1965.

106. BARR, M. L., BERTRAM, L. F., AND LINDSAY, H. A. The morphology of the nerve cell nucleus according to sex. Anat. Rec., **107**: 283, 1950.

107. MOORE, K. L , AND BARR, M. L. Nuclear morphology, according to sex in human tissues. Acta Anat., **21**: 197, 1954.

General Embryology

108. MOORE, K. L. *The Sex Chromatin*, edited by K. L. Moore. W. B. Saunders Co., Philadelphia, 1966.
109. BARR, M. L., AND CARR, D. H. Correlations between sex chromatin and sex chromosomes. Acta Cytol., **6**: 34, 1962.
110. KLINEFELTER, H. F., REIFENSTEIN, F. C., AND ALBRIGHT, F. Syndrome characterized by gynecomastia, aspermatogenesis without a-leydigism and increased excretion of FSH. J. Clin. Endocr., **2**: 615, 1942.
111. JACOBS, P. A., AND STRONG, J. A. A case of human intersexuality having a possible XXY sex determining mechanism. Nature (Lond.), **183**: 302, 1959.
112. MOORE, K. L. Sex reversal in newborn babies. Lancet, **1**: 217, 1959.
113. BERGEMANN, E. Geschlechtschromatinbestimmungen am Neugeborenen. Schweitz. med. Wschr., **10**: 292, 1961.
114. MACLEAN, N., HARNDEN, D. G., COURT BROWN, W. M., BOND, J., AND MANTLE, D. J. Sex-chromosome abnormalities in newborn babies. Lancet, **1**: 286, 1964.
115. FERGUSON-SMITH, M. A. Sex chromatin, Klinefelter's syndrome and mental deficiency. In *The Sex Chromatin*, edited by K. L. Moore. W. B. Saunders Co., Philadelphia, 1966.
116. CARR, D. H., BARR, M. L., PLUNKETT, E. R., GRUMBACH, M. M., MORISHIMA, A., AND CHU, E. H. Y. An XXXY sex chromosome complex in Klinefelter subjects with duplicated sex chromatin. J. Clin. Endocr., **21**: 491, 1961.
117. BARR, M. L., *et al.* An XY/XXXY sex chromosome mosaicism in a mentally defective male patient. J. Ment. Defic. Res., **6**: 65, 1962.
118. MOORE, K. L. Sex chromatin and gonadal dysgenesis. In *The Sex Chromatin*, edited by K. L. Moore. W. B. Saunders Co., Philadelphia, 1966.
119. FORD, C. E., JONES, K. W., POLANI, P. E., DE ALMEIDA, J. C., AND BIGGS, J. H. A sex chromosome anomaly in a case of gonadal dysgenesis (Turner's syndrome). Lancet, **1**: 711, 1959.
120. JACOBS, P. A., BAIKIE, A. G., COURT BROWN, W. M., MACGREGOR, T. N., AND MACLEAN, N. Evidence for the existence of the human "superfemale." Lancet, **2**: 423, 1959.
121. FRASER, F. C. Genetics and congenital malformations. In *Progress in Medical Genetics*, edited by A. G. Steinberg, p. 38. Grune & Stratton, Inc., New York, 1961.
122. STEVENSON, A. C. The load of hereditary defects in human populations. Radiat. Res. (Suppl.), **1**: 306, 1959.
123. FRANCOIS, J. L'Hérédité en Ophthalmologie. Masson et Cie., Paris, 1958.
124. HSIA, D. Y. Phenylketonuria: a study of human biochemical genetics. Pediat., **38**: 173, 1966.
125. STERN, C. The problem of complete Y-linkage in ɔ ɔn. Amer. J. Hum. Genet., **9**: 147, 1957.
126. STERN, C. *Principles of Human Genetics*, Ed. 2, Freeman, San Francisco, 1960.
127. WILSON, G. W. Experimental studies on congenital malformations. J. Chron. Disc., **10**: 111, 1959.
128. GIROUD, A., AND MARTINET, M. Action tératogène de l'hypervitaminose A chez la souris en fonction du stade embryonaire. C. R. Soc. Biol. (Par.), **154**: 1353, 1960.
129. HICKS, S. P. The effects of ionizing radiation, certain hormones and radiometric drugs on the developing nervous system. J. Cell. Comp. Physiol., **43**: 151, 1954.
130. CHANG, M. C., AND HUNT, D. M. Effects of *in vitro* radio-cobalt irradiation of rabbit ova on subsequent development *in vivo*, with special reference to the irradiation of maternal organism. Anat. Rec., **137**: 511, 1960.
131. NELSON, M. M., ASLING, C. W., AND EVANS, H. M. Production of multiple congenital malformations in young by maternal pteroyl-glutamic acid deficiency during gestation. J. Nutr., **48**: 61, 1952.

132. NELSON, M. M., WRIGHT, H. V., ASLING, C. W., AND EVANS, H. M. Multiple congenital abnormalities resulting from transitory deficiency of pteroylglutamic acid during gestation in rats. J. Nutr., **56:** 349, 1955.

133. LANGMAN, J., AND WELCH, G. W. Excess vitamin A and the development of the cerebral cortex. J. Comp. Neurol., **131:** 15, 1967.

134. RUNNER, M. N. Inheritance of susceptibility to congenital deformity. Metabolic clues provided by experiments with teratogenic agents. Pediatrics, **23:** 245, 1959.

135. FRASER, F. C., AND FAINSTAT, T. D. Production of congenital defects in offspring of pregnant mice treated with cortisone. Pediat., **8:** 527, 1951.

136. KALTER, H. The inheritance of susceptibility to the teratogenic action of cortisone in mice (abstract). Genetics, **39:** 185, 1954.

137. LANDAUER, W. On the chemical production of developmental abnormalities and of phenocopies in chicken embryos. J. Cell. Comp. Physiol., **43:** 261, 1954.

General Embryology

# CHAPTER 8

# Experimental Embryology

---

DETERMINATION AND INDUCTION
•HISTORICAL BACKGROUND: *preformation; epigenesis*
•INDUCTOR AND RESPONDING TISSUE
•NATURE OF THE INDUCTIVE AGENTS

DIFFERENTIATION
•MORPHOLOGICAL AND BIOCHEMICAL ASPECTS
•GENE ACTION IN PROTEIN SYNTHESIS
•GENE ACTION IN DIFFERENTIATION

GROWTH
•CELL PROLIFERATION
•INCREASE IN CELL SIZE
•DEPOSITION OF INTERCELLULAR MATERIAL
•GROWTH REGULATION IN THE EMBRYO
•CELL PROLIFERATION AFTER BIRTH: *static, expanding and renewing cell populations*

---

## *Determination and Induction*

### Historical Background

Throughout the centuries embryology has been characterized by a controversy which even today has not been solved. This difference of opinion was first clearly formulated by Aristotle, who stated that an embryo is either totally preformed and only needs to grow during further development, or develops from an undifferentiated cell which continuously acquires new specific properties. Until about 1800 it was generally believed that a fully formed miniature individual existed in the ovum and that this miniscule individual needed only the stimulus of the sperm to start growing. Others believed that the sperm contained a miniature individual and that it would begin to develop as soon as the sperm had penetrated the yolk-rich ovum. Although considerable differences existed between the "spermists" and the "ovists," both groups supported the theory of *preformation*.

During the nineteenth century considerable doubt arose as to the validity of the preformation theory since many investigators observed that during the growth of the embryo entirely new structures and organs appeared, which were not present at earlier stages. The theory which supports the progressive development of the embryo from the simple to the more complex form is known as *epigenesis*. As this theory stimulated many investigators to analyze the development of each organ from its first beginning to its final form, the foundation for our descriptive knowledge of the development of the embryo was obtained in this period.

With the recent progress in the field of molecular genetics, it seems that the old controversy between preformation and epigenesis is again being accentuated. The hereditary constitution of an individual is determined by its genes and development is essentially an unfolding of the information stored in the genes. Hence, development seems to be strictly preformationist from a genetic standpoint; from a morphological standpoint, however, development seems to follow the rules of epigenesis.

## Inductor and Responding Tissue

As soon as the main morphological characteristics of the embryo had been described, the question arose as to how embryonic cells, initially all of similar appearance, differentiate into such a variety of cells and organs as seen in the adult. In other words, which forces and conditions regulate the normal development of the individual?

Introducing the experimental approach to embryology, Wilhelm Roux[1] touched one of the blastomeres of a two-cell stage amphibian zygote with a hot needle, to examine whether the remaining living cell would develop into an entire embryo or, as the preformation theory suggested, into a half embryo. As the living cell to which the rest of the coagulated cell was attached gave rise to one half of an embryo, the result of the experiment seemed to contradict the theory of epigenesis. In later experiments, however, in which the two cells of the zygote were separated by gently pulling them apart with a loop of hair, each cell developed into a complete, normal, embryo.[2-4] Hence, the division experiments indicate that the fate of the zygote is not *determined* at the beginning of development, but that each cell has a far greater *potency* than is seen under normal conditions.

Since the fate of the cells apparently is not determined at the stage of fertilization,[5] which factors then regulate the final determination of cells and tissues? This problem was studied by Spemann,[6, 7] who made use of grafting experiments between amphibian embryos. When a piece of ectoderm removed from an *early* gastrula stage (and under normal conditions known to develop into neural plate tissue) was transplanted onto the belly side of another gastrula of the same age, the grafted ectoderm did not form neural tissue but developed into skin. It was concluded that the fate of the grafted ectoderm had not been determined prior to the grafting, but was determined by its new environment. When similar experiments were performed between two *late* gastrula stages, the ectoderm transplanted onto the belly side formed neural tissue, that is, the tissue which it would have formed when left in its original position. Hence, the fate of the ectoderm was determined some time between the early and late gastrula stages and thereafter the cells had lost their capacity to develop in another direction.

To examine which tissues might be responsible for the determination of the ectoderm, Spemann and Mangold transplanted a piece of the blastopore lip of an early amphibian gastrula stage under the belly ectoderm of a similar embryo.[8] As a result the ectoderm on the belly of the host developed into a neural groove and subsequently into a neural tube. The piece of the blastopore lip (which under normal conditions would have formed the notochord-mesoderm complex) had apparently influenced the overlying ectoderm in such a manner that the cells differentiated into nervous tissue. The conclusion was made that the tissue of the blastopore lip functions as the *primary organizer* or *primary inductor*, and determines the differentiation of the surface ectoderm into the neural plate.

With further development of the nervous system, new structures arise and these in turn act as inductors on the surrounding ectoderm. In this regard the role of the optic vesicle is best known. The optic vesicle arises as an outpocketing on each side of the forebrain and is initially separated from the overlying surface ectoderm by some loose mesenchyme. With the disappearance of the mesenchyme the optic vesicle establishes a direct and intimate contact with the surface ectoderm, which then thickens and gives rise to the lens. If the ectoderm which normally develops into a lens is removed before contact with the optic vesicle is established and replaced by a piece of ectoderm from another part of an embryo of the same age, the grafted ectoderm likewise forms a lens under influence of the optic vesicle. If the optic vesicle is grafted under the ectoderm in another part of the embryo, then that ectoderm will form a lens under influence of the transplanted optic vesicle.[9, 10] Hence, the optic vesicle acts as the *activator* or *inductor*, while the ectoderm forms the *responding tissue*. After the lens has been established, it in turn begins to function as an inductor and influences the overlying ectoderm to form the cornea.

From the above examples it is apparent that the primary inductor determines the differentiation of the neural plate. At the conclusion of this stage, secondary inductors are formed in different parts of the nervous system and these in turn give rise to the development of the lens, nasal pits and optic vesicles. At the end of this phase tertiary inductors in the form of the lens begin to function, thus giving rise to the cornea. Hence, the inductor system functions as a chain reaction; every phase in development is the result of earlier events and is a prerequisite for the following steps.

### Nature of the Inductive Agents

The induction experiments raise the fundamental question as to how an inductor can influence the responding tissue so that its development is determined in a certain direction only. Is the induction process brought about by the diffusion of chemical components from the inductor to the responding tissue, or is a cell-to-cell surface reaction required to evoke the differentiation of a cell? The first concept has been compared to a virus infection.[11-13] Brachet[14, 15] suggested that the inductive stimulus is transmitted by the transfer of microsome-like particles from the inductor to the ectoderm and that the active factor in all probability is a nucleoprotein. Weiss,[16] on the other hand, suggested that a close contact between the cells is essential for induction. He thought that a cell-to-cell surface reaction might act as "an attraction of key molecules to the new contact area followed by the building of oriented chains of molecules and the consequent redisposition of the chemical system of the cells."

The controversy between actual diffusion and surface reaction can best be demonstrated by means of lens induction experiments. In support of the surface reaction is the intimate contact which exists between the cells of the surface ectoderm and those of the optic vesicle during the induction phase. During this period, when the ectoderm cells become elongated and the nuclei become oriented perpendicular to the contact surface, it is impossible to separate the reacting layers from each other.[17, 18] In addition, when a cellophane membrane or loose mesenchyme cells prevent contact between the optic vesicle and the ectoderm, lens induction fails to occur.[19, 20] When, however, a thin sheet of agar jelly is placed between the tissues, normal differentiation of the lens occurs, despite the separation of the cells.[20] The latter observations seem to support the concept that the inductive agents are diffusible substances. Further indication about the diffusibility of the inductive substances was obtained when lens induction was studied by means of radioactive tracers.[21] A relatively selective transfer of labeled substances from the eye cup to the lens was noted. From the distribution of the radioactivity in the lens cells, it was concluded that both small and more complex molecules or particles had been transferred from the inductor to the responding tissue.

The best evidence for the existence of diffusible agents comes from experiments on the induction of the kidney.[22-25] Normal differentiation of the secretory tubules in the metanephrogenic mesenchyme of the mouse is dependent on an inductive stimulus of the Wolffian duct. This stimulus is able to pass through a filter with an average pore size of $0.1$ $\mu$ and to operate over a distance of less than $80$ $\mu$. Cytoplasmic material could not be observed in the filter with the electron microscope. In experiments with radioactive tracers, however, labeled substances were found to cross the filter and to be incorporated in the reactive mesenchyme. Hence, many of the recent experimental findings suggest the actual transfer of substances from the inductor to the responding tissue without any cellular contact. It has to be kept in mind, however, that under normal conditions an intimate cell-to-cell contact exists between the two reacting tissues. In all probability the inductive stimulus is transmitted by diffusible agents but to achieve optimal conditions the cells may have to be in close contact with each other.

As to the nature of the inducing agents, it was found that the inductive action needed for the formation of the neural plate is not only present in the blastopore and chorda-mesoderm tissue, but in almost all the tissues of the body. This inductive activity can even be found in tissues which have been killed by boiling or different chemical treatments. To bring some order in the confusion, Ebert[26] suggested that the morphological stimuli might be divided into three categories: (1) non-specific stimuli; (2) specific small molecular stimuli; and (3) specific macromolecules.

Among the non-specific stimuli, various substances of the steroid group[27] as well as a number of organic acids such as adenylic acid, thymonucleic acid and stearic acid were found to be potent inductive agents.[28] Surprisingly, also a number of non-physiological substances such as methylene blue,[29] silicon[30] and certain dyes[31] were found capable of causing induction. Since many of the above agents cannot be considered "normal" inducing factors and cause differentiation only under experimental conditions, it has been suggested that the non-specific stimuli might act by releasing the true "evocator" in the ectoderm.[29]

Among the specific small molecular substances playing a role in induction, phenylalanine is of great importance for the differentiation of the neural crest,[32, 33] while vitamin A has an influence on the keratinization of the epidermis.[34] The mechanisms by which phenylalanine and vitamin A act, however, are not fully elucidated and the importance of these compounds to normal embryonic induction is unknown.

With regard to the action of specific macromolecules, RNA in particular was thought to play an important role in the induction process.[35, 36] Histochemical observations suggested that during gastrulation a transfer of RNA occurred from the invaginating dorsal lip to the reacting ectoderm.[37] Furthermore, implants treated with ribonuclease lost their inductive activity and the inductive effect seemed to be proportional to the RNA content of the inductors. When in later years the ribonuclease experiments were repeated, treatment of the inductor tissue with the enzyme was totally ineffective.[38, 39] Hence, RNA is not an essential component in the induction process, and the misleading results of earlier experiments are most likely due to a contamination of the ribonuclease preparation by proteolytic enzymes.[15]

Since ribonuclease treatment of inducing substances does not effect the induction process, while on the contrary treatment with trypsin and pepsin completely eliminates the inductive action, the inductive capacity of many tissues is probably bound to proteins or ribonucleoproteins. Indeed, extensive biochemical experiments of Yamada[40, 41] and Tiedemann[42, 43] indicate that both proteins and ribonucleoproteins are active in the induction process. Minute quantities of both substances were found to be sufficient to cause induction. Whether the participation of ribonucleoproteins in induction means that somehow ribonucleic acids are involved in transmitting information from the inductor to the reacting cells is presently unknown.

# Differentiation

## Morphological and Biochemical Aspects

During the early phases of development, when the number of blastomeres increases rapidly, all cells are morphologically identical and are capable of performing only certain basic functions such as protein synthesis and respiration. During the formation of the germ layers, however, the cells lose their similarity and some cell groups acquire totally new functions and new morphological characteristics. Hence, the term *differentiation* indicates that a cell acquires new morphological and functional properties, which make it different from other cells.

In whatever direction a cell differentiates, the morphological changes are in all likelihood based on alterations in the intrinsic chemical machinery of the cell, and morphological differentiation is presumably a reflection of the production of a new enzyme or combination of enzymes, which in turn cause the production of new structural proteins. As the proteins synthesized in the cell vary from muscle proteins to pigment granules, it is postulated that differentiation of a particular cell type is based on the production of highly specialized and unique enzymes.[44–46]

If the appearance of specific enzymes is characteristic for differentiation, the question arises whether it is possible to demonstrate the presence of such an enzyme at the time that new proteins or new morphological characteristics arise. A typical example of an enzyme which appears in various cell types of the embryo at different times during development is formed by alkaline phosphatase. This enzyme, which causes hydrolytic splitting of monoesters of the phosphoric acid in an alkaline medium, arises first in the cells concerned with the development of the subcutaneous tissue.[47] A little later it appears in cartilage and in the hair papillae.[48] Subsequently the enzyme is found in the periosteum of bone. Hence in all cells concerned with the production of fibrous proteins and keratin, the enzyme appears about at the time that cell-specific proteins are being produced.

In recent years, immunological techniques have been applied to detect the appearance of specific proteins in differentiating cells. For this purpose organ or tissue proteins from adult animals are injected into rabbits, which subsequently form antibodies against these proteins. If a tissue or organ of the embryo with an unknown protein composition is mixed with the antibodies and an antigen-antibody reaction occurs in the form of a precipitate, the unknown tissue must contain proteins capable of reacting with the antibodies. Another method to test the presence of specific proteins in the developing embryo is to place the embryo in a tissue culture medium containing antibodies against the specific proteins. In these circumstances the antibodies may react with the antigen, present in or on the surface of the cells, and thus cause cell damage to the embryonic cells containing the specific protein.

The appearance of lens proteins in the chick embryo has been examined most thoroughly. Initially, the cells of the prospective lens placode are morphologically similar to those of the surrounding surface ectoderm. After contact with the optic vesicle has been established, the cells gradually change and become elongated, while the nuclei become oriented perpendicular to the contact surface.[18] The elongated cells can easily be distinguished from the surrounding surface ectoderm and are collectively referred to as the *lens placode.* To determine whether during formation of the lens placode specific structural proteins arise, prospective lens placodes from 10- to 18-somite chick embryos were dissected out, homogenized and mixed with antiserum containing antibodies against adult lens proteins. Despite the use of micro-precipitin methods, no reaction was observed.[49] When, however, optic vesicles together with the overlying ectoderm from 5- to 16-somite embryos were cultured in a medium containing antibodies against lens proteins, the placode cells started to degenerate shortly after the beginning of the culture period. When similar explants were cultured in a medium containing antibodies against muscle proteins, the lens placodes developed normally and formed small lenses.[50, 51] It was thus concluded that during the period of intimate contact between the optic vesicle and the overlying ectoderm, new proteins are formed in the placode cell. These proteins are apparently capable of reacting with the lens antibodies, resulting in the degeneration of the placode cells. Furthermore, since cell elongation and nuclear orientation occurred at approximately the same time that the "lens" proteins appeared, chemodifferentiation and morphological differention seem to occur simultaneously. In further experiments in which immunochemical and fluorescent antibody techniques were used, the different proteins characteristic for the adult were found to arise one after the other in the course of development.[52-56] Hence, chemical as well as morphological differentiation are continuous processes and come to a halt only when all the proteins necessary for the function of the adult organ are present.

## Gene Action in Protein Synthesis

It is evident from the foregoing discussion that cellular differentiation is based on the production of unique enzyme patterns, which in turn leads to the production of highly specific structural proteins, such as myosin, collagen and the crystallins. Since the proteins of a cell are synthesized under direct control of nucleic acids and the structure of the proteins in the cell is determined by the chromosomal DNA in the genes, the question arises as to how the genes obtain the information for differentiation and how this information is put into action.

Considerable information is presently available about the manner by which genes regulate the synthesis of proteins in the cytoplasm of the cell. Each gene is thought to be responsible for the formation of one specific protein monomer; the formation of subunits of a complex protein molecule is determined by the action of two or three separate genes. The specificity of a protein molecule depends on the kind and the sequence in which amino acids are joined together. The sequence of amino acids in turn is determined by the sequence of bases in the chromosomal DNA. Since there are only four different bases in DNA (see Chapter 1), and about 20 different amino acids in proteins, an amino acid must be determined by some sort of combination of bases rather than by a single base. Present evidence indicates that a group of three bases is responsible for each amino acid, and that triplet combinations of bases determine each of the 20 amino acids.[57, 58]

In the control of protein synthesis the chromosomal DNA acts by means of ribonucleic acid or RNA. The ribonucleic acids, which differ only slightly from the DNA molecule, form long chains but do not form regular double spirals. The type of RNA which carries the genetic information from the chromosomal DNA to the cytoplasm where it is used in protein synthesis is referred to as *messenger RNA* (m-RNA). The messenger RNA directs the arrangement of the amino acids into a particular protein molecule.

To help the amino acid molecules in recognizing the coding triplets of the messenger RNA, a second type of RNA, the *transfer RNA*, is needed. Transfer RNA carries at its end a triplet ACC, which serves for attachment of the amino acid. As soon as the amino acid is connected to transfer RNA, the complex becomes attached to a molecule of messenger RNA. When two transfer RNA molecules have found their specific places on the messenger RNA, the amino acid molecules are arranged in order and are ready to be linked by peptide bonds to form a specific peptide chain.

The interaction between the messenger RNA and the molecules of transfer RNA takes place in connection with the ribosomes, small granules of 150–250 Å in diameter, consisting of ribonucleic acid and protein in about equal amounts. At the time of protein synthesis the ribosomes attach themselves actively to molecules of messenger RNA. Since the extended length of the messenger RNA molecule by far exceeds the diameter of a single ribosome, it is thought that several ribosomes may attach themselves simultaneously to the same messenger RNA. On the other hand it seems possible that the building of a protein molecule results from the action of one ribosome. The single ribosome is assumed to travel along the length of the messenger RNA.[59] In this respect the ribosome may be compared to a lock in a zipper. One side of the zipper is represented by the messenger RNA molecule and the other side by the recognition triplets on the transfer RNA molecules. The result is the linking together of the amino acids in a chain as a protein molecule.

## Gene Action in Differentiation

During the initial stages of development, all the cells of the embryo have the ability to form a whole embryo, indicating that the nuclei of the undifferentiated cells contain all the information needed for the formation of an entire embryo. Likewise when nuclei of differentiated entodermal cells from frog larvae are transplanted into enucleated eggs, the eggs develop into perfectly normal frogs.[60, 61] Hence the nuclei of undifferentiated as well as differentiated cells contain the information necessary for all possible differentiations. The consequence of this conclusion must be that not all of them are in an active state. Some apparently are not producing messenger RNA, and do not participate in protein synthesis. During development, only some of the genes produce messenger RNA, while the rest of them are in an inactive state.[62]

It is now generally accepted that the genes are prevented from being active by the presence of a so-called *repressor*, which may be a product of a special gene (*regulator gene*). A gene becomes active when the repressor action is removed or when the gene is "*derepressed.*" During the cleavage stage no new proteins are formed and most of the genes are repressed. With the beginning of gastrulation, however, new proteins appear, indicating that some of the genes have become derepressed. Since in different parts of the embryo different enzymes and different proteins are synthesized, a different number of genes must be derepressed at various stages of development.

Although the actual mechanism of derepression is unknown, it is important to realize that DNA is not the only component of the chromosomes, but that certain proteins such as *histones* are also present in the chromosomes. The histones are thought to be wrapped around the DNA molecule and somehow to prevent the DNA from interacting with other substances in the cell and from forming messenger RNA.[63] Indeed, histones prepared from calf thymus were found to prevent or inhibit the synthesis of DNA-dependent RNA.[64, 65] On the other hand, removal of histones by trypsin treatment increased the RNA content in the cell considerably.[66]

The cytoplasm of a cell seems in the last instance to determine which genes will become derepressed. This is particularly evident in the induction process. If induction of the neural plate is carried out by emission of a protein or nucleoprotein into the cytoplasm of the reacting cells, then this protein will in all probability cause a change in the cytoplasm which reflects itself in the functioning of the genes. The change in the cytoplasm is possibly transmitted to the nucleus by an enzyme or set of enzymes, which subsequently

General Embryology

change or destroy the position of the histones repressing the activity of the genes. The result would be the emission of new messenger RNA, which in turn causes the production of new enzymes or structural proteins. The new enzymes might in turn detach other histones from the chromosomes. As development proceeds, more and more genes will be derepressed and, depending on the type of genes, differentiation in a specific direction will take place.

Differentiation is not only caused by the action of inducing substances but can also be brought about by other factors such as hormones and vitamins. When small pieces of vaginal epithelium of juvenile mice are cultured in a regular medium, the epithelium remains without any trace of cornification. If, however, B-estradiol is added to the medium, the epithelium becomes squamous and cornified.[67] Likewise, when ectoderm from chick embryos is grown in a regular tissue culture medium, it develops a squamous cornified layer. When vitamin A is added to the medium, the epithelium becomes cuboid, loses its keratinization and becomes mucus-secreting.[68, 69]

The direct interaction between epithelium and mesenchyme also creates a special condition for differentiation. The growth of epithelial structures and their special arrangement is dependent on the presence of connective tissue. When embryonic epidermis is isolated and fails to make contact with mesoderm, the epidermis soon loses its epithelial arrangement; the cells become reticulate and degenerate. In the presence of mesenchyme, however, the epithelial arrangement is maintained and the ectoderm differentiates as normal skin epidermis.[70]

Although considerable information is presently available on differentiation, many problems such as the nature of the substances produced by surrounding tissues as well as the mechanisms by which these agents influence the formation of new enzymes and structural proteins in the responding differentiating cells have not been solved.

# Growth

One of the fundamental features of development is *growth*, defined as an increase in spatial dimensions and weight. Growth may be accomplished in several manners: (1) by an increase in the number of cells; (2) by an increase in size of individual cells; and (3) by an increase in the amount of intercellular substance. Although growth of a particular organ or tissue is usually accomplished by all three components at the same time, in the following discussion each process will be dealt with separately.

## Cell Proliferation

The lifespan of a cell was originally divided into the *mitotic phase* and the *interphase* (also termed the *resting phase*). With the application of tritiated thymidine and radioautography, however, it became evident that the life of a cell consists of four different phases. Although the mitotic phase is the most easily recognizable stage, a prerequisite for cell division is the replication of the chromosomal DNA. This occurs during the so called DNA-synthetic or "S"-phase, which varies in time depending on the amount of DNA to be duplicated.[71] Immediately after the "S"-phase, the cell enters a short-lasting "$G_2$"-phase, which extends from the end of DNA-synthesis to the prophase of the mitosis. During the latter phase ("M"-phase) the previously doubled chromosomes separate and one half of each of the chromosomes moves to the daughter cells (see Chapter 1). After mitosis the daughter cells enter the so-called "$G_1$"-phase, which extends from the telophase to the beginning of the next DNA-synthetic phase. Hence, the lifespan of a cell can be expressed as $M \rightarrow G_1 \rightarrow S \rightarrow G_2 \rightarrow M \rightarrow G_1$.

Cell proliferation in the embryo begins immediately after the male and female gametes have fused and results in the formation of the morula. Despite repeated divisions of the blastomeres, the total size of the zygote, however, does not increase and the blastomeres actually decrease in size after each division. This is one of the few examples where an increase in the number of cells does not indicate growth in the sense of increase in size.

Considerable information about the rate of cell proliferation and the duration of the different phases of the cell cycle is available from studies on the spinal cord in the chick embryo. During the neural groove stage the constituent cells, known as the neuroepithelial cells, form a homogeneous population, that is, a population in which all the cells have the same morphological characteristics and behave in the same manner.[72, 73] When the duration of the different phases of the lifespan is determined by means of tritiated thymidine, the DNA-synthetic phase is found to last for five hours, the $G_2$-phase two hours, the mitosis approximately 30 minutes, while the $G_1$-phase is non existent or exceedingly brief. The total lifespan of the neuroepithelial cells is about eight hours, and since the cells of the neural plate and neural groove form a homogeneous population, the total population doubles in number every eight hours. This enormous increase in cell number in all probability accounts for the expansion of the nervous system in cephalocaudal direction and possibly is a major factor for the cephalocaudal curvature of the embryo (fig. 5-9).

At the moment that the neural groove closes, the proliferative activity of the cells changes. While previously each dividing neuro-epithelial cell would give rise to two new neuroepithelial cells, after closure some of the cells divide in such a manner that one of the daughter cells remains a neuroepithelial cell, while the other leaves the population to migrate to the periphery of the tube. This latter cell, characterized by a round pale nucleus and a darkly stained nucleolus, forms a primitive neuroblast. The neuroblast does not have the capacity to divide and is unable to participate in the process of growth by cell proliferation. During the following days, when more and more neuroblasts are formed, the neuroepithelial population becomes gradually smaller and the proliferative pool decreases in size.[74, 75]

After the majority of neuroblasts is formed, the proliferating neuroepithelial pool gives rise to a totally different type of cell, the primitive glia cell. These cells in all probability are released from the neuroepithelium without a preceding division and the result is that the proliferative pool rapidly diminishes in size.[76, 77] Finally, when the lumen of the neural tube collapses, only a few neuroepithelial cells remain. Hence, when the spinal cord reaches its final shape the neuroepithelial population is small and does not contribute to further growth by proliferative activity. Enlargement of the spinal cord is then caused by increase in cell size of the neuroblasts, by the appearance of many intercellular fiber bundles, and, to a moderate extent, by the proliferative activity of the glia cells.

**Increase in Cell Size**

Although increase in the size of individual cells is the least important factor contributing to growth, in some organs and tissues such as the lens and the central nervous system its contribution is not negligible. The neuroblast in the spinal cord initially is about the same size as the neuroepithelial cell. When differentiation begins, however, the neuroblast forms a number of cell processes representing the dendritic network and the axon, while in addition the cell body itself enlarges greatly as a result of an increase in the amount of cytoplasm containing the Golgi material, Nissl substance and endoplasmic reticulum. The central nervous system, indeed, forms a prime example of a tissue in which increase in cell size contributes to growth of the system. The large pyramidal cells (Betz) in the cerebral cortex, the Purkinje cells in the cerebellum and the anterior motor horn cells in the spinal cord may increase in size five to tenfold when compared with their original size.

Another typical example of growth by increase in cell size is found in the lens. Initially the lens forms a vesicle and the cells at the posterior pole are not much larger than those at the anterior pole (fig.

16-2). During further development, the cells at the posterior pole begin to elongate, and grow in anterior direction, thereby filling up the entire cavity of the lens vesicle. This cellular enlargement is caused by the deposition of intracellular proteins in the form of long elongated fibers. Hence, for the total growth of the embryo increase in cell size is of relatively minor importance; in a few organs and tissues, such as the lens, however, it plays an essential role.

## Deposition of Intercellular Material

One of the best examples of growth through deposition of *inter-cellular material* is found in hyaline cartilage. Initially the pre-cartilage cells are crowded together. With further development, as the cells themselves enlarge and become functional, they secrete a matrix of which the main component is formed by a chondromuco-protein. The carbohydrate constituents of this complex are formed in the Golgi complex, while the protein components are synthesized in the granular endoplasmic reticulum. After conjugation of the two components in the Golgi apparatus, they are released from the cell as chondromucoprotein. At the same time that the matrix is formed, the chondrocytes synthesize tropocollagen, which subsequently is deposited as collagen in the matrix outside the cell.[78] Fibrils grad-ually appear in the matrix and at later stages 40 per cent of the dry weight of cartilage matrix is collagen in the form of an interlacing network of fibrils. As the amount of interstitial material increases, the cells become isolated from each other and located in small com-partments. Although the hyaline cartilage cells maintain their abil-ity to divide for some time, the actual growth of the tissue occurs in the intercellular tissue. Finally small groups of cells are found in clusters separated from the other cells by large amounts of inter-cellular material. Hence, the deposition of intercellular material as seen in hyaline cartilage as well as in a number of other tissues forms a substantial contribution to the growth of the embryo.

## Growth Regulation in the Embryo

Experiments designed to examine the factors which control growth in the adult animal strongly suggest that growth of a particular organ such as the liver is regulated by functional demand.[79] Al-though this theory may be acceptable for mature and functional organs, it is difficult to see how it could be valid for prefunctional, immature organs as found in embryos.

To obtain some insight into the factors which control growth in the embryo, six-day-old embryonic livers were grafted on the chori-oallantoic membrane of four-day-old chick embryos.[80] As a result,

General Embryology

the livers of the host embryos grew approximately 30 per cent more than those of the controls. Similarly, when liver extracts were deposited onto the chorioallantois of seven-day chick embryos, hypertrophy and hyperplasia of the hepatic cells were observed two or three days after the treatment.[81] When, however, adult liver tissue was transplanted on the chorioallantoic membrane, the embryonic livers did not show a growth response.[82] It thus seems likely that treatment with embryonic tissue preparations tends to cause growth stimulation, but that growth fails to occur after treatment with adult tissue preparations.

A different reaction is found for the endocrine organs. When embryonic or fetal endocrine organs are grafted on the chorioallantoic membrane, the growth of the developing endocrine glands is inhibited, suggesting that growth of embryonic endocrine glands may be regulated by functional demand as observed in the adult. Similarly, when young chick embryos are injected with extracts of blood, erythropoiesis is inhibited as measured by a decreased hemoglobin formation.

The enlargement of the spleen in the chick embryo following transplantation of immunologically competent tissues on the chorioallantoic membrane is of particular interest. The changes in the spleen are both degenerative and constructive in nature.[83] These changes, however, are also caused by transplantation of adult bone marrow, liver, kidney, brain and skin. Since heavily x-rayed spleens, spleens of immature donors as well as of adults of inbred strains fail to cause a reaction, it seems that an immunological process in the graft-host reaction might be responsible for the destructive changes occurring in host spleens.[84] The destruction of the tissue in turn is thought to lead to a secondary proliferative response on the part of the host cells, thus causing the splenomegaly. Summarizing, it seems that the arguments in favor of the occurrence of tissue-specific growth regulating components are inconclusive and little or no information is presently available about factors regulating the growth of tissues in the embryo.

## Cell Proliferation After Birth

Although growth by cell proliferation does not stop at birth, important and large cell populations have already reached their final and total number at this stage of development. This becomes readily evident when newborn animals are given serial injections of tritiated thymidine. Large cell populations such as the anterior motor horn cells, the Purkinje cells, the ganglion cells in the dorsal root ganglia and other neuron populations in the cerebral cortex fail to incorporate tritiated thymidine, indicating that these populations have lost their ability to divide. Hence, at about the time of birth and in some cases long before birth, certain cell populations have reached their final number and fail to contribute to growth by proliferative activity. These populations, referred to as *static cell populations*, are mainly found in the central nervous system, but are also present in other tissues and organs.[85]

Although the neuronal population in the central nervous system does not proliferate after birth, growth of the central nervous system continues as a result of the proliferative activity of the glia, the increased size of the neurons themselves and the appearance of large myelinated fiber tracts.[86, 87] Thus, although at the time of birth some cell populations have become static, others are continuing to proliferate. These populations are referred to as *expanding cell populations*. Their rate of proliferation can be determined by measuring the DNA content at various times after birth. Since the amount of DNA per cell is constant, a progressive increase in DNA in a certain organ indicates a progressive increase in the number of cells.[88] Between 7 and 90 days of age the number of cells in the kidney of the rat increases approximately 6.5 times and that in the pancreas 18.2 times. Hence, the rate of proliferation in postnatal organs varies from organ to organ, and also varies between cell populations in the same organ.

Growth as an increase in spatial dimensions stops when full maturity is reached. When an adult animal, however, is treated with tritiated thymidine and the tissues are examined for DNA uptake, a number of organs and tissues show a high proliferative activity. The amount of DNA in these tissues remains constant, indicating that the total number of cells does not change. The discrepancy between the constancy in total DNA and the appearance of high DNA synthetic activity indicates that many cells are added to the population by mitosis, but that few or none are retained for addition to the population. Apparently, cells produced by mitosis are eventually lost by degeneration or migration. This phenomenon is seen particularly in the cells of the intestinal epithelium.[89, 90] Cells formed in the crypts migrate along the surface of the villus to the tips, where they subsequently fall into the lumen. Likewise, a continuous stream of lymphocytes produced in the thymus leave the organ in large numbers to enter the circulation. The cell populations where cell production is balanced by cell loss are referred to as *renewing cell populations*.[91] The magnitude of this cell renewal is impressive and it has been estimated that in the gastro-intestinal tract of the rat approximately 2 billion cells are released daily.

In most renewing cell populations division is seen in the cells that are little differentiated. These cells, referred to as *stem cells*, are

General Embryology

found in the basal layer of the skin and in the crypts between the intestinal villi. As soon as the stem cells have divided, one of the daughter cells usually leaves the population to migrate and to differentiate while the other remains in the stem cell layer to start DNA synthesis for the next division. Although renewing cell populations play an important role in the maintenance of tissues and organs of the adult animal, in the embryo they have as yet not been described.

## References

1. ROUX, W. Zur Frage der Axenbestimmung des Embryo im Froschei. Biol. Zblt., **8**: 399, 1888.
2. ENDRES, H. Ueber Anstick-und Schnürversuche an Eiern von Triton taeniatus. Schles. Ges. Vaterländ. Kultur, **73**, 1895.
3. SPEMANN, H. Entwicklungsphysiologische Studien am Triton-Ei. I. Arch. Entwmech. Org., **12**: 224, 1901.
4. SPEMANN, H. Entwicklungsphysiologische Studien am Triton-Ei. III. Arch. Entwmech. Org., **16**: 551, 1903.
5. WEISSMAN, A. Das Keimplasma. Eine Theorie des Vererbung. Fisher, Jena, 1892.
6. SPEMANN, H. Ueber Transplantationen an Amphibienembryonen im Gastrulastadium. S. B. Ges. naturf. Fr. Berl., **9**: 306, 1916.
7. SPEMANN, H. Ueber die Determination der ersten Organanlagen des Amphibienembryo. Arch. Entwmech. Org., **43**: 448, 1918.
8. SPEMANN, H., AND MANGOLD, H. Ueber Induktion von Embryonalanlagen durch Implantation artfremder Organisatoren. Arch. Entwmech. Org., **100**: 599, 1924.
9. WOERDEMAN, M. W. On lens induction. Proc. Kon. Ned. Akad. Wetensch., Amst., **42**: 290, 1939.
10. TWITTY, V. Eye. In Analysis of Development, edited by B. H. Willier, P. A. Weiss and V. Hamburger. Saunders, Philadelphia, 1955.
11. MANGOLD, O. Ist das Induktionsmittel diffusionsfähig? In "Versuche zur Analyse der Induktionsmittel in der Embryonalentwicklung." Naturwissenschaften, **20**: 971, 1932.
12. DALCQ, A. L'oeuf et son dynamisme organisateur. Michel, Paris, 1941.
13. NEEDHAM, J. Biochemistry and Morphogenesis. University Press, Cambridge, 1942.
14. BRACHET, J. The Biochemistry of Development. Pergamon Press, London, 1960.
15. BRACHET, J. Nucleic acids and growth. In Fundamental Aspects of Normal and Malignant Growth, edited by W. Nowinski. Elsevier, Amsterdam, 1960.
16. WEISS, P. Cell contact. Int. Rev. Cytol., **7**: 391, 1958.
17. WEISS, P. Perspectives in the field of morphogenesis. Quart. Rev. Biol., **25**: 177, 1950.
18. McKEEHAN, M. S. Cytological aspects of embryonic lens induction in the chick. J. exp. Zool., **117**: 31, 1951.
19. LANGMAN, J. Morphological aspects in the development of the crystalline lens in the chick embryo. Acta Morph. Neerl.-Scand., **1**: 1, 1956.
20. McKEEHAN, M. S. Induction of portions of chick lens without contact with the optic cup. Anat. Rec., **132**: 297, 1958.
21. SIRLIN, J. L., AND BRAHMA, S. K. Studies on embryonic induction using radioactive tracers. II. The mobilization of protein components during induction of the lens. Develop. Biol., **1**: 234, 1959.
22. GROBSTEIN, C. Morphologic interaction between embryonic mouse tissues separated by a membrane filter. Nature (Lond.), **172**: 869, 1953.

23. GROBSTEIN, C. Trans-filter induction of tubules in mouse metanephrogenic mesenchyme. Exp. Cell Res., **10:** 424, 1956.
24. GROBSTEIN, C. Some transmission characteristics of the tubule inducing influence on mouse metanephrogenic mesenchyme. Exp. Cell Res., **13:** 575, 1957.
25. GROBSTEIN, C. Cell contact in relation to embryonic induction. Exp. Cell Res. (Suppl.), **8:** 234, 1961.
26. EBERT, J. D. The acquisition of biological specificity. In *The Cell*, edited by J. Brachet and A. E. Mirsky. Academic Press, New York, 1959.
27. NEEDHAM, J., WADDINGTON, C. H., AND NEEDHAM, D. M. Physicochemical experiments on the amphibian organizer. Proc. roy. Soc., London, Ser. B, **114:** 393, 1934.
28. FISHER, F. G., WEHMEIER, E., LEHMANN, H., JÜHLING, L., AND HULTZSCH, K. Zur Kenntniss der Induktionsmittel in der Embryonal-Entwicklung. Ber. dtsch. chem. Ges., **68:** 1196, 1935.
29. WADDINGTON, C. H., NEEDHAM, J., AND BRACHET, J. Studies on the nature of the amphibian organization centre. III. The activation of the evocator. Proc. roy. Soc., London, Ser. B, **120:** 173, 1936.
30. OKADA, Y. K. Neural induction by means of inorganic implantation. Growth, **2:** 49, 1938.
31. BEATTY, R. A., DE JONG, S., AND ZEILINSKI, M. A. Experiments on the effect of dyes in induction and respiration in the amphibian gastrula. J. Exp. Biol., **16:** 150, 1939.
32. WILDE, C. E. The urodele neuroepithelium. II. The relationship between phenylalanine metabolism and the differentiation of neural crest cells. J. Morph., **97:** 313, 1955.
33. WILDE, C. E. The urodele neuroepithelium. III. The presentation of phenylalanine to the neural crest by archenteron roof mesoderm. J. exp. Zool. **133:** 409, 1956.
34. FELL, H. B., AND MELLANBY, E. Metaplasia produced in cultures of chick ectoderm by high vitamin A. J. Physiol. (Lond.), **119:** 470, 1953.
35. BRACHET, J. La détection histochimique des acides pentosenucléiques. Enzymologia, **10:** 87, 1941.
36. BRACHET, J. Le rôle des acides nucléiques dans l'induction chez les amphibiens. Acta Biol. Belg., **2:** 16, 1942.
37. BRACHET, J. Le rôle et la localisation des acides nucléiques au cours du développement embryonnaire. C. R. Soc. Biol. (Paris), **142:** 1241, 1948.
38. HAYASHI, Y. The effects of pepsin and trypsin on the inductive ability of pentose nucleoprotein from guinea pig liver. Embryologia, **4:** 33, 1958.
39. HAYASHI, Y. The effect of ribonuclease on the inductive ability of liver pentose nucleoprotein. Develop. Biol., **1:** 247, 1959.
40. YAMADA, T. Induction of specific differentiation by samples of proteins and nucleoproteins in the isolated ectoderm of Triturus gastrulae. Experientia, **14:** 81, 1958.
41. YAMADA, T., AND TAKATA, K. A technique for testing macromolecular samples in solution for morphogenetic effects on the isolated ectoderm of the amphibian gastrula. Develop. Biol., **3:** 411, 1961.
42. TIEDEMANN, H. Ueber die chemische Natur der organdeterminierenden Stoffe beim Organizator-Effekt Spemanns. Verh. d. Deutschen Zool. Ges., **251,** 1961.
43. TIEDEMANN, H. Biochemische Untersuchungen ueber die Induktionsstoffe und die Determination der ersten Organanlagen bei Amphibien. Colloquium d. Ges. F. physiolog. Chemie, Mosbach, **13:** 177, 1962.
44. SPIEGELMAN, S. Differentiation as the controlled production of unique enzymatic patterns. Symp. Soc. exp. Biol., **2:** 286, 1948.
45. BOELL, E. J. Biochemical differentiation during amphibian development. Ann. N. Y. Acad. Sci., **49:** 773, 1948.
46. BOELL, E. J. Energy exchange and enzyme development during embryogenesis.

General Embryology

In *Analysis of Development*, edited by B. H. Willier, P. A. Weiss and V. Hamburger. W. B. Saunders, Philadelphia, 1955.

47. MOOG, F. The physiological significance of the phosphomono-esterases. Biol. Rev., **21:** 41, 1946.

48. HARDY, M. H. The histochemistry of hair follicles in the mouse. J. Anat. (Lond.), **90:** 285, 1952.

49. TEN CATE, G., AND VAN DOORENMAALEN, W. J. Analysis of the development of the eye-lens in chicken and frog embryos by means of the precipitin reaction. Proc. Konink. Nederl. Akad. van Wetensch. (Amst.), **53:** 894, 1950.

50. LANGMAN, J., SCHALEKAMP, M., KUIJKEN, M., AND VEEN, R. Sero-immunological aspects of lens development in chick embryos. Acta Morph. Neerl.-Scand., **1:** 142, 1956.

51. LANGMAN, J. The first appearance of specific antigens during the induction of the lens. J. Embryol. exp. Morph., **7:** 193, 1959.

52. LANGMAN, J. Appearance of antigens during development of the lens. J. Embryol. exp. Morph., **7:** 264, 1959.

53. MAISEL, H., AND LANGMAN, J. An immuno-embryological study on the chick lens. J. Embryol. exp. Morph., **9:** 191, 1961.

54. ZWAAN, J., AND IKEDA, A. The changing cellular localization of alpha-crystallin in the lens of the chicken embryo studied by immunofluorescence. Dev. Biol., **15:** 348, 1967.

55. ZWAAN, J. Lens specific antigens and cytodifferentiation in the developing lens. J. Cell. Physiol., **72** (Suppl. 1): 47, 1968.

56. ZWAAN, J., AND IKEDA, A. Macromolecular events during differentiation of the chicken lens. Exp. Eye Res., **7:** 301, 1968.

57. CRICK, F. H. C. The genetic code. Sci. Amer., **207:** 66, 1962.

58. NIREMBERG, M. W. The genetic code. Sci. Amer., **208:** 80, 1963.

59. RICH, A. Polyribosomes. Sci. Amer., **209:** 44, 1963.

60. BRIGGS, R., AND KING, T. J. Changes in the nuclei of differentiating entoderm cells as revealed by nuclear transplantation. J. Morph., **100:** 269, 1957.

61. KING, T. J., AND BRIGGS, R. Transplantation of living nuclei of late gastrulae into enucleated eggs of Rana pipiens. J. Embryol. exp. Morph., **2:** 73, 1954.

62. JACOB, F., AND MONOD, J. On the regulation of gene activity. Cold Spr. Harb. Symp. quant. Biol., **26:** 193, 1961.

63. BLOCH, D. P. On the derivation of histone specificity. Proc. Nat. Acad. Sci. (Wash.), **48:** 324, 1962.

64. BARR, G. C., AND BUTLER, J. A. V. Histones and gene function. Nature (Lond.), **199:** 1170, 1963.

65. BONNER, J., HUANG, R. C., AND GILDEN, R. V. Chromosomally directed protein synthesis. Proc. Nat. Acad. Sci. (Wash.), **50:** 893, 1963.

66. ALLFREY, V. G., LITTAU, V. C., AND MIRSKY, A. E. On the role of histones in regulating ribonucleic acid synthesis in the cell nucleus. Proc. Nat. Acad. Sci. (Wash.), **49:** 414, 1963.

67. HARDY, M. H. Vaginal cornification of the mouse produced by oestrogens in vitro. Nature (Lond.), **172:** 1196, 1953.

68. WEISS, P., AND JAMES, R. Skin metaplasia in vitro induced by brief exposure to vitamin A. Exp. Cell Res. (Suppl.), **3:** 381, 1955.

69. FELL, H. B., AND MELLANBY, E. Metaplasia produced in cultures of chick ectoderm by high vitamin A. J. Physiol., **119:** 470, 1952.

70. GROBSTEIN, C. Epithelio-mesenchymal specificity in the morphogenesis of mouse sub-mandibular rudiments in vitro. J. exp. Zool., **124:** 383, 1953.

71. LAMERTON, L. F., AND FRY, R. I. M. *Cell Proliferation*. Blackwell Scientific Publications, Oxford, 1963.

Experimental Embryology

72. MARTIN, A., AND LANGMAN, J. The development of the spinal cord examined by autoradiography. J. Embryol. exp. Morph., **14:** 25, 1965.
73. LANGMAN, J., GUERRANT, R. L., AND FREEMAN, B. G. Behavior of neuroepithelial cells during closure of the neural tube. J. Comp. Neurol., **127:** 399, 1966.
74. LANGMAN, J., AND HADEN, C. The development and migration of neuroblasts in the spinal cord of the chick embryo. J. Comp. Neurol. (in press).
75. FUJITA, S. Analysis of neuron production in the central nervous system by H³-thymidine autoradiography. J. Comp. Neurol., **122:** 311, 1964.
76. LANGMAN, J., AND SYDNOR, C. F. The origin of glia in the chick embryo spinal cord. J. Comp. Neurol. (in press).
77. FUJITA, S. The matrix cell and cytogenesis in the developing central nervous system. J. Comp. Neurol., **120:** 37, 1963.
78. REVEL, J. P., AND HAY, E. D. An autoradiographic and electron microscopic study of collagen synthesis in differentiating cartilage. Zeitschr. f. Zellforsch., **61:** 110, 1963.
79. Goss, R. J. *Adaptive Growth.* Academic Press, New York, 1964.
80. WEISS, P., AND WANG, H. Growth response of the liver of embryonic chick hosts to the incorporation in the area vasculosa of liver and other organ fragments. Anat. Rec., **70:** 62, 1941.
81. ALOV, J. A., AND SEMENOVA, N. F. Activation of the division and growth of cells during regeneration. Bull. exp. Biol. Med., **46:** 1137, 1958.
82. SIMONSEN, M. The impact on the developing embryo and the newborn animal of adult homologous cells. Acta Path. Microbiol. Scand., **40:** 480, 1957.
83. DeLANNEY, L. E., AND EBERT, J. D. On the chick spleen: origin, patterns of normal development and their experimental modification. Contrib. Embryol., **37:** 57, 1962.
84. MUN, A. M., TARDENT, P., ERRICO, J., EBERT, J. D., DeLANNEY, L. F., AND ARGYRIS, T. S. An analysis of the initial reaction in the sequence resulting in homologous splenomegaly in the chick embryo. Biol. Bull., **123:** 366, 1962.
85. LEBLOND, C. P. Classification of cell populations on the basis of their proliferative behavior. Nat. Cancer Inst. Monogr., **14:** 119, 1964.
86. HOMMES, O. R., AND LEBLOND, C. P. Mitotic division of neuroglia in the normal adult rat. J. Comp. Neurol., **129:** 269, 1967.
87. ALTMAN, J. Proliferation and migration of undifferentiated precursor cells in the rat during postnatal gliogenesis. Exp. Neurol., **16:** 263, 1966.
88. ENESCO, M., AND LEBLOND, C. P. Increase in cell number as a factor in the growth of the organs and tissues of the young male rat. J. Embryol. exp. Morph., **10:** 530, 1962.
89. LEBLOND, C. P., AND STEVENS, C. E. The constant renewal of intestinal epithelium in the albino rat. Anat. Rec., **100:** 357, 1948.
90. LEBLOND, C. P., AND MESSIER, B. Renewal of chief cells and goblet cells in the small intestine as shown by radioautography after injection of thymidine-H³ in mice. Anat., Rec., **132:** 247, 1958.
91. LEBLOND, C. P., AND WALKER, B. E. Renewal of cell populations. Physiol. Rev., **36: 255, 1956.**
92. LEBLOND, C. P., GREULICH, R. C., AND PEREIRA, J. P. M. Relationship of cell formation and cell migration in the renewal of stratified squamous epithelium. In *Advances in Biology of Skin,* **5:** 39, 1964.

General Embryology

PART II

# SPECIAL EMBRYOLOGY

# CHAPTER 9

# Skeletal System

---

NORMAL DEVELOPMENT
- CARTILAGE FORMATION
- BONE FORMATION: *membranous ossification; endochondral ossification*
- VERTEBRAL COLUMN
- SKULL: *neurocranium; viscerocranium*

CONGENITAL MALFORMATIONS
- VERTEBRAL COLUMN: *cleft vertebra*
- SKULL: *microcephalus; acrocephalus*
- APPENDICULAR SKELETON: *amelia; phocomelia; micromelia; sympodia; syndactyly; lobster claw; thalidomide syndrome*

---

## *Normal Development*

### Cartilage Formation

Cartilage is formed by mesenchyme cells and appears in embryos of approximately five weeks old. In certain areas the mesenchyme cells then begin to proliferate, acquire a round shape (*chondroblasts*), and form a compact, cell-rich tissue known as *precartilage*. The intercellular spaces of precartilage contain collagenous fibers embedded in a homogeneous basophilic substance, the so-called *ground substance*. With further development, the intercellular material, the *cartilage matrix*, becomes so voluminous that the cells are pushed apart. According to the type of matrix, three different kinds of cartilage are distinguishable: (1) *hyaline cartilage*; this type is found on the articular surfaces of bones in the synovial joints and contains an intercellular substance with fine collagenous fibrils embedded in a large amount of ground substance; (2) *fibrous cartilage*; this type is found in the intervertebral discs and contains many heavy fibers embedded in a lesser amount of ground substance; and (3) *elastic cartilage*; in addition to collagenous fibers, this type contains branching yellow elastic fibers.

## Bone Formation

*Membranous Ossification.* In the areas where membranous bone tissue is formed, the mesenchyme cells proliferate and gradually change their shape. The newly formed cells, the *osteoblasts*, have a basophilic cytoplasm and a nucleus located in an eccentric position (fig. 9-1A).[1]

The osteoblasts are initially arranged in irregular fashion; later they arrange themselves in rows and secrete a collagenous material, known as *prebone* or *osteoid*. This material gives the tissue a membranous appearance, and this type of ossification is therefore called *membranous ossification.* At some distance from the osteoblasts, the prebone is transformed into bone matrix which subsequently calcifies. The calcification is believed to result from the release of the enzyme *phosphatase*, which is produced by the osteoblasts.[2] The newly formed bone is always separated from the osteoblasts by a

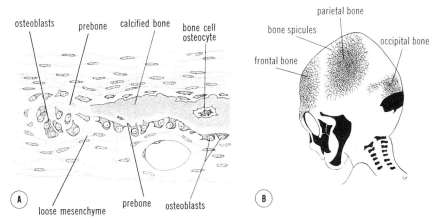

Figure 9-1. *A, Schematic drawing to show the membranous ossification. On the left side the mesenchyme cells are transformed into irregularly arranged osteoblasts which deposit the prebone. Toward the right, the osteoblasts are arranged in regular rows, where they continue to secrete prebone or osteoid. At some distance from the osteoblasts the prebone is transformed into a bone matrix, which calcifies. The newly formed bone always remains separated from the osteoblasts by a thin layer of prebone. Note how a few osteoblasts are trapped in the calcified bone to become bone cells or osteocytes. B, Schematic representation of the bones of the skull of a 3 months old embryo (drawn after a cleared preparation stained with alizarin). Note the spread of the bone spicules from the primary ossification centers in the flat bones of the skull.*

Special Embryology

thin layer of prebone. A few of the osteoblasts, however, become trapped in the bone itself and form the *bone cells* or *osteocytes* (fig. 9-1A). With time, a number of needle-like *bone spicules* are formed which progressively radiate from the primary ossification centers toward the periphery (fig. 9-1B).

When ossification of the primary center is well on its way, the entire primordium is surrounded by dense mesenchyme which forms the *periosteum*. On the inner surface of this layer the mesenchymal cells differentiate into osteoblasts, which deposit parallel bony plates on the surface of the primary ossification center. These parallel plates of bone formed by the periost are known as *periosteal* or *compact bone*.

With each new layer of bone added to the surface, some osteoblasts are trapped to become the bone cells or *osteocytes*. These cells are located in small lacunae and are in contact with each other by means of small canals, the *canaliculi*. The osteoblasts so lost are continuously replaced by new ones formed by the periosteum.

In postnatal life membranous bones, as found in the skull, enlarge by apposition of new layers on the outer surface, and by simultaneous osteoclastic resorption from the inside.[3]

*Endochondral Ossification.* By the seventh week of development the long bones of the extremities are represented by hyaline cartilage "models," surrounded by a layer of dense vascular mesenchyme (fig. 9-2A). This mesenchyme initially forms the *perichondrium*, but later develops into the *periosteum*.

Soon a vascular bud invades the center of the cartilage model, and around the erosion sites the cartilage cells respond in such a manner that eventually four zones can be recognized. Each zone represents a specific stage in the formation of the endochondral bone tissue (fig. 9-2B): (1) a zone in which the cartilage cells show abundant mitoses, the so-called active growth region; (2) a zone of cell hypertrophy; (3) a zone where the cells die and the intercellular matrix becomes impregnated with calcium salts; and (4) a zone of invading capillaries which occupy the lacunae left by the dead cells.

Accompanying the invading capillaries are specialized mesenchymal cells, the *osteoclasts*, which break down the calcified matrix, thus causing the initial small lacunae to fuse. Other specialized mesenchyme cells, the *osteoblasts*, arrange themselves along the walls of the newly formed large lacunae and deposit bone along the remaining calcified cartilaginous spicules (fig. 9-2B, C). This process, known as *endochondral ossification*, gives rise to bone-coated cartilage spicules (*mixed spicules*).

Shortly after their formation, a great number of the centrally lo-

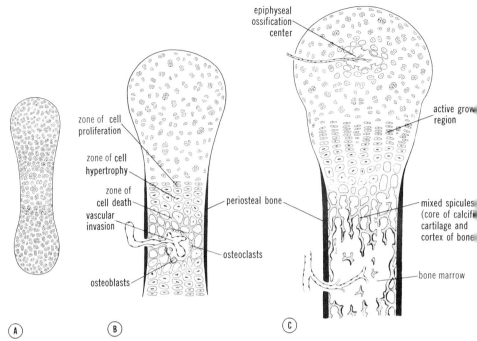

Figure 9-2. *Schematic representation of the endochondral ossification. A, Hyaline cartilage model. B, Around the erosion site, where a vascular bud invades the center of the shaft, can be recognized: (1) zone of cell proliferation, (2) zone of cell hypertrophy, (3) zone of cell death where the matrix is impregnated with calcium salts, (4) lacunar zone with osteoclasts and osteoblasts. Note the deposition of periosteal bone along the periphery of the shaft. C, The central bone spicules disappear while the lateral ones reinforce the wall of the bone. Note that the ossification in the epiphysis proceeds in a manner similar to that in the shaft.*

cated spicules are broken down by osteoclasts, leaving only the lateral ones intact to reinforce the walls of the bone. As a result of this resorption, a broad marrow appears in the center of the bone (fig. 9-2C).

From the primary ossification center in the shaft or *diaphysis* of the bone, the endochondral ossification progresses gradually toward the ends of the cartilaginous "model." Although the cartilage cells close to the marrow cavity are swollen, those farther away are small and crowded, and multiply actively, thus forming a region of active growth at each end of the marrow cavity (fig. 9-2C).

At birth, the diaphysis of the bone is usually completely ossified but the two extremities, known as the *epiphyses*, are still cartilaginous. Shortly thereafter, however, ossification centers arise in the epiphyses, and the endochondral ossification proceeds here in a

Special Embryology

manner similar to that in the diaphysis (fig. 9-2C). Finally, the epiphyses are composed of spongy bone covered by a cartilaginous shell.

A cartilage plate remains temporarily between the diaphyseal and epiphyseal ossification centers. This plate, known as the *epiphyseal plate*, plays an important role in the growth in length of the bone (fig. 9-3). On both sides of the plate endochondral ossification proceeds, rapidly on the diaphyseal side and very slowly on the epiphys-

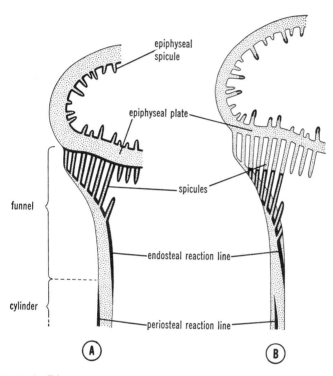

Figure 9-3. A, *Diagram representing part of the head and shaft of a long bone in a young, growing rat killed a few hours after subcutaneous injection of radiophosphorus* ($P^{32}$). *(Phosphorus is incorporated at the sites of active bone deposition.) The heavy black lines indicate the surfaces where the radioactive material is deposited, that is, on each side of the epiphyseal plate, the spicules of the metaphysis and epiphysis, the endosteal surface of the funnel-shaped portion, and the periosteal surface of the cylindrical portion of the shaft. B, Diagram showing the distribution of radiophosphorus several days after the injection. The radioactive material is now found in the spicules well below and above the epiphyseal plate, and in the interior of the compact zone of the shaft. The radioactive line found in the endosteal surface of the funnel soon after injection is now deeply embedded in the bone along most of the length of the funnel and is even resorbed by osteoclastic activity at the wider end* (modified after Leblond and Greulich).

eal side. When the bone has acquired its full length the epiphyseal plates disappear and the epiphyses unite with the shaft of the bone.

In the long bones an epiphyseal plate is found on each extremity; in the smaller ones, such as the phalanges, an epiphyseal plate is present only at one extremity; and in irregular bones, such as the vertebrae, one or more primary centers of ossification, and usually several secondary centers, are found.[4]

Whereas growth in length takes place at the epiphyseal plates, growth in thickness is more complicated. In the straight part of the shaft, the so-called *cylinder*, the bone grows by deposition of new layers of periosteal bone on the outer surface, and by simultaneous osteoclastic resorption on the inside or *endosteal surface* (fig. 9-3). As a result, the outer as well as the inner diameter of the shaft increases. In the epiphyseal region, growth in thickness is caused by a radial expansion of the cartilaginous shell and by progressive endochondral ossification on the inside. Since the increase in size in the epiphyseal region is greater than that in the shaft, the two extremities of the shaft become funnel-shaped (fig. 9-3). In these regions, growth in thickness is entirely different. Here, new bone is deposited on the endosteal surface, while resorption takes place on the outer surface.[5]

## Vertebral Column

During the fourth week of development, the cells of the sclerotomes migrate medially to surround the spinal cord and notochord (fig. 5-6*D*), thus forming a long mesenchymal column. This column retains traces of its segmental origin as the sclerotomic blocks are separated by less dense areas containing the *intersegmental arteries* (fig. 9-4*A*).

During further development the caudal portion of each sclerotome segment condenses and joins the cephalic part of the underlying sclerotome, thereby incorporating the intersegmental tissue into the *precartilaginous vertebral body* (fig. 9-4*B*). Hence, the body of the vertebra is intersegmental in origin.[6]

Cells originating from the cephalic part of the underlying sclerotome segment fill the space between two precartilaginous vertebral bodies and so contribute to the formation of the *intervertebral disc*.[7] While the notochord regresses entirely in the region of the vertebral bodies, it persists and enlarges in the region of the intervertebral disc. Here it undergoes mucoid degeneration and forms the *nucleus pulposus*, which is later surrounded by the circular fibers of the *annulus fibrosis*. Combined, these two structures form the *intervertebral disc* (fig. 9-4*C*).[8]

Special Embryology

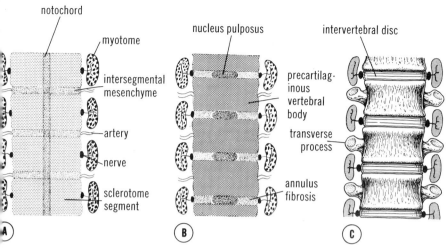

notochord
myotome
nucleus pulposus
intervertebral disc
intersegmental mesenchyme
precartilaginous vertebral body
artery
transverse process
nerve
sclerotome segment
annulus fibrosis

A          B          C

Figure 9-4. *Scheme to show the formation of the vertebral column at various stages of development. A, At the fourth week of development the sclerotomic segments are separated by less dense intersegmental tissue. Note the position of the myotomes, intersegmental arteries, and segmental nerves. B, The precartilaginous vertebral bodies are formed by the upper and lower halves of two successive sclerotomes and the intersegmental tissue. The notochord degenerates except in the region of the intervertebral disc, where it forms the nucleus pulposus. C, The vertebral column in the adult. The myotomes overbridge the intervertebral discs.*

The rearrangement of the sclerotomes into the definitive vertebrae causes the myotomes to overbridge the intervertebral discs, and this alteration gives them the opportunity of moving the spine (fig. 9-4B, C). For the same reason, the intersegmental arteries, at first located between the sclerotomes, now pass midway over the vertebral bodies. The spinal nerves, however, come to lie near the intervertebral discs and leave the vertebral column through the intervertebral foramina.

## Skull

The skull can be divided into two parts: the *neurocranium*, which forms a protective case around the brain, and the *viscerocranium*, which forms the skeleton of the face. Both portions are initially formed by dense mesenchyme; later some parts are converted into membranous bone, and others into cartilage. The latter, in turn, may persist throughout life or undergo endochondral ossification.

*Neurocranium.* The neurocranium is most conveniently divided into two portions: (1) the *base of the skull* or *chondrocranium*, which undergoes endochondral ossification; and (2) the *flat bones*, which undergo membranous ossification.

An important role in the formation of the base of the skull is played by the notochord. Chondrification of the mesenchyme surrounding this structure results in the formation of the *parachordal cartilage* or *basal plate* (fig. 9-5A). This plate extends from the sella turcica to the occipital somites which form four fairly typical sclerotomes. The most cephalic of these sclerotomes disappears, but the remaining three persist and form an unsegmented cartilage, fusing with the basal plate.[9] Hence, the base of the occipital bone is formed by the parachordal cartilage and the bodies of the occipital sclerotomes (fig. 9-5B). Later, the occipital bone extends dorsally around the neural tube to form the *occipital tectum*. Although the original segmentation of the occipital sclerotomes is lost, some evidence of it is retained in the structure of the hypoglossal canal. Occasionally, the hypoglossal nerve leaves the skull through a canal which is divided by a bony bridge into two separate compartments.

Rostral to the basal plate are found the *hypophyseal cartilages* and the *trabeculae cranii* (fig. 9-5A). These cartilages soon fuse to form the body of the *sphenoid* and *ethmoid*, respectively. In this

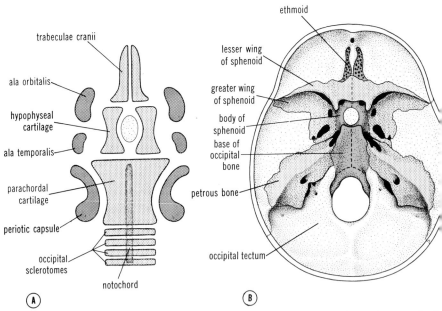

Figure 9-5. A, *Diagram showing the different components that play a role in the formation of the base of the skull or chondrocranium (modified after Clara)* B, *Schematized dorsal view of the chondrocranium in the adult, showing the derivatives of the various components represented in A.*

Special Embryology

manner an elongated median plate of cartilage, extending from the nasal region to the anterior border of the *foramen magnum*, is formed.

A number of other mesenchymal condensations arise on either side of the median plate. The most rostral of these, the *ala orbitalis* or *orbitosphenoid*, forms the lesser wing of the sphenoid bone. Caudally, it is followed by the *ala temporalis* or *alisphenoid*, which gives rise to the greater wing of the sphenoid. These components later fuse with the median plate and with each other, except for the openings through which a number of cranial nerves leave the skull (fig. 9-5B).

A third component, which lies lateral to the parachordal plate is formed by the *periotic capsule*.[10] This cartilage, which surrounds the otic vesicle, gives rise to the petrous and mastoid parts of the temporal bone. These two parts later fuse with the ala temporalis and the parachordal plate to form the definitive temporal bone. The base of the skull is thus formed by cartilage which subsequently is transformed into bone by endochondral ossification.

In contrast to the base of the skull, the sides and roof are formed by flat bones, which undergo membranous ossification (fig. 9-1B). At birth the flat bones of the skull are separated from each other by narrow seams of connective tissue, the *sutures*. At points where more than two bones meet, the sutures are wide and known as the

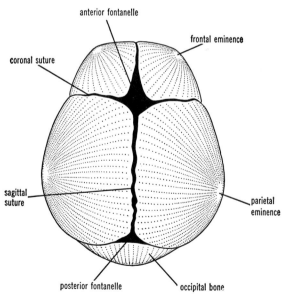

Figure 9-6. *Skull of a newborn, seen from above. Note the anterior and posterior fontanelles and the sutures.*

*fontanelles* (fig. 9-6). The most prominent of these is the *anterior fontanelle*, which is found where the two parietals and two frontals meet. In the first few years after birth, palpation of this fontanelle may give valuable information as to whether ossification of the skull is proceeding normally or intracranial pressure is normal.

*Viscerocranium.* The viscerocranium is formed mainly by the first two pharyngeal arches. The first or mandibular arch gives rise to a dorsal portion, the *maxillary process*, which extends forward beneath the region of the eye, and a ventral portion, known as *Meckel's cartilage* or the mandibular process. The dorsal tip of the mandibular process, along with that of the second pharyngeal arch (*Reichert's cartilage*), later give rise to the *incus*, the *malleus* and the *stapes*. Ossification of the three ossicles begins in the fourth month, thus making these the first bones to become fully ossified (see also Chapters 13 and 17).

# Congenital Malformations

### Vertebral Column

The formation and subsequent rearrangement of the segmental sclerotomes into the definitive vertebrae is a complicated process and it is not uncommon that two successive vertebrae fuse asymmetrically or that half a vertebra is missing. Likewise, it is not infrequently noted that the regular number of vertebrae is increased or decreased. One of the most serious vertebral defects, however, is the result of imperfect fusion or non-union of the vertebral arches. Such an abnormality, known as *cleft vertebra*, is usually accompanied by abnormalities of the spinal cord which herniates through the cleft and is thus exposed to the outside (see Chapter 15).

### Skull

Abnormalities of the skull are manifold. They are frequently associated with brain defects, which in turn are often incompatible with life (see Chapter 15). When the sutures between the various flat bones of the skull close prematurely, the result is *microcephalus* or *acrocephalus*.

### Appendicular Skeleton

The abnormalities of the extremities vary greatly. In the most extreme form, all four extremities are absent (*amelia*), or represented only by hands and feet attached to the trunk by a small, irregularly shaped bone. Such a defect is known as *phocomelia*. Sometimes all segments of the extremities are present, but abnormally short (*micromelia*).

In addition to complete or partial absence of the extremities, the lower limbs may be fused (*sympodia* or *sirenomelia*), a defect always associated with a profound disturbance in the formation of the pelvis. The single lower extremity then contains one femur, two or three bones below the knee, and five or six digits in the foot. Sometimes abnormal fusion involves only the fingers of one hand, a condition known as *syndactyly*.

Abnormalities consisting of absence of a bone or part of a bone usually involve only one extremity, whereas those in which an excessive number of bones is present are mostly bilateral. For example, absence of a thumb is usually unilateral, whereas duplication is often bilateral.

A *lobster claw* deformity consists of an abnormal cleft between the central metacarpal bones and soft tissues, dividing the hand into two parts. The third metacarpal and phalangeal bones are almost always absent.

Although abnormalities of the limbs such as phocomelia and amelia are mainly of hereditary nature, the high incidence of children with phocomelia born in West Germany a few years ago led to a review of the prenatal histories of the affected children.[11] It was thus noted that many of the mothers had taken *thalidomide*, a drug widely used as a sleeping pill and anti-nauseant. In several cases neither the physician nor the mother could remember any exposure to the drug, but examination of the pharmacist's records showed that it had indeed been prescribed.[12] It is now well established that thalidomide, when taken in the early stages of pregnancy, may cause a characteristic syndrome of malformations, consisting of absence or gross deformities of the long bones, intestinal atresia, and cardiac anomalies (see Chapter 7).[13-15]

# References

1. PRITCHARD, J. J. The osteoblast. In *The Biochemistry and Physiology of Bone*, edited by G. H. Bourne. Academic Press, Inc., New York, 1956.
2. BOURNE, G. H. (editor). Phosphatase and bone. In *The Biochemistry and Physiology of Bone*. Academic Press, Inc., New York, 1956.
3. HANCOX, N. M. The osteoclast. In *The Biochemistry and Physiology of Bone*, edited by G. H. Bourne. Academic Press, Inc., New York, 1956.
4. GARDNER, E. Osteogenesis in the human embryo and fetus. In *The Biochemistry and Physiology of Bone*, edited by G. H. Bourne. Academic Press, Inc., New York, 1956.
5. LEBLOND, C. P., AND GREULICH, R. C. Autoradiographic studies of bone formation

and growth. In *The Biochemistry and Physiology of Bone*, edited by G. H. Bourne. Academic Press, Inc., New York, 1956.

6. SENSENIG, E. C. The early development of the human vertebral column. Contrib. Embryol., **33:** 21, 1949.
7. PRADER, A. Die frühembryonal Entwicklung der menschlichen Zwischenwirbelscheibe. Acta Anat. (Basel), **3:** 68, 1947.
8. PEACOCK, A. Observations on the prenatal development of the intervertebral disc in man. J. Anat., **85:** 260, 1951.
9. AREY, H. B. The history of the first somite in human embryos. Contrib. Embryol., **27:** 235, 1938.
10. BAST, T. H., AND ANSON, B. J. *The Temporal Bone and the Ear.* Charles C Thomas, Springfield, Ill., 1949.
11. LENZ, W. Thalidomide and congenital abnormalities. Lancet, **1:** 1219, 1962.
12. SPEIRS, H. L. Thalidomide and congenital abnormalities. Lancet, **1:** 303, 1962.
13. WEICKER, H., AND HUNGERLAND, H. Thalidomid-embryopathie. I. Vorkommen inner und ausserhalb Deutschlands. Deutsch. Med. Wschr., **87:** 922, 1962.
14. VICKERS, T. H. Congenital abnormalities and thalidomide. Med. J. Aust., **1:** 649, 1962.
15. DEVITT, R. E. F., AND KENNY, S. Thalidomide and congenital abnormalities. Lancet, **1:** 430, 1962.

CHAPTER 10

# Muscular System

---

- CROSS-STRIATED MUSCULATURE: *myotome; occipital and preotic myotomes; limb musculature; pharyngeal arch musculature*
- SMOOTH MUSCULATURE

---

## Cross-Striated Musculature

### Myotome

Shortly after the cells of the myotome have been formed by the overlying dermatome (figs. 5-6C, D and 10-1A), they become elongated and spindle-shaped, and are known as primitive muscle cells or *myoblasts*. During further development the myotome enlarges and extends ventrally toward the coelomic cavity (fig. 10-1B). Although it was initially thought that the muscle tissue developing in the somatic mesoderm layer was formed by migration of the myotome cells (fig. 10-1B), from recent experiments it has become evident that the musculature in the ventro-lateral body wall develops by differentiation of local mesoderm cells.[1]

By the end of the fifth week the musculature in the body wall is divided into a small dorsal portion, the *epimere*, and a larger ventral part, the *hypomere* (fig. 10-2A). The two portions are temporarily connected by a plate of mesenchyme, known as the *intermuscular septum*. The nerve innervating the segmental muscles is also divided into a *dorsal primary ramus* for the epimere, and a *ventral primary ramus* for the hypomere (fig. 10-2A).

The muscles of the epimeres form the extensor muscles of the vertebral column, while those of the hypomeres give rise to the lateral and ventral flexor musculature (fig. 10-2B). The latter splits into three layers which, in the thorax, are represented by the *external*

Muscular System

141

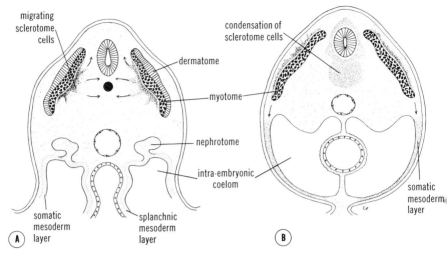

Figure 10-1. *A, Diagrammatic transverse section through a 4-week embryo, showing the migration of the sclerotome cells. The cells of the myotome form a continuous layer in close contact with the dermatome. B, Similar section as in A, showing the condensation of mesenchyme cells around the spinal cord and the migration of the dermatome cells under the overlying ectoderm. The cells of the myotome migrate in a ventral direction until they reach the intra-embryonic coelom.*

intercostal, the *internal intercostal,* and a deep *intracostal* or *transverse thoracic muscle.* In the abdominal wall these three muscle layers consist of the *external oblique,* the *internal oblique,* and the *transverse abdominis muscles* (fig. 10-2B). The muscles in the wall of the thorax maintain their segmental character, owing to the ribs; in the abdominal wall, however, the muscles of the various segments fuse to form large sheets of muscle tissue.

In addition to the above three ventro-lateral muscle layers, a ventral longitudinal column arises at the ventral tip of the hypomeres (fig. 10-2B). In the abdominal region this column is represented by the *rectus abdominis muscle,* and in the cervical region by the *infrahyoid musculature.* In the thorax the longitudinal muscle normally disappears but is occasionally represented by the *sternalis muscle.*

### Occipital and Preotic Myotomes

In the region of the head the development of the myotomes is not so clear. Initially, four pairs of occipital somites can be distinguished, but the most cephalic of these disappears soon after its formation.[2] The myoblasts of the three remaining occipital myotomes are believed to migrate forward and to form the extrinsic and in-

142

trinsic musculature of the tongue (fig. 10-3A).[3, 4] Indeed, their innervation by the hypoglossal nerve, which represents the occipital group of segmental nerves, gives considerable support to the theory that the tongue musculature is derived from the occipital somites.

Although the origin of the extrinsic muscles of the eye has not been traced in mammalian embryos, it has been suggested that these muscles originate from mesoderm surrounding the prochordal plate.[5] This mesoderm is thought to form three myotomes known as the *preotic myotomes* (fig. 10-3A). The eye muscles derived from these myotomes are later innervated by the third, fourth, and sixth cranial nerves.

## Limb Musculature

In the sixth week of development, the limb buds appear on the ventro-lateral surface of the embryo as small flattened paddles (fig. 5-12A). The arms buds lie opposite the lower six cervical and upper two thoracic segments (fig. 10-3A); the lower limb buds opposite the

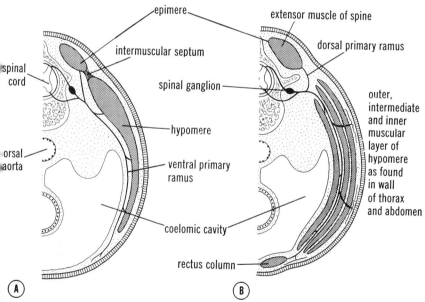

Figure 10-2. A, *Transverse section through the thoracic region of a 5-week embryo. The dorsal portion of the body wall musculature (epimere) is connected to the ventral portion (hypomere) by a mesenchymatous intermuscular septum. The innervating nerve is divided into a dorsal primary ramus for the epimere, and a ventral primary ramus for the hypomere. B, Similar sections as in A, at a later stage of development. The hypomere has formed three separate muscle layers and a ventral longitudinal muscle (modified after Clara).*

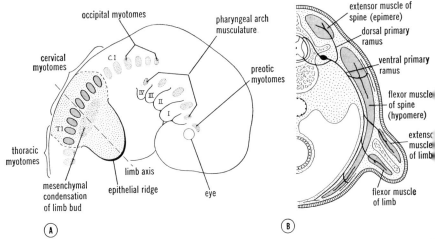

Figure 10-3. A, *Schematic representation of the myotomes in the head, neck and thorax region of a 7-week embryo. The upper limb bud is attached opposite the lower six cervical and upper two thoracic segments. Note the localization of the preotic and occipital myotomes and the condensation of mesenchyme at the base of the limb bud. B, Transverse section through the region of attachment of the limb bud. Note the dorsal (extensor) and ventral (flexor) muscular component of the limb.*

lower four lumbar and upper three sacral segments. The leg buds are always somewhat behind in development when compared with the arm buds.

The first indication of the limb musculature is found in the seventh week of development as a condensation of mesenchyme near the base of the buds (fig. 10-3A). Whether in the human embryo this mesenchyme is derived from the somatic mesoderm layer or from the adjacent somites, as has been shown in some lower vertebrates, is unknown.[6] Similarly, whether the muscles in the limb buds differentiate *in situ* or are derived from cells which migrate into the buds from the mesenchymal condensation at the base is a problem which needs further examination.

With elongation of the limb buds the muscular tissue, as yet undifferentiated, splits into ventral (flexor) and dorsal (extensor) components (fig. 10-3B). Although initially the muscles of the limbs have a segmental character, with time they fuse and are then composed of muscle tissue derived from several segments.

The spinal nerves penetrate into the limbs as soon as the buds are formed. At first they enter with isolated dorsal and ventral branches, but soon these branches unite to form large dorsal and ventral nerves. Thus the *radial nerve*, which supplies the extensor musculature, is formed by a combination of the dorsal segmental branches, whereas the *ulnar* and *median nerves,* which supply the flexor musculature, are formed by combination of the ventral branches. Immediately after the nerves have entered the limb buds, they establish an intimate contact with the differentiating mesodermal condensations, and it is not improbable that the early contact between the nerve and the differentiating muscle cells is a prerequisite for their complete functional differentiation. Muscle regeneration in amputated limb buds of amphibian larvae occurs only when the nerves are permitted to enter the blastema of the regenerating stump.[7]

The spinal nerves not only play an important role in the differentiation and motor innervation of the limb musculature, but also provide the sensory innervation for the dermatomes. Since the tis-

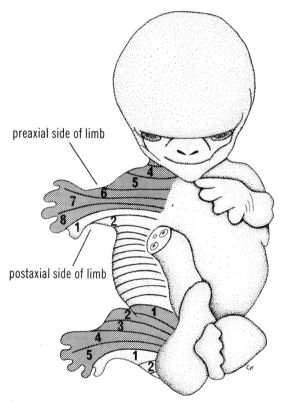

preaxial side of limb

postaxial side of limb

Figure 10-4. *Schematic drawing of the dermatome pattern in the human fetus. Note that at the early stages of development the dermatome pattern strongly reflects the primitive segmental arrangement. With further development the primitive pattern disappears, but an orderly sequence can still be recognized in the adult.*

sues of the dermatome, however, do not migrate beyond the boundaries of their own segment, the sensory supply of the body surface strongly reflects the primitive segmental arrangement (fig. 10-4). Although in the region of the limb buds the original dermatomal pattern changes greatly with growth of the extremities, an orderly sequence can still be recognized in the adult. The cranial spinal nerves supply the preaxial side of the limb, the caudal ones the postaxial side and the intermediate spinal nerves the distal portions of the limbs.

*Pharyngeal Arch Musculature*

When the embryo is approximately 7 weeks old, mesodermal cells located in the pharyngeal arches differentiate into myoblasts and migrate subsequently in various directions (fig. 10-3A). Despite their extensive migration in the region of the face, the origin of the muscles can always be traced, as they remain innervated by the nerve of the arch of origin (see Chapter 13).

Postnatal growth of the cross-striated muscle fibers is mainly due to enlargement of pre-existing fibers. The gradual increase in the number of nuclei in the myotubes, however, indicates that new cells continuously are added to existing fibers.[8] When a few muscle fibers are damaged in case of injury, regeneration may be complete; if, however, damage is extensive, the injured muscle fibers are replaced by fibrous tissue.[9, 10]

## Smooth Musculature

Smooth muscle tissue develops mainly from the mesoderm layer surrounding the gastrointestinal tract and its derivatives. These mesodermal cells form the muscle coat of the gut, trachea, and bronchi, as well as that of the vessels found in the mesenteries. The vessels which develop in the limb buds, head, and body wall obtain their muscular coat from local mesenchyme. In fact, mesenchyme anywhere in the body is a potential source of smooth muscle tissue.

The smooth muscles of the iris form an exception. These muscles, the *sphincter* and *dilator pupillae*, are thought to differentiate from the ectoderm of the optic cup[11, 12] (see Chapter 16).

## References

1. STRAUSS, W. L., AND RAWLES, M. E. An experimental study of the origin of the trunk musculature and ribs in the chick. Am. J. Anat., **92:** 471, 1953.
2. AREY, H. B. The history of the first somite in human embryos. Contrib. Embryol. **27:** 235, 1938.
3. BATES, M. N. The early development of the hypoglossal musculature of the cat. Amer. J. Anat., **83:** 329, 1948.

Special Embryolog

4. Deuchar, E. M. Experimental demonstration of tongue muscle origin in chick embryos. J. Embryol. Exp. Morph., **6**: 527, 1958.
5. Gilbert, P. W. Origin and development of head cavities in the human embryo. J. Morph., **90**: 149, 1952.
6. Glücksmann, A. Über die Entwicklung der Amniotenextremitäten und ihre Homologie mit den Flossen. Z. Anat. Entwicklungsgesch., **102**: 498, 1934.
7. Singer, M. The influence of the nerve in regeneration of the amphibian extremity. The Quart. Rev. Biol., **27**: 169, 1952.
8. Enesco, M. Increase in the number of nuclei in various striated muscles of the growing rat. Anat. Rec., **139**: 225, 1961.
9. Godman, J. C. On the regeneration and redifferentiation of mammalian striated muscle. J. Morph., **100**: 27, 1957.
10. Walker, B. E. The origin of myoblasts in normal and dystrophic mice. Anat. Rec., **142**: 289, 1962.
11. Collin, R. Recherches sur le développement du muscle sphincter de l'iris. Bibliographie Anat., **11**: 183, 1902.
12. Nussbaum, M. Die Entwicklung der Binnenmuskeln des Auges der Wirbeltiere. Arch. Mikroskop. Anat. Entwichlungsmech., **58B**: 199, 1901.

# CHAPTER 11

# Urogenital System

Functionally, the urogenital system can be divided into two entirely different components: (1) the *urinary system*, which excretes waste products and excess water by means of an intricate tubular system in the kidneys; and (2) the *genital system*, which assures continuation of the human race by the production of the germ cells.

Embryologically and anatomically, the two systems are intimately interwoven. Both develop from a common mesodermal ridge along the posterior wall of the abdominal cavity, and the excretory ducts of both systems initially enter a common cavity, the cloaca.

With further development, the overlapping of the two systems is particularly evident in the male. Here, the primitive excretory duct first functions as a urinary duct, but later is transformed into the main genital duct. Moreover, in the adult, the urinary as well as the genital organs discharge their products to the outside through a common duct, the penile urethra.

Despite the close association of the two systems with regard to their development and adult anatomical relationship, for purposes of description the two systems will be discussed separately.

# URINARY SYSTEM

NORMAL DEVELOPMENT
- FORMATION OF THE EXCRETORY UNIT
- PRONEPHROS
- MESONEPHROS
- METANEPHROS: *collecting system; excretory system*
- BLADDER AND URETHRA

CONGENITAL MALFORMATIONS
- CONGENITAL CYSTIC KIDNEY
- PELVIC AND HORSESHOE KIDNEY
- RENAL AGENESIS
- DOUBLE URETER
- URACHAL CYST AND FISTULA

## Normal Development

### Formation of the Excretory Unit

In the third week of development, the intra-embryonic mesoderm differentiates into three distinct parts: (1) the *paraxial portion* which forms the somites; (2) the *lateral plate* which splits into the somatic and splanchnic mesoderm layers lining the intra-embryonic coelom; and (3) the *intermediate mesoderm* which temporarily connects the paraxial tissue and the lateral plate (fig. 11-1A).

In the cervical region the intermediate mesoderm is segmented; in the thoracic and lumbar regions, however, it forms a solid, unsegmented mass of tissue, the *nephrogenic cord* (fig. 11-2A). From this partly segmented, partly unsegmented intermediate mesoderm the excretory units of the urinary system arise.

In the following paragraph is given a general description of the development of the intermediate mesoderm into the excretory units. In the cervical region the intermediate mesoderm loses its contact with the somite and forms segmentally arranged cell clusters, known as the *nephrotomes* (fig. 11-1A, B). The nephrotomes grow in lateral direction and obtain a lumen. The newly-established tubules, the *nephric tubules*, open medially into the intra-embryonic coelom, while at their opposite ends they grow in a caudal direction. During the caudal growth the tubules of succeeding segments unite and form a longitudinal duct on each side of the embryo (fig. 11-2). While this occurs small branches of the dorsal aorta cause invaginations in the wall of the nephric tubule as well as in that of the coelomic cav-

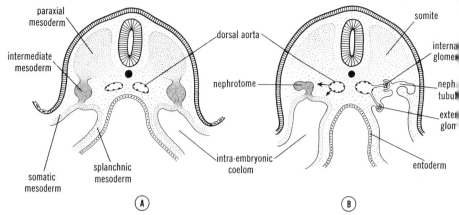

Figure 11-1. *Schematic transverse sections through the cervical region of embryos at various stages of development to show the formation of the nephric tubule. A, At 21 days; B, at 25 days. Note the formation of the external and internal glomeruli, and the open connection between the coelomic cavity and the nephric tubule (modified after Heuser).*

ity, thus forming the *internal* and *external glomeruli*, respectively (fig. 11-1*B*). Together the glomeruli and the nephric tubule form the *excretory unit*. In the lower vertebrates each cervical segment is characterized by one excretory tubule and one internal and external glomerulus.

In the thoracic, lumbar and sacral regions of the higher vertebrates, the intermediate cell mass loses its contact with the somite as well as with the coelomic cavity. The external glomeruli, therefore, fail to develop. In addition, the segmentation disappears and the tissue of the *nephrogenic cord* forms two, three or even more excretory tubules and several internal glomeruli per segment.

Though the structure of the excretory units from the cervical to the sacral region is basically the same, three different, slightly overlapping kidney systems are formed during intra-uterine life in man.[1, 2] The earliest and simplest of these is the *pronephros*, a vestigial structure found in the cervical region (fig. 11-2*B*). It is replaced by a more advanced system, the *mesonephros*, which extends from the lower cervical to the upper lumbar segments. This system in turn is replaced by the *permanent kidney* or *metanephros*, which arises in the lower lumbar and sacral regions.

## Pronephros

The pronephric system is functional in the early development of fish and amphibia, but not in the higher vertebrates. In the human embryo the pronephros is represented by 7 to 10 solid or tubular

Special Embryology

arranged cell groups in the cervical region (fig. 11-2*B*). The first formed vestigial nephrotomes regress before the last ones are formed and at the end of the fourth week all indications of the pronephric system have disappeared. Neither internal nor external glomeruli develop and it is doubtful whether a collecting tube, the so-called *longitudinal pronephric duct*, is ever established (fig. 11-2).

## Mesonephros

During regression of the pronephric system, the first excretory tubules of the mesonephros begin to appear. These tubules, which lack a connection with the coelomic cavity, lengthen rapidly, form

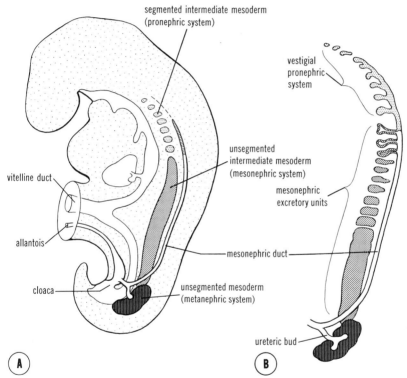

Figure 11-2. *A, Schematic diagram showing the relation of the intermediate mesoderm of the pronephric, mesonephric and metanephric systems. In the cervical and upper thoracic regions the intermediate mesoderm is segmented; in the lower thoracic, lumbar and sacral regions it forms a solid, unsegmented mass of tissue, the nephrogenic cord. Note the longitudinal collecting duct, initially formed by the pronephros but later taken over by the mesonephros. B, Schematic representation of the excretory tubules of the pronephric and mesonephric systems in a 5-week-old embryo. The ureteric bud penetrates the metanephric tissue. Note the remnant of the pronephric excretory tubules and longitudinal collecting duct.*

an "S" shaped loop, and acquire a glomerulus at their medial extremity (fig. 11-3A). Here the tubule forms the *Bowman's capsule.* At the opposite end the tubule enters the longitudinal collecting duct, known as the *mesonephric* or *Wolffian duct* (figs. 11-2 and 11-3A). In the upper thoracic region, each segment gives rise to one excretory tubule and one glomerulus; in the lower thoracic and lumbar regions, which develop later, each segment forms two, three or even four tubules, each with several glomeruli.

In the middle of the second month, the mesonephros forms a large ovoid organ on each side of the midline (fig. 11-3B). It projects into the coelomic cavity and is attached to the posterior abdominal wall by a broad mesentery. Since the developing gonad is located on the medial side of the mesonephros, the ridge formed by both organs is known as the *urogenital ridge* and the mesentery as the *urogenital mesentery* (fig. 11-3A). While the caudal tubules of mesonephros are still differentiating, the cranial tubules and glomeruli show many degenerative changes and by the end of the second month the ma-

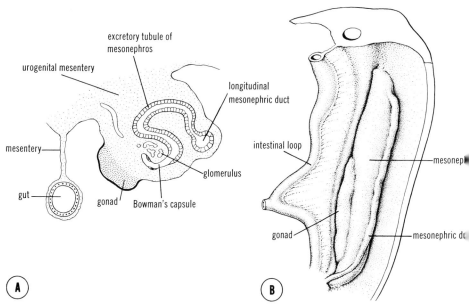

Figure 11-3. A, *Transverse section through the lower thoracic region of a 5-week embryo, showing the formation of an excretory tubule of the mesonephric system. Note the appearance of the capsule of Bowman and the gonadal ridge. The mesonephros and gonad are attached to the posterior abdominal wall by a broad urogenital mesentery. B, Drawing to show the relationship of the gonad and the mesonephros. Note the size of the mesonephros with regard to that of the gonad. The longitudinal mesonephric duct (Wolffian duct) runs along the lateral side of the mesonephros.*

Special Embryology

jority of the excretory tubules and glomeruli have disappeared.[3] A few of the caudal tubules, however, persist and parts of these tubules are later found in close contact with the testis and the ovary. The fate of the longitudinal mesonephric duct differs with the sex of the embryo. In the male it persists as the *ductus deferens*, but in the female it disappears almost entirely (see "Genital System").

Though functional activity of the mesonephric system has been shown to exist in embryos of the cat, rabbit, and pig, and great resemblances in ultrastructure have been found to exist between the mesonephros and the metanephros, functional activity of the mesonephros has not been demonstrated in the human embryo.[4, 5]

## Metanephros

During regression of the mesonephric system, a third urinary organ known as the *metanephros* or *permanent kidney* appears. Its excretory units develop from the intermediate mesoderm, which forms the caudal continuation of the nephrogenic cord and is known as the *metanephric blastema* (fig. 11-4). The excretory units develop in the same manner as in the mesonephric system. The development of the collecting ducts, however, differs from the other kidney systems in that it is formed by an outbudding of the mesonephric duct.

### Collecting System

The development of the collecting ducts of the permanent kidney begins with the formation of the *ureteric bud,* an outgrowth of the

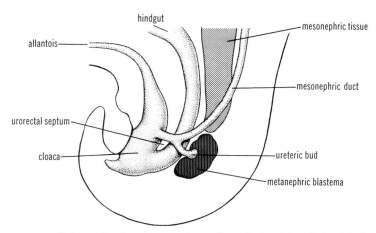

Figure 11-4. *Schematic drawing to show the relationship of the hindgut and cloaca at the end of the fifth week. The ureteric bud begins to penetrate the metanephric blastema. Note the urorectal septum which will grow in caudal direction to divide the cloaca into the urogenital sinus and anorectal canal.*

dorsomedial wall of the mesonephric duct close to its entrance into the cloaca (figs. 11-2A and 11-4). The bud grows dorsocranially, thereby penetrating the metanephric blastema, which as a cap is molded over its distal end (fig. 11-4). This end subsequently dilates forming the *primitive pelvis*; simultaneously it splits into a cranial and caudal portion, the future *major calyces* (fig. 11-5A, B).

Shortly later one or sometimes two additional calyces are formed near the middle of the pelvis. Each calyx, while penetrating deeper into metanephric tissue, forms two new buds, which are also known as *secondary collecting tubules*. The newly formed buds continue to subdivide until 12 or more generations of tubules have been formed (fig. 11-5).[6] While at the periphery more tubules are continuously formed until the end of the fifth month, the secondary tubules enlarge and absorb the tubules of the third and fourth generations, thus forming the *minor calyces* of the renal pelvis. Hence, the tubules of the fifth generation are the first collecting tubules to open into the minor calyces (fig. 11-5D). During further development the collecting tubules of the fifth and successive generations elongate considerably and converge on the minor calyx, thus forming the *renal pyramid* (fig. 11-5D). Since the third, fourth and fifth generations of collecting tubules sometimes give rise to three or four buds instead of two, the total number of collecting ducts entering a minor calyx may vary from 10 to 25. Hence, the ureteric bud gives rise to the ureter, the renal pelvis, the major and minor calyces and approximately one to three million collecting tubules.

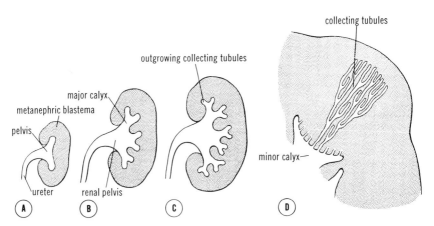

Figure 11-5. *Schematic drawings showing the development of the renal pelvis, calyces and collecting tubules of the metanephros. A, At 6 weeks; B, end of sixth week; C, 7 weeks; D, newborn. Note the pyramid form of the collecting tubules entering the minor calyx.*

Special Embryology

*Excretory System*

While the collecting tubules penetrate the metanephric blastema, this tissue proliferates continuously to keep pace with the growth of the ureteric tree. Each newly formed tubule is covered at its distal end by a so-called *metanephric tissue cap* (fig. 11-6A). Subsequently cells separate from the tissue cap to form a cell cluster on each side of the tubule. These cell clusters differentiate and form small vesicles, the *renal vesicles*, which in turn give rise to small tubules (fig. 11-6B, C).

The renal vesicle and the tubule together form a *nephron*. The proximal end of the nephron becomes invaginated by a small capillary loop, and forms the *Bowman's capsule* of the renal glomerulus (fig. 11-6C, D). The distal end breaks into one of the collecting tubules, thus establishing a passageway from the glomerulus to the collecting unit. Continuous lengthening of the nephron or *excretory*

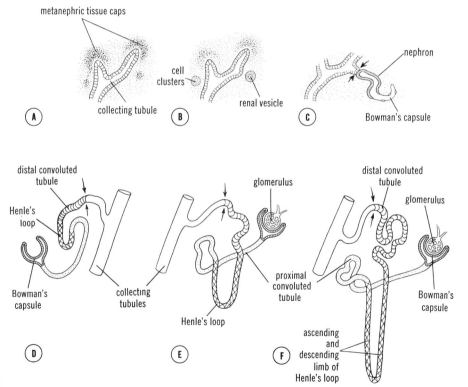

Figure 11-6. *Schematic representation of the development of a metanephric excretory unit. Arrows indicate the place where the excretory unit establishes an open communication with the collecting system, thus allowing for the flow of urine from the glomerulus into the collecting ducts.*

*tubule* results in the formation of the *proximal convoluted tubule,* the *loop of Henle,* and the *distal convoluted tubule* (fig. 11-6*E, F*).

The nephrons belonging to the second, third and fourth generations of collecting tubules are vestigial and disappear when these tubules are incorporated into the minor calyces.[7]

The metanephros, initially located in the lower lumbar and sacral regions, later shifts to a more cranial position. This so-called *ascent of the kidney* is thought to be caused by a diminution of the body curvature as well as by the continuous cranial growth of the ureteric bud (fig. 11-7).[8] While this occurs the gonad and the remnants of the mesonephros migrate in caudal direction. The metanephros or definitive kidney becomes functional at the end of pregnancy.[4, 9]

### Bladder and Urethra

During the fourth to seventh weeks of development, the cloaca is subdivided into a posterior portion, the *anorectal canal,* and an anterior portion, the *primitive urogenital sinus* (fig. 11-8). This is accomplished by the formation of a transverse mesodermal ridge, which arises in the angle between the allantois and the hindgut. The ridge, known as the *urorectal septum,* proliferates strongly and grows in the direction of the cloacal membrane, with which it fuses by the end of the seventh week. At the site of fusion the *primitive perineal body* is formed. The cloacal membrane itself is then divided into the *urogenital membrane,* anteriorly, and the *anal membrane,* posteriorly (fig. 11-8*C*).

Three portions of the primitive urogenital sinus can be distinguished: (1) the upper and largest part is the *urinary bladder* (fig. 11-9*A*). Initially the bladder is continuous with the allantois, but

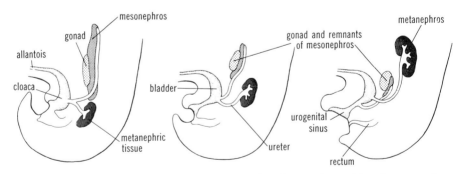

Figure 11-7. *Ascent of the kidney. Note the change in position between the metanephros and mesonephric system. The mesonephric system degenerates almost entirely and only a few remnants persist in close contact with the gonad. In both the male and female embryo the gonad descends from its original level to a much lower position.*

Special Embryology

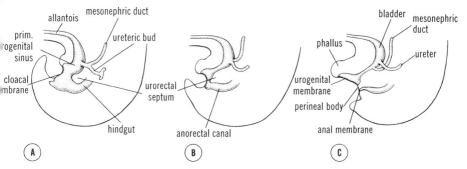

Figure 11-8. *Diagrams showing the division of the cloaca into the urogenital sinus and anorectal canal. Note that the mesonephric duct is gradually absorbed into the wall of the urogenital sinus and that the ureters enter separately. A, End of the fifth week; B, 7 weeks; C, 8 weeks.*

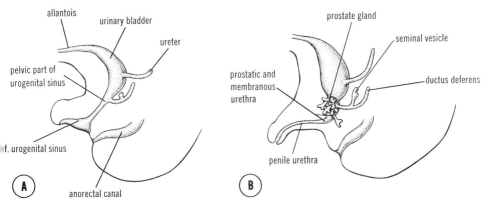

Figure 11-9. *A, Development of the urogenital sinus into the urinary bladder, the pelvic part of the urogenital sinus and the definitive urogenital sinus. B, In the male the urogenital sinus develops into the prostatic, membranous and penile portions of the urethra. The prostate gland is formed by outbuddings of the urethra, while the seminal vesicles are formed by an outbudding of the ductus deferens.*

when the latter shrinks and its lumen is obliterated, a thick fibrous cord, the *urachus*, connects the apex of the bladder with the umbilicus.[10] In the adult the fibrous ligament is known as the *median umbilical ligament*. (2) A rather narrow canal, the *pelvic part of the urogenital sinus*, also known as the *phallic part of the urogenital sinus*, is considerably flattened from side to side and is separated from the outside by the urogenital membrane (fig. 11-9A).

The development of the definitive urogenital sinus differs greatly between the two sexes. In the male, two distinct parts can be distinguished (fig. 11-9B): (1) a pelvic portion which forms the *prostatic urethra* and the *membranous urethra*; and (2) a long phallic portion which forms the *penile urethra*. In the female, the definitive urogenital sinus forms a small portion of the urethra and the *vestibule* (see "Genital System").

During division of the cloaca into the primitive urogenital sinus and the anorectal canal, the position of the mesonephric ducts and ureters is greatly altered. As a result of growth changes the mesonephric ducts are gradually absorbed into the wall of the urinary bladder (fig. 11-10). Consequently the ureters, initially outbuddings of the mesonephric ducts, enter the bladder separately (fig. 11-10*B*). Later, the orifices of the ureters move further cranially, while those of the mesonephric ducts move close together to enter the upper part of the urethra (fig. 11-10*C*, *D*).[11] Since both the mesonephric ducts and the ureters are of mesodermal origin, the mucosa of the bladder formed by incorporation of the ducts, the *trigone of the bladder*, is mesodermal in origin. The remaining part of the bladder is derived from the urogenital sinus and is entodermal in origin. With time, the mesodermal lining of the trigone is replaced by entodermal epithelium, so that finally the inside of the bladder is completely lined with epithelium of entodermal origin.[12]

At the end of the third month, the epithelium of the cranial portion of the urethra begins to proliferate and forms a number of outbuddings which penetrate the surrounding mesenchyme. In the male these buds form the *prostatic gland* (fig. 11-9*B*), whereas in the female they give rise to the *urethral* and *para-urethral glands*.

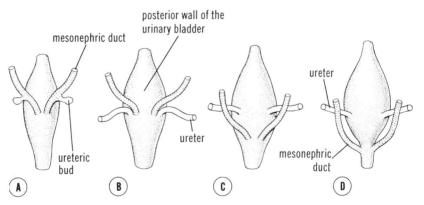

Figure 11-10. *Schematic drawings to show the relationship of the ureters and mesonephric ducts during development. Initially the ureter is formed by an outgrowth of the mesonephric duct, but with time it obtains a separate entrance into the urinary bladder.*

Special Embryology

# Congenital Malformations

## Congenital Cystic Kidney

Under normal conditions, the collecting tubules unite with the excretory units of the metanephric blastema, thus allowing for the flow of urine from the glomeruli to the renal pelvis (fig. 11-6). According to the "non-union" theory of the formation of renal cysts, the collecting and excretory tubules occasionally fail to join. The excretory units develop then in a normal manner and may even form functional glomeruli. Accumulation of urine in the convoluted tubules, however, causes them to dilate and gradually to form cysts lined with cuboidal epithelium. These cysts, usually found in the cortex of the kidney, may be so numerous that insufficient active renal tissue remains.

Sometimes one or more cysts are found close to the pelvis of the kidney. These cysts are thought to be remnants of the nephrons of the second, third or fourth order. When their corresponding collecting tubules are absorbed into the minor calyces, the nephrons usually disappear.[13] In recent years the non-union theory has become discredited and it is presently thought that the main cause for cyst formation in the kidney may be found in abnormal development of the collecting system.[14, 15] In some cases cyst formation was found to result from hyperplasia of the wall of the collecting tubules, while in others abnormal differentiation of the ureteric bud, resulting in dilated, constricted or sometimes atretic tubules was held responsible.

## Pelvic and Horseshoe Kidney

From their initial position in the pelvis, the kidneys normally ascend to the lumbar region (fig. 11-7). During this ascent they pass through the arterial fork formed by the umbilical arteries, but occasionally one of the kidneys fails to do so. It then remains in the pelvis close to the common iliac artery and is known as a *pelvic kidney* (fig. 11-11A). Sometimes both kidneys are pushed so close together during their passage through the arterial fork that the lower poles fuse. This results in the formation of a *horseshoe kidney* (fig. 11-11B).[16] The horseshoe kidney is usually located at the level of the lower lumbar vertebrae, since its ascent is prevented by the root of the *inferior mesenteric artery* (fig. 11-11B). The ureters arise from the anterior surface of the kidney and pass ventral to the isthmus in caudal direction.

## Renal Agenesis

Bilateral or unilateral renal agenesis is presumably caused by an early degeneration of the ureteric bud. When the ureteric bud does not reach the metanephric tissue cap, the latter fails to proliferate, possibly indicating that under normal conditions the ureteric outgrowth has an inductive influence on the metanephric mesoderm. The uterus and a major portion of the vagina are also absent. A newborn child with total renal agenesis dies shortly after birth.[17]

## Double Ureter

Early splitting of the ureteric bud into two parts may result in partial or complete duplication of the ureter (fig. 11-12A, B). The metanephric blastema may then be divided into two completely separate parts, each with its own renal pelvis and ureter. More frequently, however, the two parts have a number of lobes in common, as a result of the intermingling of the collecting tubules. In rare cases one ureter opens into the bladder, while the other enters the vagina, urethra, or vestibule.

## Urachal Cyst and Fistula

When the lumen of the intraembryonic portion of the allantois, extending from the urinary bladder to the umbilicus, persists over its entire length, urine may drain from the umbilicus. This abnor-

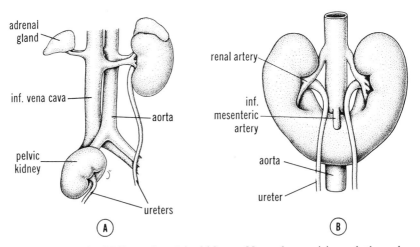

Figure 11-11. A, *Unilateral pelvic kidney. Note the position of the adrenal gland on the affected side. B, Horseshoe kidney, ventral view. Note the position of the inferior mesenteric artery.*

Special Embryology

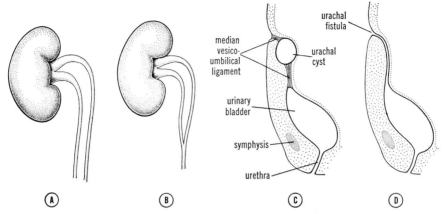

median
vesico-
umbilical
ligament

urachal
fistula

urachal
cyst

urinary
bladder

symphysis

urethra

(A)          (B)          (C)          (D)

Figure 11-12. *A and B, Complete and partial double ureter; C, urachal cyst; D, urachal fistula connecting the urinary bladder with the umbilicus.*

mality is known as a *urachal fistula* (fig. 11-12*D*).[18] If only a localized area of the intraembryonic allantois persists, secretory activity of its lining results in a cystic dilatation, the *urachal cyst* (fig. 11-12*C*). These cysts are not malignant, but in later life they may enlarge and become filled with fluid.

### References—Urinary System

1. FRASER, E. A. The development of the vertebrate excretory system. Biol. Rev., **25**: 159, 1950.
2. TORREY, R. W. The early development of the human nephros. Contrib. Embryol., **35**: 175, 1954.
3. ALTSCHULE, M. D. The changes in the mesonephric tubules of human embryos ten to twelve weeks old. Anat. Rec., **46**: 81, 1930.
4. GERSH, I. The correlation of structure and function in developing mesonephros and metanephros. Contrib. Embryol., **26**: 33, 1937.
5. LEESON, T. S. The fine structure of the mesonephros of the 17-day rabbit embryo. Exp. Cell Res., **12**: 670, 1957.
6. HUBER, G. C. Renal tubules. In *Special Cytology*, edited by E. V. Cowdry, Vol. 2. Paul B. Hoeber, Inc., New York, 1932.
7. KAMPMEYER, O. F. The metanephros or so-called permanent kidney in part provisional and vestigial. Anat. Rec., **33**: 115, 1926.
8. GRUENWALD, P. The normal changes in the position of the embryonic kidney. Anat. Rec., **85**: 163, 1943.
9. WELLS, L. J., AND BELL, E. T. Functioning of the fetal kidney as reflected by stillborn infants with hydroureter and hydronephrosis. Arch. Path., **42**: 274, 1946.
10. BEGG, R. C. The urachus; its anatomy, histology and development. J. Anat., **64**: 170, 1930.
11. FRAZER, J. E. The terminal part of the Wolffian duct. J. Anat., **69**: 455, 1935.
12. GYLLENSTEN, L. Contributions to embryology of the urinary bladder; development of definitive relations between openings of the Wolffian ducts and ureters. Acta Anat., **7**: 305, 1949.

13. McKENNA, C. M., AND KAMPMEYER, O. F. Consideration of development of poly-cystic kidney. Trans. Amer. Assn. Genitourin. Surg., **26:** 373, 1933.
14. OSATHANONDH, V., AND POTTER, E. L. Pathogenesis of polycystic kidneys. Arch. Path., **77:** 459, 1964.
15. BAXTER, T. J. Cysts arising in the renal tubules. Arch. Dis. Childh., **40:** 464, 1965.
16. GORDON-TAYLOR, G. On horseshoes and horseshoe kidneys, concave downwards. Brit. J. Urol., **8:** 112, 1936.
17. DAVIDSON, W. M., AND ROSS, G. I. M. Bilateral absence of kidneys and related congenital anomalies. J. Path. Bact., **68:** 459, 1954.
18. MAHONEY, P. J., AND ENNIS, D. Congenital patent urachus. New Engl. J. Med., **215:** 193, 1936.

Special Embryology

# GENITAL SYSTEM

## NORMAL DEVELOPMENT
- GONADS: *genital ridge; primordial germ cells; indifferent gonad; testis; ovary*
- GENITAL DUCTS: *indifferent stage; genital ducts in the male; genital ducts in the female*
- EXTERNAL GENITALIA: *indifferent stage; external genitalia in the male; external genitalia in the female*
- DESCENT OF THE TESTIS

## CONGENITAL MALFORMATIONS
- HYPOSPADIA
- EPISPADIA
- ECTOPIA OR EXSTROPHY OF THE BLADDER
- CRYPTORCHISM
- CONGENITAL INGUINAL HERNIA
- DUPLICATION AND ATRESIA OF THE UTEROVAGINAL CANAL
- OVARIAN HYPOPLASIA
- PSEUDOHERMAPHRODITISM AND INTERSEXUALITY

## *Normal Development*

### Gonads

Although the sex of the embryo genetically is determined at the time of fertilization, the gonads do not acquire male or female morphological characteristics until the seventh week of development.

### *Genital or Gonadal Ridge*

The gonads appear in a 4-week embryo as a pair of longitudinal ridges, the *genital* or *gonadal ridges*, on each side of the midline between the mesonephros and the dorsal mesentery (figs. 11-3*B* and 11-13). They are formed by proliferation of the coelomic epithelium and a condensation of the underlying mesenchyme. Germ cells do not appear in the genital ridges until the sixth week of development.[1, 2]

### *Primordial Germ Cells*

In mammalian and human embryos the primordial germ cells appear at an early stage of development, and are initially located in

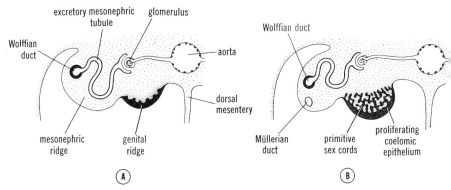

Figure 11-13. *A, Diagrammatic transverse section through the lumbar region of a 4-week embryo, showing the genital ridge, located between the dorsal mesentery and the mesonephros. B, Similar section, as in A, of a 6-week embryo, showing the indifferent gonad with the primitive sex cords (modified after Giroud).*

the wall of the yolk sac close to the allantois (fig. 11-14A).[3-7] From here they migrate by ameboid movement along the dorsal mesentery of the hindgut toward the region of the genital ridges (fig. 11-14B). In the sixth week of development the primordial germ cells invade the genital ridges; if they fail to reach the ridges, the gonads do not develop. Hence, the primordial germ cells have an inductive influence on the development of the ovary and testis.

*Indifferent Gonad*

Shortly before and during the arrival of the primordial germ cells the coelomic epithelium of the genital ridge proliferates and epithelial cells penetrate the underlying mesenchyme. Here they form a number of irregularly shaped cords, the *primitive sex cords*, which gradually surround the invading primordial germ cells (fig. 11-13B). In both male and female embryos these cords remain connected to the surface epithelium, and at this stage of development it is impossible to differentiate between the male and female gonad. Hence, the gonad is known as the *indifferent gonad*.

*Testis*

If the embryo is genetically male, the primitive sex cords continue to proliferate during the sixth to eighth weeks of development, and penetrate deep into the medulla of the gonad. They form a series of well-defined cell cords, anastomosing with one another and known as the *testis cords* (fig. 11-15A). Toward the hilus of the gland the cords break up into a network of tiny cell strands which later give rise to the tubules of the *rete testis* (fig. 11-15B).

Special Embryology

During further development, the testis cords lose contact with the surface epithelium, and by the end of the seventh week they are separated from it by a dense layer of fibrous connective tissue, the *tunica albuginea*. The epithelium on the surface of the gonad

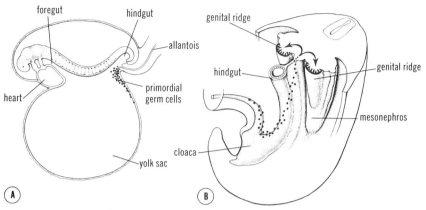

Figure 11-14. A, *Schematic drawing of a three-week-old embryo showing the primordial germ cells in the wall of the yolk sac, close to the attachment of the allantois (after Witchi). B, Drawing to show the migration path of the primordial germ cells along the wall of the hindgut and the dorsal mesentery into the genital ridge. Note the position of the genital ridge and mesonephros.*

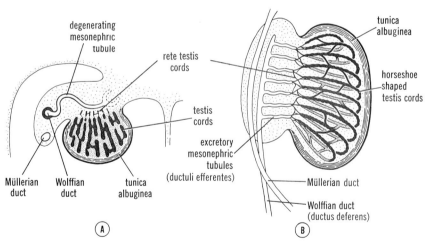

Figure 11-15. A, *Transverse section through the testis in the eighth week of development. Note the tunica albuginea, the testis cords, and the rete testis. The glomerulus and Bowman's capsule of the mesonephric excretory tubule are in regression. B, Schematic representation of the testis and the genital ducts in the fourth month of development. The horseshoe-shaped testis cords are continuous with the rete testis cords. Note the ductuli efferentes (excretory mesonephric tubules) which enter the Wolffian duct (modified after Giroud).*

flattens and disappears, and the tunica albuginea then forms the capsule of the testis.

In the fourth month the testis cords become horseshoe-shaped, and their extremities are continuous with the cell strands of the rete testis (fig. 11-15B).[8, 9] Later, the two extremities of the testis cord narrow to form the *tubuli recti*, while the arch becomes convoluted and is known as the *tubulus contortus*.

During fetal life the testis cords are composed of primitive germ cells and epithelial cells (fig. 1-11A). The latter are derived from the surface of the gland and eventually develop into the *sustentacular cells of Sertoli*.[10] The cords remain solid until puberty, but when sexual maturity is reached they acquire a lumen, thus forming the *seminiferous tubules*. Once the seminiferous tubules are canalized, they rapidly join the rete testis ductuli, which in turn enter the *vasa efferentia*. These efferent ductules, five to twelve in number, are the remaining parts of the excretory tubules of the mesonephric system. They function as the connecting link between the ductuli of the rete testis and the *mesonephric* or *Wolffian duct*, which in the male is known as the *ductus deferens* (fig. 11-15B). The *interstitial cells of Leydig* develop from the mesenchyme located between the seminiferous tubules and are particularly abundant in the fourth to sixth months of development.

*Ovary*

Whereas in the male the primitive sex cords are well defined, in the female they are broken up by invading mesenchyme into irregular cell clusters (fig. 11-16A). These clusters, containing groups of primitive germ cells, are mainly located in the medullary part of the ovary. Later they disappear and are replaced by vascular stroma which forms the *ovarian medulla*.

The surface epithelium of the female gonad, unlike that of the male, remains thick and continues to proliferate. It thus gives rise to a second generation of cords, the *cortical cords*, which penetrate the underlying mesenchyme but remain close to the surface of the gland (fig. 11-16A). These cords are also split into isolated cell clusters, each surrounding one or more primitive germ cells (fig. 11-16B). The germ cells subsequently develop into the oogonia, while the surrounding epithelial cells, descendants of the surface epithelium, form the *follicular cells* (see Chapter 1). It is generally accepted that the primary medullary cords are a distinctly male feature, whereas the secondary cortical cords are characteristic of the female gonad.[1, 11]

Although in the female a number of excretory mesonephric tubules (ductuli efferentes) are present as in the male (fig. 11-16B), the ab-

Special Embryology

sence of medullary tubules in the form of a rete ovarii explains why the germ cells are shed from the surface of the ovary and not transported by way of medullary tubules to the main genital duct.

## Genital Ducts

### Indifferent Stage

In the sixth week of development, both male and female embryos have two pair of genital ducts: (1) the *mesonephric* or *Wolffian ducts*, extending from the mesonephros to the cloaca; and (2) the *paramesonephric* or *Müllerian ducts*, newly formed ducts which run parallel to the Wolffian ducts (fig. 11-17A, B).

The Müllerian duct arises as a longitudinal invagination of the coelomic epithelium on the antero-lateral surface of the urogenital ridge (fig. 11-16A). Cranially the duct opens in the coelomic cavity with a funnel-like structure; caudally, it runs first lateral to the mesonephric duct, but then crosses it ventrally to grow in caudomedial direction (fig. 11-17). In the midline it comes in close contact with the Müllerian duct from the opposite side. The two ducts are initially separated by a septum, but later fuse to form the *uterovaginal canal* (fig. 11-19A). The septum between the ducts may per-

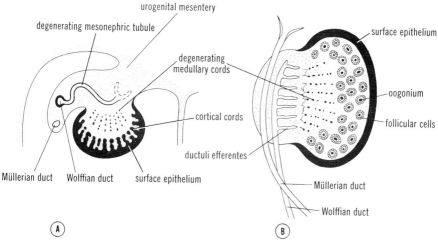

Figure 11-16. *A, Transverse section through the ovary at the seventh week of development, showing the degeneration of the primitive (medullary) sex cords and the formation of the cortical cords. B, Schematic drawing of the ovary and genital ducts in the fifth month of development. Note the degeneration of the medullary cords. The excretory mesonephric tubules (ductuli efferentes) do not communicate with the rete. The cortical zone of the ovary contains groups of oogonia surrounded by follicular cells.*

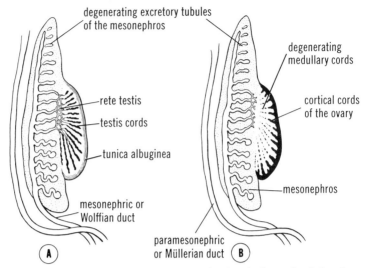

degenerating excretory tubules
of the mesonephros

degenerating
medullary cords

rete testis

cortical cords
of the ovary

testis cords

tunica albuginea

mesonephros

mesonephric or
Wolffian duct

paramesonephric
or Müllerian duct

A

B

Figure 11-17. *Diagram of the genital ducts in the sixth week of development in male (A) and in the female (B). The Wolffian and Müllerian ducts are present in both the male and female. Note the excretory tubules of the mesonephros and their relationship to the developing gonad.*

sist for a considerable time. The caudal tip of the combined ducts continues to grow in caudal direction until it comes in contact with the posterior wall of the urogenital sinus. On the inside of the sinus the Müllerian ducts cause a small swelling, the *Müllerian tubercle* (fig. 11-19A). The Wolffian ducts open into the urogenital sinus on either side of the utero-vaginal canal.

Depending upon the sex of the embryo, either the Wolffian or the Müllerian duct comes to full development. If the embryo is male, the Wolffian duct forms the main genital duct (*ductus deferens*) and the Müllerian duct disappears almost entirely; if the embryo is female, the Müllerian duct comes to full development, thereby forming the *oviducts*, the *uterus* and a major portion of the *vagina*, while the Wolffian duct disappears except for a few remnants.

*Genital Ducts in the Male*

As the mesonephros regresses, the excretory tubules located cranial to the gonad disappear completely. Those located in the region of the developing testis, the *epigenital tubules*, lose their glomeruli and become somewhat shortened (fig. 11-18A). During further development, these tubules establish contact with the cords of the rete testis and finally form the *ductuli efferentes* of the testis (fig. 11-18B). The excretory tubules of the mesonephros located along the caudal pole

Special Embryology

of the testis are known as the *paragenital tubules* (fig. 11-18A). These tubules, which remain functional until the end of the third month, do not join the cords of the rete testis; in addition they lose contact with the Wolffian duct (fig. 11-18B). The vestiges of these ductuli are collectively known as the *paradidymis*.

Despite the regression of the majority of the excretory tubules of the mesonephros, the Wolffian duct persists (except for its most cranial portion, the *appendix epididymis*), and forms the main genital duct (fig. 11-18). Immediately below the entrance of the ductuli efferentes it elongates greatly and becomes highly convoluted, thus forming the *epididymis*. From the tail of the epididymis to the outbudding of the *seminal vesicle*, the Wolffian duct obtains a thick muscular coat and is known as the *ductus deferens*.

By the end of the eighth week the paramesonephric or Müllerian duct in the male has degenerated entirely, except for a small portion at its cranial end which persists as the *appendix testis*. The fate of its caudal part is not precisely known. According to some authors it develops into the *utriculus prostaticus*, or *uterus masculinus*, a small diverticulum in the wall of the prostatic urethra. Other authors, how-

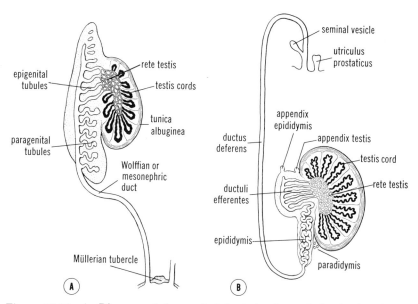

Figure 11-18. *A, Diagram of the genital ducts in the male in the fourth month of development. The Müllerian duct has degenerated except for the appendix testis and the utriculus prostaticus. B, The genital duct after descent of the testis. Note the horseshoe-shaped testis cords, the rete testis and the ductuli efferentes entering the ductus deferens. The paradidymis is formed by the remnants of the paragenital mesonephric tubules.*

Urogenital System

169

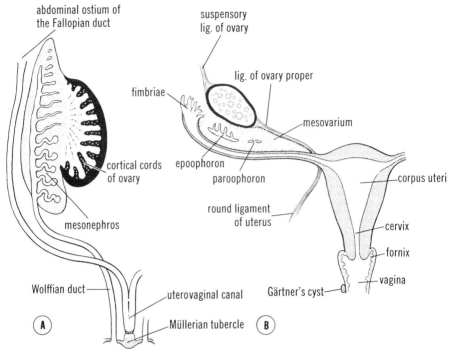

Figure 11-19. A, *Schematic drawing of the genital ducts in the female at the end of the second month of development. Note the Müllerian tubercle and the formation of the uterovaginal canal. B, The genital ducts after descent of the ovary. The only parts remaining of the mesonephric system are the epoophoron, paroophoron and Gärtner's cyst. Note the suspensory ligament of the ovary, the ligament of the ovary proper and the round ligament of the uterus.*

ever, believe that it disappears entirely and that the utriculus prostaticus is formed by an outpocketing of the urogenital sinus (fig. 11-18B).[12]

### Genital Ducts in the Female

The Müllerian duct develops into the main genital duct of the female. Initially three parts can be recognized: (1) a cranial vertical portion which opens into the coelomic cavity; (2) a horizontal part which crosses the Wolffian duct; and (3) a caudal vertical part which fuses with its partner from the opposite side (fig. 11-19A).

With the descent of the ovary, the first two parts develop into the *oviduct* or *Fallopian tube* (fig. 11-19B). The coelomic opening of the duct is then known as the *abdominal ostium of the Fallopian tube*.

The course of the second part of the Müllerian duct has a profound effect on the position of the structures in the pelvis. When it

Special Embryology

courses in medio-caudal direction, the urogenital ridges change in position and gradually come to lie in a transverse plane (fig. 11-20A, B). When the Müllerian ducts reach each other in the midline, a broad transverse pelvic fold is established (fig. 11-20C). This fold, which extends from the lateral sides of the fused Müllerian ducts (the *uterovaginal canal*) towards the pelvis, is known as the *broad ligament of the uterus*. In its upper border is found the oviduct and on its posterior surface the ovary (fig. 11-20C).

Considerable confusion exists about the origin of the human vagina. Initially it was believed that the *uterovaginal canal*, formed by fusion of the two Müllerian ducts, gave rise to both the uterus and the entire vagina. This view was abandoned since it was observed that solid evaginations of the posterior wall of the urogenital sinus became canalized and in this manner participated in the formation of the vagina. According to this theory the upper four-fifths of the vagina is derived from the uterovaginal canal, while the lower one-fifth is of urogenital sinus origin. The third and most recent theory indicates that the vagina is entirely derived from the urogenital sinus.

The solid caudal tip of the Müllerian ducts reaches the posterior wall of the urogenital sinus in the ninth week of development (figs. 11-21A and 11-22A). Shortly later two solid evaginations grow out from the pelvic part of the urogenital sinus in the region of the Müllerian ducts (figs. 11-21B and 11-22B). These evaginations, known as the *sinovaginal bulbs*, proliferate strongly and form a solid plate, the *vaginal plate*.[13] This plate, which enfolds the solid end of the uterovaginal canal, begins to obtain a lumen at its caudal end in embryos of approximately 11 weeks (figs. 11-21B and 11-22B). In the meantime proliferation continues at the cranial end of the plate, thus

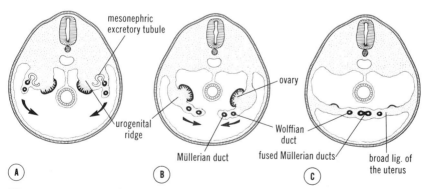

Figure 11-20. *Transverse sections through the urogenital ridge at progressively lower levels. Note that the Müllerian ducts approach each other in the midline to fuse. As a result of the fusion of the ducts, a transverse fold, the broad ligament of the uterus, is formed in the pelvis. The gonads come to lie at the posterior aspect of the transverse fold.*

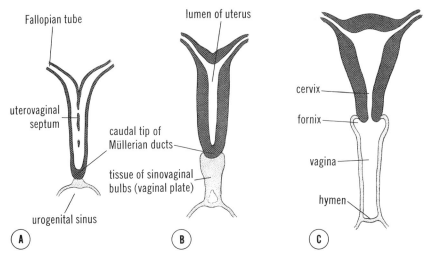

Figure 11-21. *Schematic drawing showing the formation of the uterus and vagina. A, At 9 weeks. Note the disappearance of the uterovaginal septum. B, At the end of the third month. Note the tissue of the sinovaginal bulbs, extending between the uterus and the urogenital sinus. C, Newborn. The vagina and the fornices are formed by vacuolization of the tissue of the sinovaginal bulbs.*

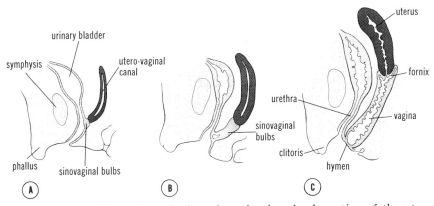

Figure 11-22. *Schematic sagittal sections showing the formation of the uterus and vagina at various stages of development. At present it is believed that the vagina is entirely formed by the sinovaginal bulbs. At first the uterovaginal canal is in close connection with the urethral part of the urogenital sinus, but with further development it descends until it opens into the vestibule.*

increasing the distance between the lumen of the uterus and that of the urogenital sinus. By the fifth month the vaginal outgrowth is entirely canalized and the winglike expansions of the plate around the end of the uterus form the *vaginal fornices* (fig. 11-22C).

The lumen of the vagina remains separated from that of the uro-

Special Embryology

genital sinus by a thin tissue plate, known as the *hymen* (figs. 11-21*C*
and 11-22*C*). It consists of the epithelial lining of the sinus and a thin
layer of mesoderm.

The uterovaginal canal, which gives rise to the *corpus* and the
*cervix of the uterus*, is surrounded by a layer of mesenchyme. With
time this mesenchyme forms the thick muscular coat of the uterus,
known as the *myometrium*. The vagina, derived from the sinovaginal
bulbs, is surrounded by only a few muscle fibers.

Although in the female the mesonephric system does not play any
role with regard to the transport of the oocytes, some remnants of
the excretory tubules and a small portion of the mesonephric or
Wolffian duct may be found in the adult. They are located in the
mesovarium, where they form the *epoophoron* (fig. 11-19*B*). The
more caudally located mesonephric tubules form a remnant known
as the *paroophoron*. The Wolffian duct disappears entirely except for
a small cranial portion found in the epoophoron, and occasionally a
small caudal portion, which later in life may form a cyst, *Gärtner's
cyst*, in the wall of the vagina (fig. 11-19*B*).

## External Genitalia

### Indifferent Stage

In the third week of development mesenchyme cells, originating
in the region of the primitive streak, migrate around the cloacal membrane to form a pair of slightly elevated folds, the *cloacal folds* (fig.
11-23*A*). Directly in front of the cloacal membrane the folds unite to
form the *genital tubercle*. When, in the sixth week, the cloacal membrane is subdivided into the urogenital and anal membranes, the
cloacal folds are likewise subdivided into the *urethral folds* anteriorly,
and the *anal folds* posteriorly (fig. 11-23*B*).

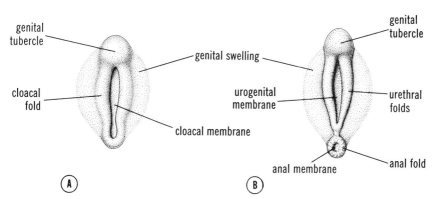

Figure 11-23. *The indifferent stage of the external genitalia. A, At approximately 4 weeks; B, at approximately 6 weeks.*

In the meantime another pair of elevations, the *genital swellings*, become visible on each side of the urethral folds (fig. 11-23B). In the male these swellings later differentiate into the *scrotal swellings* (fig. 11-24A), and in the female into the *labia majora* (fig. 11-25B). By the end of the sixth week, however, the external appearance of the external genitalia is identical in the male and female, and it is impossible to distinguish between the two sexes.

*External Genitalia in the Male*

Further development of the external genitalia in the male is characterized by the rapid elongation of the genital tubercle which now is called the *phallus* (fig. 11-24A). During this elongation the phallus pulls the urethral folds forward so that they form the lateral walls of the deep *urogenital* or *urethral groove*. This groove, formed after the disappearance of the urogenital membrane, extends along the caudal aspect of the elongated phallus, but does not reach the most distal part of the glans.[14] The epithelial lining of the groove is of entodermal origin and forms the *urethral plate* (fig. 11-24B).

At the end of the third month the two urethral folds close over the urethral plate, thus forming the *penile part of the urethra* (fig. 11-24B).[15] This canal does not extend to the tip of the phallus. The most distal portion of the glandular urethra is formed during the

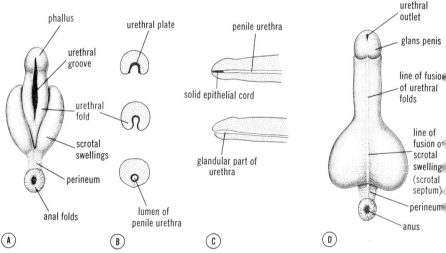

Figure 11-24. A, *Development of the external genitalia in the male at 10 weeks. Note the deep urethral groove flanked by the urethral folds. B, Transverse sections through phallus during the formation of the penile urethra. The urogenital groove is bridged over by the two urethral folds. C, Development of the glandular portion of the penile urethra. D, In the newborn.*

Special Embryology

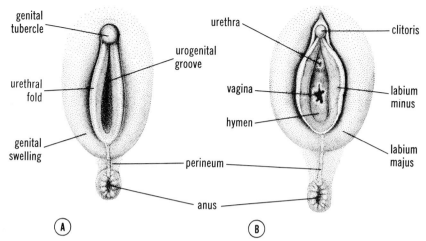

Figure 11-25. *Development of the external genitalia in the female at 5 months* *(A), and in the newborn (B).*

fourth month when ectodermal cells from the tip of the penis pene- trate inward and form a short epithelial cord extending toward the lumen of the urethra. This cord later obtains a lumen, thus forming the *definitive external urethral meatus* at the tip of the glans (fig. 11-24C).

The genital swellings known in the male as the scrotal swellings are initially located in the inguinal region. With further development they move caudally, and each swelling then makes up a half of the scrotum. The two are separated from each other by the *scrotal sep- tum* (fig. 11-24D).[16]

*External Genitalia in the Female*

The changes in the external genitalia of the female are less pro- found than those in the male. The genital tubercle elongates only slightly and forms the *clitorus* (fig. 11-25A, B); the urethral folds do not fuse as in the male, but develop into the *labia minora*. The genital swellings enlarge greatly and form the *labia majora*. The urogenital groove is open to the surface and forms the *vestibule* (fig. 11-25B).

## Descent of the Testis

Toward the end of the second month the testis and the remaining portions of the mesonephros are attached to the posterior abdominal wall by a rather narrow *urogenital mesentery*. Initially this peritoneal fold was broad, but with degeneration of the major portion of the mesonephros, the attachment becomes increasingly narrow and serves mainly as a mesentery for the testis (figs. 11-3A and 11-20). In cranial direction the peritoneal folds extended from the upper pole of the testis and mesonephros toward the diaphragm, but with regression of the mesonephros the fold gradually has disappeared. In caudal direction the fold, enforced by mesenchyme and remnants of the mesonephros, becomes ligamentous and is known as the *caudal genital ligament* (fig. 11-26A). In the inguinal region the caudal genital ligament is continuous with a band of mesenchyme, marking the future inguinal canal, which in turn continues into a mesenchymal condensation in the genital (scrotal) swelling. Although the mesenchymatous column, extending from the caudal pole of the testis to the genital swelling, consists of three different components, it is referred to as the *gubernaculum testis.*

As a result of the rapid growth of the body during the second month of development and the failure of the gubernaculum to elongate correspondingly, the testis comes to lie approximately 10 segments below its level of origin. By the beginning of the third month it lies in close proximity to the inguinal region (fig. 11-26B). Hence the *descent of the testis* is not an active migration, but is a relative shift in position with regard to the body wall. The blood supply from the

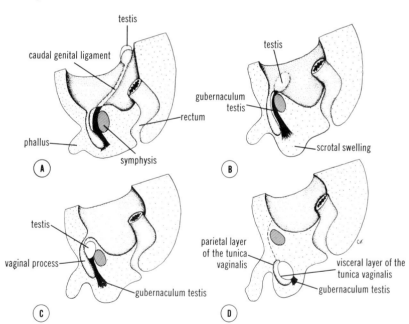

Figure 11-26. *Schematic representation of the descent of the testis. A, During the second month; B, middle of the third month; C, seventh month; D, shortly after birth. The coelomic cavity evaginates into the scrotal swelling, where it forms the vaginal process (tunica vaginalis).*

Special Embryology

aorta is retained and the testicular vessels descend from the original level to the inguinal region.

At the beginning of the third month the peritoneum of the coelomic cavity forms an evagination on each side of the midline into the ventral abdominal wall. These evaginations follow the course of the gubernaculum testis through the inguinal canal into the scrotal swellings (fig. 11-26C). The extension of the coelomic cavity into the scrotal swellings is known as the *vaginal process*. Hence, the vaginal process, accompanied by the muscular and facial layers of the body wall, evaginates into the scrotal swelling. It has to be realized that the ligamentous fibers of the gubernaculum testis remain outside the vaginal process at all times.

The testis remains in its abdominal position in close proximity to the inguinal canal until the seventh month of development. Only then does it continue its descent through the inguinal ring and over the rim of the pubic bone into the scrotal swelling (fig. 11-26C). Once arrived in the scrotum at the time of birth, the testis is covered by a reflected fold of the vaginal process (fig. 11-26D). The peritoneal lining of the vaginal process, covering the testis, is known as the *visceral layer of the tunica vaginalis;* the remainder of the peritoneal sac forms the *parietal layer of the tunica vaginalis* (fig. 11-26D). The narrow canal, connecting the vaginal process with the peritoneal abdominal cavity, is obliterated at birth or shortly thereafter.[17] The final descent of the testis is accompanied by a shortening of the gubernaculum, but whether or not this shortening causes the descent of the testis is still controversial.[18-20] Undoubtedly, however, the descent of the testis is also controlled by hormones such as gonadotrophins and androgens.[21]

In the female the descent of the gonad is considerably less than in the male and the ovary is finally located just below the rim of the true pelvis. The cranial genital ligament is thought to form the *suspensory ligament of the ovary*, whereas the caudal ligament forms the *ligament of the ovary proper* and the *round ligament of the uterus* (fig. 11-19B). The latter extends into the labia majora.

# Congenital Malformations

## Hypospadia

Under normal conditions the urethral groove is closed and transformed into the penile urethra by fusion of the urethral folds (fig. 11-24B). When the fusion is incomplete, abnormal openings of the urethra may be found along the inferior aspect of the penis. Most frequently these abnormal orifices are near the glans, along the

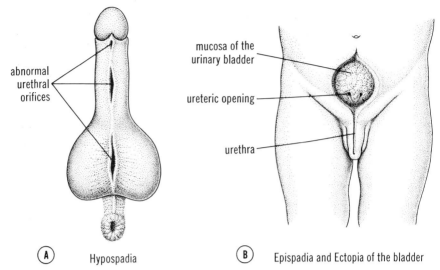

<table>
<tr><td>(A) Hypospadia</td><td>(B) Epispadia and Ectopia of the bladder</td></tr>
</table>

Labels on figure A: abnormal urethral orifices

Labels on figure B: mucosa of the urinary bladder; ureteric opening; urethra

Figure 11-27. *A, Hypospadia. The drawing shows the various locations of abnormal urethral orifices. B, Epispadia combined with ectopia of the bladder. The mucosa of the bladder is exposed to the surface, and the orifices of the ureters can readily be seen. In this case the urethral slit extends along the length of the penis.*

shaft, or near the base of the penis (fig. 11-27A). In rare cases the urethral meatus may even be located along the scrotal raphe. When fusion of the urethral folds fails entirely, the urethral meatus forms a sagittal slit along the entire length of the penis. The two scrotal swellings then closely resemble the labia majora.

### Epispadia

This abnormality is characterized by the presence of the urethral meatus on the dorsum of the penis, and is thought to be caused primarily by an abnormal position of the genital tubercle. Instead of having developed at the anterior margin of the cloacal membrane, the tubercle seems to have formed in the region of the urorectal septum. Hence a portion of the cloacal membrane is then found cranial to the genital tubercle, and the outlet of the urogenital sinus comes to lie on the cranial aspect of the penis (fig. 11-27B).[22] Occasionally, the two sides of the genital tubercle do not fuse at all, and this results in a so-called *divided penis.*

### Ectopia or Exstrophy of the Bladder

Ectopia of the bladder, seen frequently in combination with epispadia, is caused in all probability by a too large cloacal membrane.[23, 24] Under normal conditions the abdominal wall in front of

Special Embryology

the bladder is formed by primitive streak mesoderm, which migrates around the cloacal membrane.[25] When this migration is prevented as a result of the excessive size of the membrane, the rupture of the cloacal membrane may extend in cranial direction further than normal, thus establishing an *ectopia of the bladder*. The mucosa of the bladder is then exposed to the surface of the body, and the ureters and urethra can be readily seen (fig. 11-27B). At regular intervals urine escapes from the ureteric orifices.[26]

## Cryptorchism

At about the time of birth, but with wide individual variation, the testes arrive in the scrotum. In certain cases one or both testes may remain in the pelvic cavity above the inguinal ring until puberty and then descend or remain indefinitely in the pelvic position.[27] This condition is known as *cryptorchism*, and seems to be due to abnormal endocrine conditions and/or failure of the gubernaculum to shorten. An undescended testis is unable to produce mature spermatozoa, most likely because of the high temperature in the abdominal cavity.[28]

## Congenital Inguinal Hernia

Failure of the testis to descend into the scrotum is often accompanied by a *congenital inguinal hernia*. The connection between the coelomic cavity and the vaginal process in the scrotal sac normally closes after the descent of the testes (fig. 11-26C, D). If this passageway remains open the intestinal loops may descend into the scrotum, thus causing a *congenital inguinal hernia* (fig. 11-28B). Sometimes the obliteration of this passageway is irregular, leaving small cysts along its course. Later these cysts may secrete excess fluid, resulting in the formation of a *hydrocele* (fig. 11-28C).

## Duplication and Atresia of the Uterovaginal Canal

Under normal conditions the uterus is formed by fusion of the caudal parts of the Müllerian ducts. Lack of fusion in a localized area or throughout the length of the ducts may explain all different types of duplication of the uterus. In its extreme form the uterus is double (*uterus didelphys*) (fig. 11-29A). In the least severe form, the fundus of the uterus is slightly indented in the middle (*uterus arcuatus*) (fig. 11-29B). One of the more commonly found anomalies is the *bicornuate uterus*, in which the uterus has two horns entering a common vagina (fig. 11-29C). This condition is normal in many of the mammals below the primates.

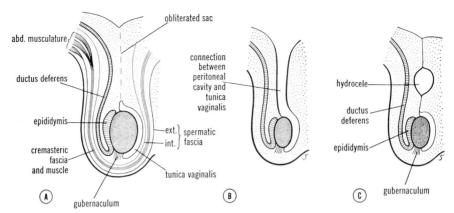

Figure 11-28. *A, Diagrammatic drawing of the testis, epididymis, ductus deferens, and the various layers of the abdominal wall which surround the testis in the scrotum. B, Vaginal process in open communication with the coelomic cavity. In such a case, portions of the intestinal loops often descend toward the scrotum, thus causing an inguinal hernia. C, Hydrocele.*

Another group of malformations is caused by complete or partial atresia of one or both of the Müllerian ducts. If one side is involved, the rudimentary part lies as an appendage to the well developed side, but since its lumen usually does not communicate with the vagina, complications frequently ensue (*uterus bicornis unicollis with one rudimentary horn*) (fig. 11-29D). If the atresia involves both sides partially, an *atresia of the cervix* may result (fig. 11-29E).[29] If the sinovaginal bulbs fail to fuse or do not develop at all, a *double vagina* or *atresia of the vagina*, respectively, result (fig. 11-29A, F).

**Ovarian Hypoplasia**

Ovarian hypoplasia, often associated with hypoplasia of the internal genitalia and hypertrophy of the clitoris, is found in persons showing *Turner's syndrome*. The cells of patients suffering from this syndrome are characterized by 45 chromosomes—44 autosomes and one X chromosome (see Chapter 7).[30]

**Pseudohermaphroditism and Intersexuality**

A *true hermaphrodite* is an individual in whom the gonads and external genitalia of both sexes are present. Though patients with both active testicular and ovarian tissue exist, true hermaphrodites with male and female genitalia have never been observed.[31, 32]

Under *pseudohermaphroditic* conditions, the genotypic sex is masked by a phenotypic appearance that closely resembles the other sex. In the male pseudohermaphrodite the gonad is a testis,

Special Embryology

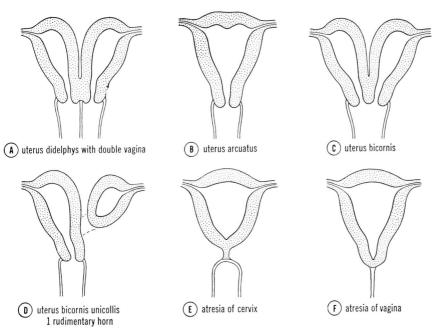

(A) uterus didelphys with double vagina    (B) uterus arcuatus    (C) uterus bicornis

(D) uterus bicornis unicollis
1 rudimentary horn    (E) atresia of cervix    (F) atresia of vagina

Figure 11-29. *Schematic representation of the main abnormalities of the uterus and vagina, caused by persistence of the uterovaginal septum or obliteration of the lumen of the uterovaginal canal.*

but the sex ducts and secondary sex characteristics resemble closely those of the female. The sex of these individuals has frequently been wrongly interpreted at birth, a mistake to become manifest at puberty. Though a few years ago the true sex of such an individual could be determined only by internal examination of the duct system and sex gland, presently the true sex is determined by the "sex chromatin" technique. (For further details, see Chapter 7.)

### References—Genital System

1. GRUENWALD, P. The development of the sex cords in the gonads of man and mammals. Amer. J. Anat., **70:** 359, 1942.
2. GILLMAN, J. The development of the gonads in man, with a consideration of the role of fetal endocrines and histogenesis of ovarian tumors. Contrib. Embryol., **32:** 81, 1948.
3. WITCHI, E. Migrations of germ cells of human embryos from the yolk sac to the primitive gonadal folds. Contrib. Embryol., **32:** 67, 1948.
4. M'INTZ, B. Embryological phases of mammalian gametogenesis. J. Cell. Comp. Physiol., **56:** 31, 1960.
5. CHIQUOINE, A. D. Identification, origin and migration of the primordial germ cells. Anat. Rec., **110:** 135, 1954.
6. EVERETT, N. B. The present status of the germ cell problem in vertebrates. Biol. Rev., **20:** 45, 1945.

7. McKay, D. G., Hertig, A. J., Adams, E. C., and Danziger, S. Histochemical observations on the germ cells of human embryos. Anat. Rec., **117:** 201, 1953.

8. Clermont, Y., and Huckins, C. Microscopic anatomy of the sex glands and seminiferous tubules in growing adult male albino rats. Amer. J. Anat., **108:** 79, 1961.

9. Wilson, K. W. Origin and development of the rete ovarii and the rete testis in the human embryo. Contrib. Embryol., **17:** 69, 1926.

10. Mancini, R. E., Narbaitz, R., and Lavieri, J. C. Origin and development of the germinative epithelium and Sertoli cells in the human testis: cytological, cytochemical and quantitative study. Anat. Rec., **136:** 477, 1960.

11. Witschi, E. *Development of Vertebrates*. W. B. Saunders Co., Philadelphia, 1956.

12. Vilas, E. Über die Entwicklung des Utriculus prostaticus beim Menschen. Z. Anat. Entwicklungsgesch., **99:** 599, 1933.

13. Bulmer, D. The development of the human vagina. J. Anat. (Lond.), **91:** 490, 1957.

14. Spaulding, M. M. The development of the external genitalia in the human embryo. Contrib. Embryol., **13:** 67, 1921.

15. Glenister, T. W. A correlation of the normal and abnormal development of the penile urethra and of the infra-umbilical abdominal wall. Brit. J. Urol., **30:** 117, 1958.

16. Politzer, G. Über die Entwicklung des Dammes beim Menschen; nebst Bemerkungen über die Bildung der äusseren Geschlechtsteile und über die Fehlbildungen der Kloake und des Dammes. Z. Anat. Entwicklungsgesch., **97:** 622, 1932.

17. Mitchell, G. A. G. The condition of the peritoneal vaginal process at birth. J. Anat., **73:** 658, 1939.

18. Wyndham, N. R. A morphological study of testicular descent. J. Anat., **77:** 179, 1943.

19. Backhouse, K. M., and Butler, H. The development of the coverings of the testis cord. J. Anat., **92:** 645, 1958.

20. Backhouse, K. M., and Butler, H. The gubernaculum testis of the pig. J. Anat. (Lond.), **94:** 107, 1960.

21. Wells, L. J. Descent of the testis; anatomical and hormonal considerations. Surgery, **14:** 436, 1943.

22. Patten, B. M., and Barry, A. Genesis of exstrophy of the bladder and epispadia. Amer. J. Anat., **90:** 35, 1952.

23. Marshall, V. F., and Muecke, E. C. Variations in exstrophy of the bladder. J. Urol., **88:** 766, 1962.

24. Muecke, E. C. The role of the cloacal membrane in exstrophy: the first successful experimental study. J. Urol., **92:** 659, 1964.

25. Wyburn, G. M. The development of the infra-umbilical portion of the abdominal wall, with remarks on the aetiology of ectopia vesicae. J. Anat., **71:** 201, 1937.

26. Unson, A. C., Lattimer, J. K., and Melicow, M. M. Types of exstrophy of the urinary bladder and concomitant malformations. Pediatrics, **23:** 927, 1959.

27. Scorer, C. G. Incidence of incomplete descent of the testicle at birth. Arch. Dis. Child., **31:** 198, 1956.

28. Moore, K. L., Graham, M. A., and Barr, M. L. Detection of chromosomal sex in hermaphrodites from skin biopsy. Surg. Gynec. Obstet., **96:** 641, 1953.

29. Jones, W. S. Obstetric significance of female genital anomalies. Obstet. Gynec. (N. Y.), **10:** 113, 1957.

30. Ford, C. E., Jones, K. W., Polani, P. E., de Almeida, J. C., and Briggs, J. H. A sex-chromosome anomaly in a case of gonadal dysgenesis (Turner's syndrome). Lancet, **1:** 711, 1959.

31. Overzier, C. *Die Intersexualität*. G. Thieme, Stuttgart, 1961.

32. Greene, R., Mathews, D., Hughesden, P. E., and Howard, A. A case of true hermaphroditism. Brit. J. Surg., **40:** 263, 1954.

# CHAPTER 12

# Cardiovascular System

## NORMAL DEVELOPMENT OF
## THE HEART

---

- •BLOOD VESSEL FORMATION: *extra-embryonic; intra-embryonic*
- •FORMATION AND POSITION OF THE HEART TUBE: *formation of the heart loop; development of the sinus venosus*
- •FORMATION OF THE CARDIAC SEPTA: *septum formation in the atrium and atrioventricular canal; septum formation in the ventricles; septum formation in the truncus arteriosus and conus cordis*
- •FORMATION OF THE CARDIAC VALVES: *atrioventricular valves; semilunar valves*

---

## Blood Vessel Formation

### Extra-Embyronic Blood Vessels

The vascular system of the human embryo appears at the middle of the third week, when the embryo is no longer able to satisfy its nutritional requirements by diffusion alone. At this stage mesenchymal cells in the chorion, the connecting stalk, and the wall of the yolk sac proliferate and form isolated cell clusters, known as the *angiogenetic cell clusters* (fig. 12-1).

When subsequently a lumen is formed in the clusters by the appearance and confluence of intercellular clefts, the centrally located cells are detached and develop into primitive blood cells (fig. 12-2). The peripherally located cells flatten and form the endothelial lining of the so-called *blood islands.*[1, 2] From now on, the blood islands approach each other rapidly by sprouting of the endothelial cells and, after fusion, form a plexiform network. This network in turn is transformed into small blood vessels presumably under the influence of hemodynamic factors.[3]

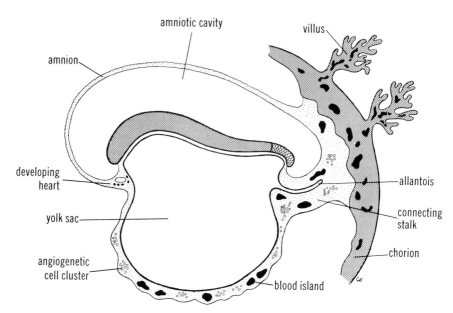

Figure 12-1. *Extra-embryonic blood vessel formation in the chorion, the connecting stalk, and the wall of the yolk sac in a presomite embryo of approximately 19 days (modified from Keibel and Elze). Note the position of the pericardial cavity and developing heart.*

In this manner the angiogenetic cell clusters in the wall of the yolk sac give rise to the *vitelline vessels*, and those in the chorion to the *umbilical vessels* (fig. 12-3). Through continuous budding these extra-embryonic vessels gradually penetrate the embryo proper.

*Intra-Embryonic Blood Vessels*

Originally the intra-embryonic vessels were thought to be extensions of the ingrowing extra-embryonic vessels.[4] It is now generally accepted that they develop independently from angiogenetic cell clusters, which appear in the splanchnic mesoderm layer of the late pre-somite embryo (fig. 12-4B).[5] At first the clusters are located on the lateral sides of the embryo, but they rapidly spread in cephalic direction (fig. 12-4A). With time they acquire a lumen, unite and form a plexus of small blood vessels.[2] This plexus gradually becomes horseshoe-shaped (fig. 12-4A). The lateral portions of the plexus coalesce into single endothelial tubes, but the central portion temporarily maintains its plexus form. The intra-embryonic coelomic cavity located over this anterior central portion of the plexus later develops into the pericardial cavity (fig. 12-4C). Hence, at this stage

Special Embryology

of development the pericardial cavity lies anterior to the *prochordal plate*.

In addition to the horseshoe-shaped plexus, other clusters of angiogenetic cells appear bilaterally, parallel and close to the midline of the embryonic shield. These clusters also acquire a lumen and form a pair of longitudinal vessels, the *dorsal aortae*. At a later stage

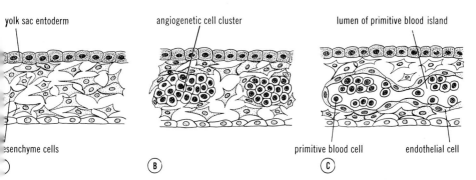

Figure 12-2. *Successive stages of blood vessel formation in the wall of the yolk sac. A, Undifferentiated mesenchyme; B, formation of angiogenetic cell clusters; C, blood island formation. Note the differentiation of mesenchymal cells into the primitive blood cells and the endothelial cells.*

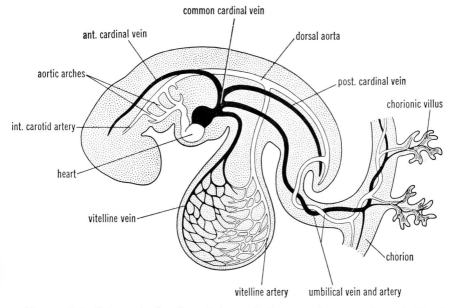

Figure 12-3. *Schematic drawing of the main intra- and extra-embryonic blood vessels in a 4 mm. embryo (end of the fourth week). Only the vessels of the left side of the embryo are represented.*

these vessels gain connections with the horseshoe-shaped plexus which will form the heart tube.

## Formation and Position of the Heart Tube

The position and formation of the heart tube are profoundly influenced by growth processes taking place in other parts of the embryo. Initially the central portion of the horseshoe-shaped plexus is located anterior to the prochordal plate and the neural plate (figs. 12-4C and 5-9). With the closure of the neural plate and the subsequent formation of the brain vesicles, however, the central nervous system grows so rapidly in cephalic direction that it extends over the central cardiogenic area and the future pericardial cavity (figs. 12-5A, B, 12-7 and 5-9). During this growth the rapidly expanding brain pulls the prochordal plate (future buccopharyngeal membrane) and the central portion of the cardiogenic plate forward. The result is that the buccopharyngeal membrane and the cardiogenic plate, including the pericardial portion of the intra-embryonic coelomic cavity, are rotated about 180 degrees along a transverse axis. Hence, the central portions of the cardiogenic plate and peri-

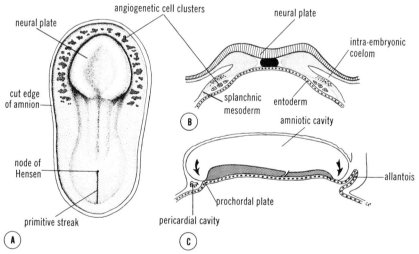

Figure 12-4. A, Dorsal view of a late presomite embryo (approximately 1.4 mm.) after removal of the amnion. The angiogenetic cell clusters formed in the splanchnic mesoderm in front of the neural plate and on each side of the embryo are visible through the overlying ectoderm and somatic mesoderm layer (modified after Davis). B, Transverse section through similar embryo to show the position of the angiogenetic cell clusters in the splanchnic mesoderm layer. C, Cephalo-caudal section through similar embryo showing the position of the pericardial cavity and angiogenetic cell clusters in front of the prochordal plate.

Special Embryology

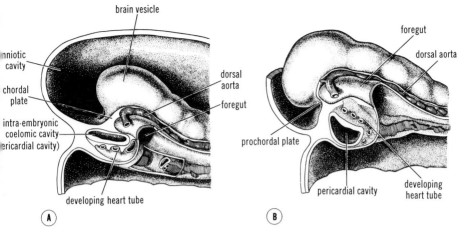

brain vesicle

foregut

amniotic cavity

dorsal aorta

chordal plate

dorsal aorta

intra-embryonic coelomic cavity (pericardial cavity)

foregut

prochordal plate

developing heart tube

pericardial cavity

developing heart tube

A

B

Figure 12-5. *Drawings to show the result of the rapid growth of the brain vesicles on the position of the pericardial cavity and the developing heart tube. Initially the angiogenetic cell clusters and the pericardial cavity are located in front of the prochordal plate (figs. 12-1 and 12-4C). As a result of the rotation along a transverse axis through the prochordal plate, the cardiogenic plexus finally comes to lie dorsally to the pericardial cavity.*

cardial cavity, initially located rostral to the buccopharyngeal plate (fig. 12-4C), become located ventrally and caudally to these structures. Simultaneously, the originally flat embryonic shield folds in transverse direction. As a result the two lateral endothelial heart tubes come closer to each other (fig. 12-6). With further lateral folding of the embryo the endocardial tubes fuse, beginning at the cephalic end of the original horseshoe-shaped structure and extending in caudal direction. Hence, a single endocardial tube is formed (fig. 12-6).[6]

The developing primitive heart tube, located in the splanchnic mesoderm tissue of the pericardial cavity, bulges gradually more and more into the pericardial cavity. This invagination continues until the heart tube with its investing layer lies completely within the pericardial cavity. The tube remains attached temporarily to the dorsal side of the pericardial cavity by a fold of mesodermal tissue, the *dorsal pericardium* (figs. 12-6C, D, and 12-7). A ventral pericardium is never formed.

While these events occur the mesoderm adjacent to the endocardial tubes gradually thickens, and by the time the tubes have fused, it surrounds them as the *myoepicardial mantle* (fig. 12-6C, D). This layer is at first separated from the endothelial wall of the tube by a gelatinous substance, the *cardiac jelly*.[7] Later the jelly is invaded by mesenchymal cells. Finally the wall of the heart tube consists of

Cardiovascular System

187

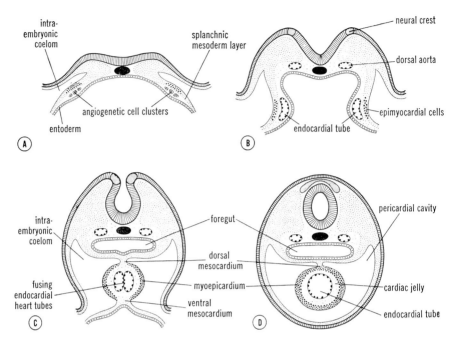

Figure 12-6. *Schematic transverse sections through embryos at different stages of development, showing the formation of a single heart tube from paired primordia. A, Early presomite embryo (approximately 17 days); B, late presomite embryo (approximately 18 days); C, at four somites (approximately 21 days); D, at eight somites (approximately 22 days) (adapted from several sources).*

three layers: (1) the *endocardium*, forming the internal endothelial lining of the heart; (2) the *myocardium*, forming the muscular wall, and (3) the *epicardium* or *visceral pericardium*, covering the outside of the tube.

The embryo is now approximately 23 days, has seven somites, and is about 2.2 mm. long. The time between the first appearance of the intra-embryonic vessels and the formation of the heart tube is about 3 days. By this time the heart begins to beat.

*Formation of the Heart Loop*

At first the heart forms a straight tube inside the pericardial cavity. The intra-pericardial part consists of the future *bulboventricular portion*. The atrial portion and the sinus venosus are still paired and lie outside the pericardium in the mesenchyme of the septum transversum (fig. 12-8A).

During subsequent development, the bulboventricular portion of the heart tube grows much more rapidly than the pericardial cavity.

188                                                  Special Embryology

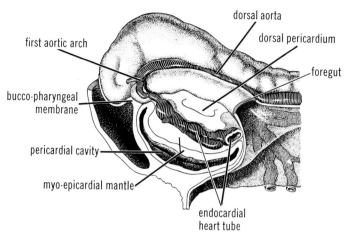

first aortic arch

bucco-pharyngeal membrane

pericardial cavity

myo-epicardial mantle

dorsal aorta

dorsal pericardium

foregut

endocardial heart tube

Figure 12-7. *Drawing of the cephalic end of an early somite embryo. The developing endocardial heart tube and its investing layer bulge into the pericardial cavity. Note the dorsal mesocardium.*

Because its two ends are fixed to the surrounding tissues outside the pericardial cavity, elongation of the tube cannot be accomplished in a longitudinal direction and the tube is therefore forced to bend. The cephalic portion of the loop bends in ventral and caudal direction and slightly to the right (fig. 12-8*B, C*). As a result the *bulboventricular sulcus* becomes visible on the outside, while on the inside a fold or flange is formed, known as the *bulboventricular fold* (fig. 12-10). As a second consequence of the bending and torsion, the *atrioventricular junction* comes to lie on the left side of the pericardial cavity, while the right side is occupied by the greatly elongated *bulbus cordis*. The cardiac loop thus consists of a cephalic or ascending limb (the bulbus), and a descending limb formed by the embryonic ventricle (figs. 12-8 and 12-9*A*).

While the cardiac loop is being formed, considerable changes occur and local expansions become visible throughout the length of the tube. The atrial portion, initially a paired structure located outside the pericardial cavity, forms a common atrium through fusion of the right and left sides. During this fusion, the atrium becomes incorporated into the pericardial cavity and shifts in dorso-cranial direction (fig. 12-9*A*).[8] As a result the *atrioventricular junction* assumes a more cranial position. This junction remains narrow and forms the *atrioventricular canal*, which connects the left side of the common atrium and the early embryonic ventricle (fig. 12-10). The junction between the ventricle and the bulbus cordis, externally indicated by the *bulboventricular sulcus*, likewise remains narrow and is called the *primary interventricular foramen*. The bulbus cordis, formed by the ascending limb of the cardiac loop, is narrow except for its proximal third. This portion will form the *trabeculated part of the right ventricle* (figs. 12-9B and 12-10). The midportion, known as the *conus cordis*, will form the outflow tracts of both ventricles. The distal part of the bulbus, the *truncus arteriosus*, will form the roots and proximal portion of the aorta and pulmonary artery (fig. 12-9).

At the end of the loop formation, the smooth-walled heart tube begins to form primitive trabeculae in two sharply-defined areas just proximal and distal to the primary interventricular foramen (fig. 12-10). The atrial portion and the other portions of the bulbus remain temporarily smooth-walled. Though the heart still consists of a single tube, its external appearance already suggests its future four-chambered condition. The primitive ventricle, which is now trabeculated, is called the *primitive left ventricle*, since it will form the major portion of the definitive left ventricle. Likewise, the trabeculated proximal one third of the bulbus cordis may be referred to as the *primitive right ventricle* (fig. 12-10).

The trunco-conal portion of the heart tube, initially located on the right side of the pericardial cavity, shifts gradually to a more medial position. This change in position is the result of the formation of two transverse dilatations of the atrium, bulging on each side of the bulbus cordis (figs. 12-9B and 12-10). The truncus arteriosus is then lo-

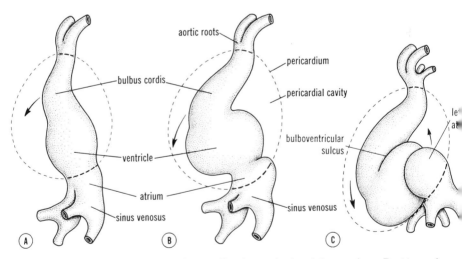

Figure 12-8. *Formation of the cardiac loop. A, At eight somites; B, 11 somites; C, 16 somites. Broken line indicates pericardium. Note how the atrium gradually assumes an intra-pericardial position (modified from Kramer).*

Special Embryology

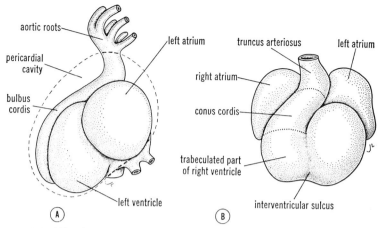

Figure 12-9. *The heart of a 5 mm. embryo (approximately 28 days). A, Seen from the left; B, in frontal view (modified after Kramer).*

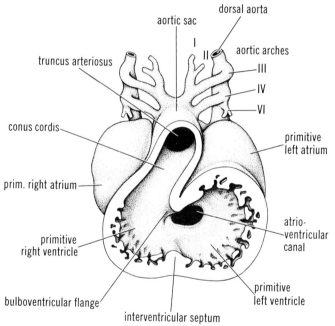

Figure 12-10. *Frontal section through the heart of a 6 mm. embryo showing the primary interventricular foramen and the entrance of the atrium into the primitive left ventricle. Note the bulboventricular flange.*

cated in a depression between the right and left atria and the conus assumes an oblique position, lying between the roof of the primitive left ventricle and the antero-medial wall of the atrium (figs. 12-9 and 12-10).

Cardiovascular System

### Development of the Sinus Venosus

Since the sinus venosus greatly contributes to the definitive form of the atrium, it will be necessary to describe its development briefly.

The *sinus venosus* maintains its paired condition longer than any other portion of the heart tube. In the 4 mm. embryo it consists of a small *transverse portion* and the *right* and *left sinus horns* (fig. 12-11 A). Each horn receives blood from three important veins: (1) the *vitelline* or *omphalomesenteric vein;* (2) the *umbilical vein;* and (3) the *common cardinal vein*. At first the communication between the transverse portion of the sinus and the atrium is wide. Soon, however, the entrance of the sinus becomes narrow and shifts to the right as a result of the development of a deep fold, the *sinu-atrial fold*, which separates the left portion of the sinus venosus from the left side of the atrium (fig. 12-11B). With the obliteration of the left um-

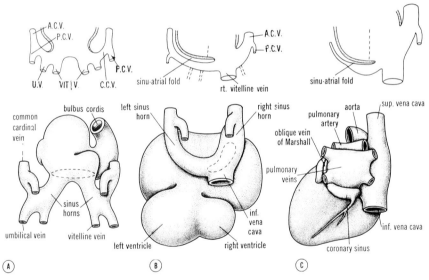

Figure 12-11. *Three stages in the development of the sinus venosus and great veins, seen from dorsal to show the formation of the coronary sinus and the incorporation of the right sinus horn into the wall of the right atrium. Broken line in A and B indicates the entrance of the sinus venosus into the atrial cavity. A, At 18 somites (approximately 24 days); B, approximately 35 days; C, in the newborn. Each drawing is accompanied by a scheme to show in transverse section the great veins and their relation to the atrial cavity. A.C.V., anterior cardinal vein; P.C.V., posterior cardinal vein; C.C.V., common cardinal vein; U.V., umbilical vein; Vit. V., vitelline vein (modified after several sources).*

Special Embryology

bilical vein at the 5 mm. stage and the left vitelline vein at the 7 mm. stage, the left sinus horn rapidly loses its importance. When finally the left common cardinal vein is obliterated at the 60 mm. stage (10 weeks), the distal part of the left sinus horn remains as the *oblique vein of Marshall*, while the proximal portion of the horn and the transverse portion of the sinus become the coronary sinus (fig. 12-11C).[9]

As a result of the obliteration of the veins on the left side, the right sinus horn and veins enlarge greatly in size. Subsequently the right horn, which forms the only communication between the original sinus venosus and the atrium, is gradually incorporated into the right atrium (fig. 12-11C). Its entrance, the *sinu-atrial orifice*, is flanked on each side by a valvular fold, the *right* and *left venous valves* (fig. 12-12A). On the right this fold is formed by a sinu-atrial fold. Another, though much smaller fold, the *left venous valve*, is formed on the left side of the orifice. Dorso-cranially, the valves fuse, thereby forming a ridge, known as the *septum spurium* (fig. 12-12A). Initially the valves are large, but when the right sinus horn is entirely incorporated into the atrium, the left venous valve and the septum spurium fuse with the developing atrial septum (fig. 12-12B). The superior portion of the right venous valve disappears entirely. The inferior portion fuses locally with the septum, which develops between the orifice of the right vitelline vein (inferior vena cava) and the orifice of the coronary sinus. The remainder of the valve is divided into two parts: (1) the *valve of the inferior vena cava*, and (2) the *valve of the coronary sinus* (fig. 12-12B).

## Formation of the Cardiac Septa

The major septa of the heart are formed between the 27th and 37th days of development, when the embryo grows in length from 5 mm. to approximately 16-17 mm. Before discussing the formation of any particular septum, the different methods by which a partition can be formed will be briefly reviewed.

One method, thought to be the most common, involves two actively growing masses of tissue which approach each other until they fuse, thereby dividing the lumen into two separate canals. Such a septum does not have to arise from two opposing cell masses, but may also be formed by active growth of a single cell mass which continues expanding until it reaches the opposite side of the lumen. Cell proliferation is the basic prerequisite for such a septum formation.

The other manner in which a septum may be formed is completely different and does not involve cell proliferation. When, for example,

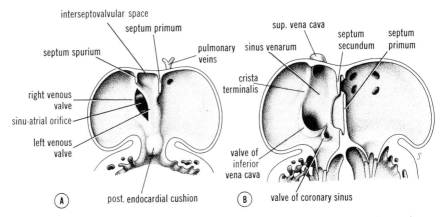

Figure 12-12. *Coronal sections through the heart at the level of the atrioventricular canal seen from ventral to show the development of the venous valves. A, At 7- to 8-mm. stage (5 weeks); B, newborn (modified after His).*

a narrow strip of tissue in the wall of the atrium or ventricle would fail to grow, while the areas on each side of it would expand rapidly, a narrow ridge would be formed between the two expanding portions. When growth of the expanding portions continues on either side of the narrow portion, the two walls approach each other and eventually fuse. If this occurs, the fused walls form a septum. It is evident, however, that such a septum will never completely divide the original lumen, but will leave a narrow communicating canal between the two expanded sections. Such a canal or opening may be closed secondarily by tissue contributed by neighboring proliferating tissues.

*Septum Formation in the Atrium and Atrioventricular Canal*

As a result of the expansion of the atrium on each side of the truncus arteriosus (fig. 12-10), a depression is formed in the roof of the common atrium. When this depression deepens, a more or less sickle-shaped crest appears in the lumen of the atrium. This crest is probably formed by fusion of the two adjacent, opposing walls of the atrium and is considered to represent the first portion of the septum primum (figs. 12-12A and 12-13A). The two limbs of the crest extend in the direction of the endocardial cushions formed in the atrioventricular canal. The opening between the right and left primitive atrium is the *foramen* or *ostium primum* (fig. 12-13A). With further development extensions of the superior and inferior endocardial cushions grow along the edge of the septum primum, thereby gradually closing the ostium primum. This process is completed in em-

Special Embryology

bryos of about 10 mm. Before closure is completed, however, perforations appear in the septum primum. When these perforations coalesce, the *ostium secundum* is formed, thus ensuring a free communication between the right and left primitive atrium (fig. 12-13 *B*).

The incorporation of the right sinus horn into the right atrium and of the common pulmonary vein into the left atrium plays an important role in the formation of the *septum secundum*. Initially the space between the septum spurium and septum primum, known as the *interseptovalvular space*, bulges out (figs. 12-12*A* and 12-13*A*). When the lumen of the right atrium expands as a result of the incorporation of the sinus horn, the roof of the interseptovalvular space folds in. The result is the formation of a new septum, the *septum secundum* (figs. 12-12*B* and 12-13*C*). This septum never forms a complete partition in the atrial cavity, but has a concave free edge (fig. 12-13*C*). Its anterior limb extends downward to the septum in the atrioventricular canal.[9, 10] During further development the left

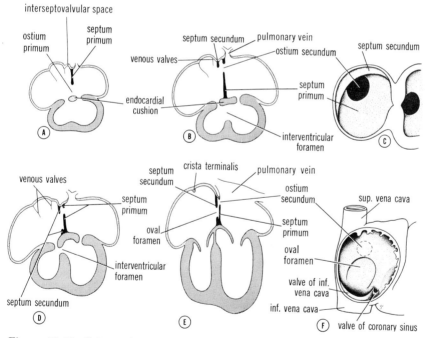

Figure 12-13. *Schematic representation of the atrial septa at various stages of development. A, At 6 mm. (approximately 30 days); B, 9 mm. (approximately 33 days); C, same stage as in B, but seen from the right; D, 14 mm. (approximately 37 days); E, newborn; F, view of the atrial septum seen from the right, same stage as in E.*

Cardiovascular System                                                                 195

venous valve and the septum spurium approach and fuse with the right side of the septum secundum, thus enforcing and extending it (fig. 12-12). Eventually the free concave edge of the septum secundum overlaps the ostium secundum and the passage between the two atrial cavities consists of an obliquely elongated cleft, known as the *oval foramen* (fig. 12-13*E, F*). After birth when the lung circulation begins and the pressure in the left atrium increases, the upper edge of the septum primum is pressed against the septum secundum, thus obliterating the oval foramen and separating the right and left atria. In about 20 per cent of cases fusion of the septum primum and septum secundum is incomplete, and a narrow oblique cleft remains between the two atria. This condition is known as *probe patency* of the oval foramen.

While the primitive right atrium enlarges by incorporation of the right sinus horn, the primitive left atrium likewise expands greatly. A single embryonic pulmonary vein develops as an outgrowth of the posterior left atrial wall, just to the left of the septum primum (fig. 12-13).[8, 11, 12] This vein gains connection with the splanchnic plexus of veins in the region of the developing lung buds. During further development the primitive pulmonary vein and parts of its branches become incorporated into the left atrium, thus forming the large smooth-walled part of the adult atrium. In the fully developed heart, the original embryonic left atrium is represented by little more than the trabeculated atrial appendage. The intrapulmonary portion of the splanchnic venous plexus ultimately loses its connections with the systemic veins and drains exclusively by way of the pulmonary veins. On the right side the original embryonic right atrium becomes the right atrial appendage containing the pectinate muscles.

Simultaneously with the expansion and septum formation in the atrium, two mesenchymal cushions, the *atrioventricular endocardial cushions*, appear at the superior and inferior borders of the atrioventricular canal (figs. 12-10 and 12-14). At this stage (5 mm.) the atrioventricular canal gives access only to the primitive left ventricle and is separated from the bulbus cordis by the *bulbo- (cono-) ventricular flange* (fig. 12-10). This flange will have to recede to allow blood coming through the atrioventricular canal to enter directly into the primitive right ventricle (proximal portion of the bulbus cordis). By the 9 mm. stage the posterior extremity of the flange terminates almost midway along the base of the superior endocardial cushion and is much less prominent than before (fig. 12-14). Hence, the flange appears to shift to the left and gradually to disappear. Since the atrioventricular canal simultaneously enlarges to the right, blood passing through the atrioventricular orifice now has direct access to the primitive left as well as the primitive right ventricle. A

Special Embryology

further consequence of the disappearance of the bulboventricular flange is that the primitive left ventricle gains access to the postero-medial portion of the conus cordis by way of the primary interventricular foramen (see below) (fig. 12-14).

In addition to the inferior and superior endocardial cushions, two other cushions, the *lateral atrioventricular cushions*, appear on the right and left borders of the canal (fig. 12-14). The main cushions, in the meantime, project further into the lumen and by the 10 mm. stage they fuse with each other, resulting in a complete division of the canal into right and left atrioventricular orifices (fig. 12-15). At the same time the cushions begin to arch in such a manner that they are concave towards the ventricles and convex to the side of the atria (fig. 12-13E). The free margin of the atrial septum meets the convex side of the fused endocardial cushions, thus closing the *foramen primum* (fig. 12-13).

*Septum Formation in the Ventricles*

In a 5 mm. embryo, the communication between the primitive left ventricle and primitive right ventricle (proximal portion of the bul-

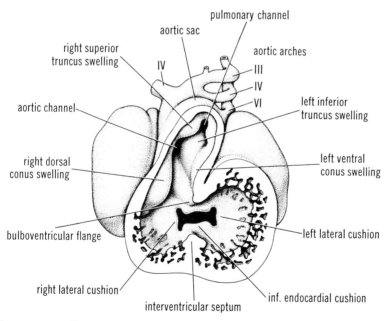

Figure 12-14. *Frontal section through the heart of a 9 mm. embryo. At this stage of development blood from the atrial cavity enters the left primitive ventricle as well as the right primitive ventricle. Note the development of the cushions in the A.V. canal. The swellings in the truncus and conus are clearly visible.*

Cardiovascular System                                    197

bus cordis) is formed by the *primary interventricular foramen* (fig. 12-10). This foramen is bordered inferiorly by the muscular interventricular septum, and superiorly and posteriorly by the bulboventricular flange. The two are continuous with each other and form a ring around the primary interventricular foramen.

By the end of the fourth week, the two primitive ventricles begin to dilate. This is accomplished by continuous growth of the myocardium on the outside, and continuous diverticulation and trabecula formation on the inside (figs. 12-10, 12-14 and 12-16). If the myocardium would grow on the outside without trabecula formation on the inside, the myocardium would become too thick and solid. The ventricles of the embryonic heart thus consist of an enormous mass of trabeculae and a relatively thin, compact, outer layer.

The medial walls of the expanding ventricles become apposed and gradually fuse together, forming the major portion of the *muscular ventricular septum* (fig. 12-16). Sometimes the fusion between the two walls is not complete, which manifests itself as a more or less deep apical cleft between the two ventricles.

*Septum Formation in the Truncus Arteriosus and Conus Cordis*

At about the 6 mm. stage a pair of opposing ridges appear in the cephalic part of the truncus. These ridges, the *truncus swellings*, are located on the right superior wall (*right superior truncus swelling*) and on the left inferior wall (*left inferior truncus swelling*) (fig. 12-14). They rapidly enlarge, touch each other, and fuse to form the *truncus septum*, which divides the truncus into an *aortic* and *pulmonary channel*. The right superior truncus swelling grows distally and to the left, while the left inferior swelling grows distally and to the right. Hence, while growing in the direction of the truncoaortic sac, the swellings twist around each other.

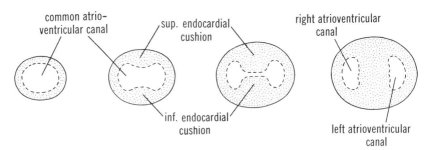

Figure 12-15. *Formation of the septum in the atrioventricular canal. From left to right, 4, 6, 9 and 12 mm. stages, respectively. The initial circular opening becomes gradually widened in transverse direction.*

Special Embryology

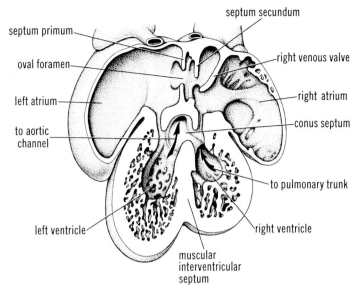

septum secundum

septum primum

oval foramen

left atrium

to aortic channel

right venous valve

right atrium

conus septum

to pulmonary trunk

left ventricle

right ventricle

muscular interventricular septum

Figure 12-16. *Posterior view of a frontal section through the heart of a 15 mm. embryo. The conus septum is completed and blood from the left ventricle enters the aorta. Note the septa in the atrial region.*

The *trunco-aortic sac* is formed by the most distal portion of the undivided truncus and the adjacent aortic sac, from which the six aortic arches originate (fig. 12-14). During further development the origin of the fourth aortic arches (which are closely related to the fused origins of the first three arches) shift somewhat to the right, while the origin of the sixth arches shifts to the left (fig. 12-14). The result is that the origins of the sixth arches become aligned with the pulmonary channel, and those of the fourth with the aortic channel. At the same time the dorsal wall of the trunco-aortic sac forms a short, rather thick septum between the origins of the fourth and sixth arches, the *aorticopulmonary septum*. The edge of this septum approaches the distal rim of the truncus septum and fuses with it. The partition of the trunco-aortic area is now complete and the manner in which this occurs accounts in part for the spiral course of the aorta and pulmonary artery around each other.

At about the time that the truncus swellings appear, similar swellings develop along the right dorsal and left ventral walls of the *conus cordis* (fig. 12-14). They initially grow slower than the truncus swellings, but after the truncus septum has been completed, the conus swellings grow toward each other and in a distal direction toward the truncus septum. The *right dorsal conus swelling* becomes continuous with the *right superior truncus swelling*

Cardiovascular System                                                      199

and the *left ventral conus swelling* with the *left inferior truncus swelling* (fig. 12-14). In the 7 mm. embryo the proximal extremity of the right dorsal conus swelling terminates to the right of the right lateral cushion of the atrioventricular canal and is separated from it by a groove (fig. 12-14). This position gradually changes as a result of the enlargement and a shift to the right of the atrioventricular canal. The right dorsal conus swelling finally terminates at the superior border of the right atrioventricular orifice. To the right it blends with the right lateral cushion and to the left with the right tubercle of the superior endocardial cushion. The left ventral conus swelling extends proximally along the right side of the upper part of the septal band (fig. 12-17).

When the two conus swellings have fused, the septum divides the conus into an anterolateral portion, which together with the primitive right ventricle form the *definitive right ventricle* (figs. 12-16 and 12-17). The posteromedial portion of the conus becomes continuous with the primitive left ventricle, thus forming the *definitive left ventricle*.

The large interventricular foramen, found above the muscular interventricular septum, becomes reduced in size with the completion of the conus septum (fig. 12-16). During further development

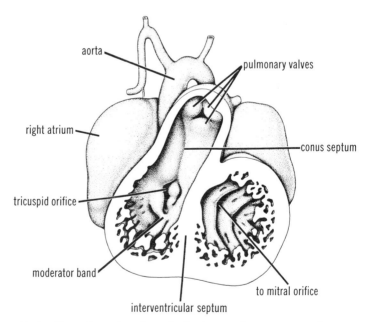

Figure 12-17. *Frontal section through the heart of a 16 mm. embryo. Note the conus septum and the position of the pulmonary valves.*

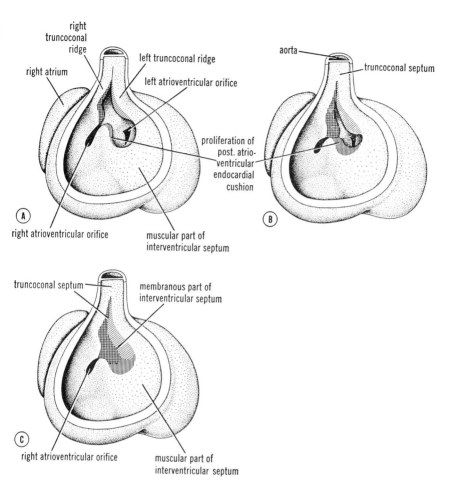

Figure 12-18. *Schematic drawings showing the development of the truncoconal ridges and the closure of the interventricular foramen. The proliferations of the right and left truncoconal ridges, combined with the proliferation of the posterior atrioventricular cushion, eventually close the interventricular foramen and form the membranous portion of the interventricular septum. A, At 6 weeks (12 mm.); B, beginning of seventh week (14.5 mm.); C, end of seventh week (20 mm.) (modified after Hamilton, Boyd and Mossman).*

closure of this foramen is accomplished by the outgrowth of tissue from the inferior endocardial cushion along the top of the muscular interventricular septum (fig. 12-18).[13] This tissue fuses with the abutting parts of the conus septum. After complete closure of the secondary interventricular foramen, this region is quite thick and only later does part of it become thin and fibrous to form the *membranous part of the interventricular septum.*

## Formation of the Cardiac Valves

### Atrioventricular Valves

After fusion of the endocardial cushions has divided the atrioventricular canal into right and left orifices (fig. 12-15), each orifice is surrounded by localized proliferations of mesenchymal tissue (fig. 12-19A). When subsequently the tissue located on the ventricular surface of these proliferations becomes hollowed out, the newly formed valves remain attached to the ventricular wall by muscular

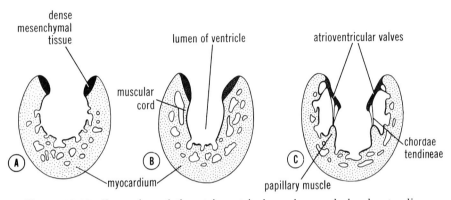

Figure 12-19. *Formation of the atrioventricular valves and chordae tendineae. Note how the valves are hollowed out from the ventricular side, but remain attached to the ventricular wall by the chordae tendineae (modified after Gegenbauer).*

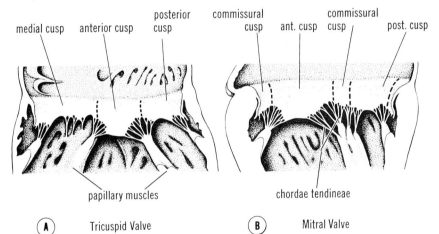

Figure 12-20. *Drawing showing the relationship of the papillary muscles to the tricuspid and mitral valves. Note the presence of the commissural cusps in the mitral valve.*

Special Embryology

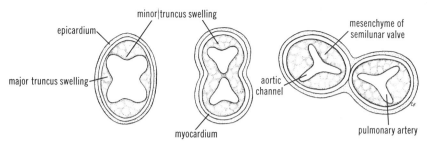

Figure 12-21. *Transverse sections through the truncus arteriosus at the level of the semilunar valves at 5, 6 and 7 weeks of development (A, B and C, respectively) (after Kramer).*

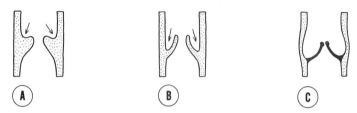

Figure 12-22. *Longitudinal sections through the semilunar valves. From left to right, sixth, seventh and ninth weeks of development, respectively.*

cords only (fig. 12-19*B*). Finally the muscular tissue in the cords on the ventricular side of the valves degenerates and is replaced by dense connective tissue. The valves then consist of connective tissue covered by endocardium and are connected to thickened trabeculae in the wall of the ventricle, the *papillary muscles*, by means of the *chordae tendineae* (figs. 12-19*C* and 12-20). In this manner two valve leaflets are formed in the left atrioventricular canal, the *bicuspid* or *mitral valve*, and three on the right side, the *tricuspid valve* (fig. 12-20).

*Semilunar Valves*

When the partitioning of the truncus has almost been completed, the primordia of the semilunar valves become visible as small tubercles. These tubercles are found on the main truncus swellings and one of each pair is assigned to the pulmonary and aortic channels, respectively (fig. 12-21). Opposite the fused truncus swellings, a third tubercle appears in both channels. Gradually the tubercles are hollowed out at their upper surface, thus forming the *semilunar valves* (fig. 12-22). This process is already well advanced at the 16 mm. stage and virtually completed in the 40 mm. embryo.

# References—Normal Development of the Heart

1. EVANS, H. M. The development of the vascular system. In *Manual of Human Embryology*, edited by F. Keibel and F. P. Mall. J. B. Lippincott Co., Philadelphia, 1912.
2. REAGAN, F. P. Experimental studies on the origin of vascular endothelium and of erythrocytes. Amer. J. Anat., **21:** 39, 1917.
3. HUGHES, A. F. W. The histogenesis of the arteries of the chick embryo. J. Anat., **77:** 266, 1943.
4. HIS, W. Lecithoblast und Angioblast der Wirbeltiere. Abhandl. Math.-Phys. Kl. Sachs. Akad. Wiss. Leipzig, **26:** 173, 1900.
5. McCLURE, C. F. W. The endothelial problem. Anat. Rec., **22:** 219, 1921.
6. GOSS, C. M. The development of the median coordinated ventricle from the lateral hearts in rat embryos with three to six somites. Anat. Rec., **112:** 761, 1952.
7. KRAMER, T. C. The partitioning of the truncus and conus and the formation of the membranous portion of the interventricular septum in the human heart. Amer. J. Anat., **71:** 343, 1942.
8. LOS, J. A. The development of the pulmonary veins and the coronary sinus in the human embryo. Doctoral thesis, University of Leyden, 1958.
9. ODGERS, P. N. B. The formation of the venous valves, the foramen secundum and the septum secundum in the human heart. J. Anat., **69:** 412, 1935.
10. VAN MIEROP, L. H. S., ALLEY, R. D., KAUSEL, M. W., AND STRANAHAN, A. The anatomy and embryology of endocardial cushion defects. J. Thor. Cardiov. Surg., **43:** 71, 1962.
11. AUER, J. The development of the human pulmonary veins and its major variations. Anat. Rec., **101:** 581, 1948.
12. NEILL, C. A. Development of the pulmonary veins. Pediatrics, **18:** 880, 1956.
13. ODGERS, P. N. B. The development of the pars membranacea septi in the human heart. J. Anat., **72:** 247, 1939.

Special Embryology

# ABNORMAL DEVELOPMENT OF THE HEART

---

- ABNORMALITIES OF THE ATRIAL SEPTUM: *probe patency; ostium secundum defect; common atrium; premature closure of the oval foramen*
- ABNORMALITIES OF THE ATRIOVENTRICULAR CANAL: *persistent atrioventricular canal; ostium primum defect; tricuspid atresia*
- ABNORMALITIES OF THE INTERVENTRICULAR SEPTUM: *defect of the membranous septum; common ventricle*
- ABNORMALITIES OF THE TRUNCUS AND CONUS: *tetralogy of Fallot; persistent truncus arteriosus; transposition of the great vessels*
- ABNORMALITIES OF THE SEMILUNAR VALVES: *pulmonary valvular stenosis and atresia; aortic valvular stenosis and atresia*
- ABNORMALITIES IN POSITION OF THE HEART: *dextrocardia; ectopia cordis*
- CAUSES OF CARDIOVASCULAR ABNORMALITIES: *fetal environment; genetic factors; experimentally produced malformations*

---

## Abnormalities of the Atrial Septum

The septum primum and septum secundum usually fuse in such a manner that no opening remains between the right and left atria. In 20 to 25 per cent of all adult hearts, however, a probe can be passed through the oval foramen obliquely upward from the right atrium toward the left. This condition, known as *probe patency of the oval foramen*, does not normally allow intracardiac shunting of blood. Since it occurs frequently in otherwise normal hearts, the condition is not considered a true abnormality.[1]

A more serious abnormality is the *ostium secundum* defect. This defect, which is characterized by a large opening between the left and right atria, is caused either by excessive resorption of the septum primum (fig. 12-23A) or by inadequate development of the septum secundum (fig. 12-23B). Depending on the size of the opening, considerable intracardiac shunting may occur.[2]

The most serious abnormality in this group is the complete absence of the atrial septum (fig. 12-23C). This condition, known as *common atrium* or *cor triloculare biventriculare*, is always associated with serious defects elsewhere in the heart.[3]

Occasionally the oval foramen closes during prenatal life. This abnormality, known as *premature closure of the oval foramen*, leads to massive hypertrophy of the right atrium and ventricle, and underdevelopment of the left side of the heart.[4] Death usually occurs shortly after birth.

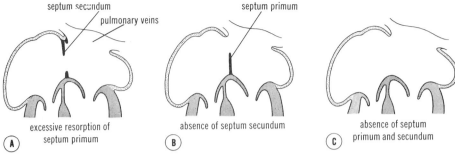

septum secundum

pulmonary veins

septum primum

**A** excessive resorption of septum primum

**B** absence of septum secundum

**C** absence of septum primum and secundum

Figure 12-23. *A, Ostium secundum defect caused by excessive resorption of the septum primum. B, Similar defect caused by failure of development of the septum secundum. C, Common atrium or cor triloculare biventriculare—complete failure of the septum primum and septum secundum to form.*

### Abnormalities of the Atrioventricular Canal

Under normal conditions the endocardial cushions of the atrioventricular canal not only divide this canal into a right and left orifice, but also participate in the formation of the membranous portion of the interventricular septum and in the closure of the ostium primum. Hence, whenever the cushions fail to fuse, the result is a *persistent atrioventricular canal*, combined with a defect in the cardiac septum (fig. 12-24A). This septal defect has an atrial and ventricular component, separated by abnormal valve leaflets in the single atrioventricular orifice (fig. 12-24B).

Occasionally the endocardial cushions in the atrioventricular canal fuse only partially. The defect in the atrial septum is then similar to that in the above-described abnormality, but the interventricular septum is closed (fig. 12-24C). This defect, known as the *ostium primum defect*, is usually combined with a cleft in the anterior leaflet of the mitral valve and in the septal leaflet of the tricuspid valve (fig. 12-24B).[5]

Another important abnormality in the partitioning of the atrioventricular canal is caused by the obliteration of the right atrioventricular orifice. This abnormality, known as *tricuspid atresia* (fig. 12-25A), is characterized by the absence or fusion of the tricuspid valves. The defect is always associated with: (1) patency of the oval foramen, (2) ventricular septal defect, (3) underdevelopment of the right ventricle, and (4) hypertrophy of the left ventricle.[6]

### Abnormalities of the Interventricular Septum

Under normal conditions the membranous part of the interventricular septum is formed by the right and left truncoconal ridges

Special Embryology

and by material of the superior atrioventricular cushion. Considering the complicated formation of this portion of the interventricular septum, it is not surprising that defects may easily arise. Indeed, a *defect of the membranous septum* is frequently seen (fig. 12-25B).

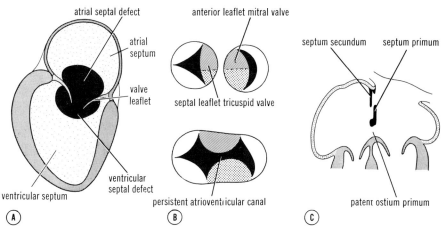

Figure 12-24. *A, Persistent common atrioventricular canal. This abnormality is always accompanied by a septum defect in the atrial as well as in the ventricular portion of the cardiac partition. B, Valves in the atrioventricular orifices under normal conditions (top) and in the case of a persistent atrioventricular canal (below). C, Ostium primum defect caused by incomplete fusion of the atrioventricular endocardial cushions.*

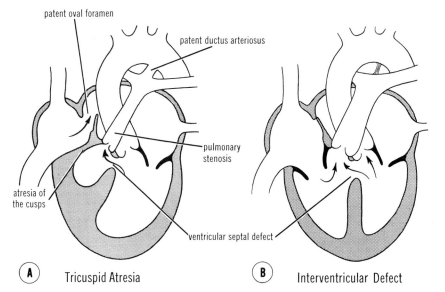

Figure 12-25. *A, Tricuspid atresia. Note the small right ventricle and the large left ventricle. B, Isolated defect in the membranous portion of the ventricular septum.*

Although it is commonly found as an isolated lesion, it may be associated with abnormalities in the partition of the truncoconal region. Depending on the size of the opening, the blood carried by the pulmonary artery may be 1.2 to 1.7 times more abundant than that carried by the aorta.[4] Occasionally the defect is not restricted to the membranous part, but involves the muscular part of the septum as well.[7]

### Abnormalities of the Truncus and Conus

The most frequently seen abnormality of this region is the *tetralogy of Fallot* (fig. 12-26A). Classically, this cardiac abnormality is described as consisting of: (1) pulmonary stenosis, (2) ventricular septal defect, (3) overriding aorta, and (4) hypertrophy of the right ventricle. Hence the term "tetralogy." The basic defect in this cardiac malformation is an unequal division of the conus, due to an anterior displacement of the truncoconal septum. This results in a narrow right ventricular outflow region, that is, an *infundibular stenosis*, and a large defect of the interventricular septum. The aorta arises directly above the septal defect from both ventricular cavities, and the resulting high pressure on the right side causes hypertrophy of the right ventricular wall. This abnormality is regarded as the most important type of malformations causing cyanosis. The defect is compatible with life.[8, 9]

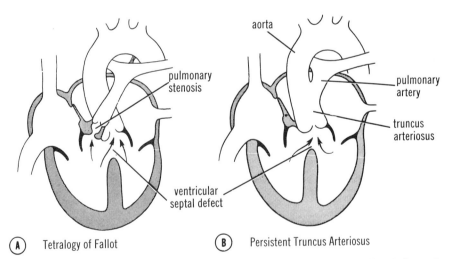

(A) Tetralogy of Fallot      (B) Persistent Truncus Arteriosus

Figure 12-26. *A, Tetralogy of Fallot characterized by: (1) stenosis of the pulmonary tract, (2) overriding aorta, (3) ventricular septal defect, and (4) hypertrophy of the right ventricle. B, Persistent truncus arteriosus. The pulmonary artery originates from the common truncus.*

Special Embryology

Under normal conditions the truncus and conus are divided into the aorta and the pulmonary artery by the fusion and descent of the two spiral ridges. If these ridges fail to fuse and to descend toward the ventricles, a *persistent truncus arteriosus* results (fig. 12-26B). In such a case the pulmonary artery arises some distance above the origin of the undivided truncus. Since the ridges also participate in the formation of the interventricular septum, the persistent truncus is always accompanied by a defective interventricular septum. The undivided truncus thus overrides both ventricles and receives blood from both sides.[10]

Sometimes the truncoconal septum fails to follow its normal spiral course, and descends straight downward (fig. 12-27A). As a consequence the aorta originates from the right ventricle, and the pulmonary artery from the left. This condition, known as *transposition of the great vessels*, is one of the most common cardiac abnormalities. Sometimes it is associated with a defect in the membranous part of the interventricular septum.[11, 12]

## Abnormalities of the Semilunar Valves

In this important group of abnormalities the semilunar valves of the pulmonary artery or aorta are fused for a variable distance and may even form an imperforated diaphragm. In case of a *valvular stenosis of the pulmonary artery* the fused valves may form a dome, which projects into a poststenotic dilation of the pulmonary ar-

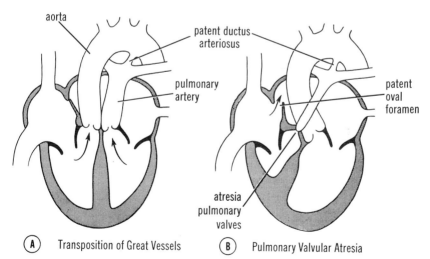

(A) Transposition of Great Vessels    (B) Pulmonary Valvular Atresia

Figure 12-27. *A, Transposition of the great vessels. B, Pulmonary atresia with normal aortic root. The only access route to the lungs is by way of the patent ductus arteriosus.*

Cardiovascular System

tery.[13] When the valves are completely fused, the trunk of the pulmonary artery is narrow or even atretic (fig. 12-27B). The patent oval foramen then forms the only outlet for blood from the right side of the heart. The ductus arteriosus is always patent and represents the only access route to the pulmonary circulation.[14]

In case of *aortic valvular stenosis* (fig. 12-28A), the fusion of the thickened valves may be so complete that only a pinhole opening remains. The size of the aorta itself, however, is usually normal.[15] Occasionally a *subaortic stenosis* may be seen. In these cases a ring of fibrous tissue is found circling the outflow tract of the left ventricle just below the aortic valves.[16]

When fusion of the semilunar aortic valves is complete—a condition known as *aortic valvular atresia* (fig. 12-28B)—the aorta, left ventricle, and left atrium are markedly underdeveloped. The abnormality is usually accompanied by a wide open ductus arteriosus, which delivers blood into the aorta.[17]

## Abnormalities in the Position of the Heart

In addition to the malformations described above, the position of the heart itself may be abnormal. Most frequently seen is the *dextrocardia*. In this condition the heart is located in the right side of the thorax and the abnormality is usually associated with a total or partial *situs inversus*.[18]

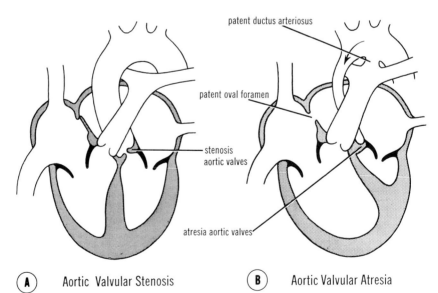

patent ductus arteriosus

patent oval foramen

stenosis aortic valves

atresia aortic valves

A  Aortic Valvular Stenosis          B  Aortic Valvular Atresia

Figure 12-28. *A, Aortic valvular stenosis. B, Aortic atresia. Arrow in arch of the aorta indicates direction of blood flow. The coronary arteries are supplied by this retroflux. Note the small left ventricle and the large right ventricle.*

Special Embryology

A rare anomaly is the *ectopia cordis*. The heart is then located on the surface of the chest. Basically this malformation is caused by failure of the embryo to close in the midline (sternal cleft).[19]

## Causes of Cardiovascular Abnormalities

### Fetal Environment

In 1941, Gregg[20] observed that German measles affecting pregnant women in the first 10 weeks of gestation was frequently followed by cataract, deafness, and congenital heart malformations in the newborn. This observation has since been confirmed repeatedly, and at present it is generally accepted that German measles may cause congenital heart malformations. The risk of giving birth to a defective infant following infection has been estimated at approximately 10 per cent.[21] In order of frequency the following heart and vessel abnormalities are seen: persistent ductus arteriosus, ventricular septal defect, Fallot's tetralogy, atrial septal defect, and pulmonary valvular stenosis.[21-23]

### Genetic Factors

There are many reports of family pedigrees showing more than one member affected with congenital heart malformations; this suggests that these malformations may be transmitted genetically. In contrast to these reports, however, recent authors are less inclined to incriminate genetic factors. Even though the familial incidence of cardiac defects has been noted in some cases, no definite mode of inheritance has so far been determined.[24-27]

### Experimentally Produced Heart Malformations

A great variety of congenital cardiovascular abnormalities have recently been produced by treating pregnant rats and mice with a number of teratogenic agents, *e.g.*, injection of trypan blue,[28, 29] vitamin A deficiency,[30] x-irradiation,[31] oxygen deficiency,[32] and pteroylglutamic acid deficiency.[33, 34] Although in many instances the abnormalities produced were strikingly similar to those observed in man, it must be kept in mind that these results were obtained with animals and are not necessarily applicable to man.

## References—Abnormal Development of the Heart

1. WRIGHT, R. R., ANSON, B. J., AND CLEVELAND, H. C. The vestigial valves and the interatrial foramen of the adult human heart. Anat. Rec., **100:** 331, 1948.
2. DEXTER, L. Atrial septal defects. Brit. Heart J., **18:** 209, 1956.
3. ROGERS, H. M., AND EDWARDS, J. E. Cor triloculare biventriculare. Amer. Heart J., **45:** 623, 1953.

4. EDWARDS, J. E. Congenital malformations of the heart and great vessels. In *Pathology of the Heart*, edited by S. E. Gould, p. 266. Charles C Thomas, Springfield, Ill., 1953.
5. ROGERS, H. M., AND EDWARDS, J. E. Incomplete division of the atrioventricular canal with patent interatrial foramen primum. Amer. Heart J., **36:** 28, 1948.
6. EDWARDS, J. E., AND BURCHELL, H. B. Congenital tricuspid atresia; a classification. Med. Clin. N. Amer., **33:** 1177, 1949.
7. MASON, D. G., AND HUNTER, W. C. Localized congenital defects of the cardiac interventricular septum. Amer. J. Path., **13:** 835, 1937.
8. BRINTON, W. D., AND CAMPBELL, M. Necropsies in some congenital diseases of the heart, mainly Fallot's tetralogy. Brit. Heart J., **15:** 335, 1953.
9. BAFFES, T. G., JOHNSON, F. R., POTT, W. J., AND GIBSON, S. Anatomic variations in tetralogy of Fallot. Amer. Heart J., **46:** 657, 1953.
10. COLLETT, R. W., AND EDWARDS, J. Persistent truncus arteriosus. Surg. Clin. N. Amer., **29:** 1245, 1949.
11. HARRIS, J. S., AND FARBER, S. Transposition of the great cardiac vessels. Arch. Path., **28:** 427, 1939.
12. TAUSSIG, H. B. Complete transposition of the great vessels. Amer. Heart J., **16:** 728, 1938.
13. ABRAHAMS, D. G., AND WOOD, P. Pulmonary stenosis with normal aortic root. Brit. Heart J., **13:** 519, 1951.
14. GREENWOLD, P. Congenital pulmonary atresia with intact ventricular septum. In *Proceedings of the 29th Scientific Session of the American Heart Association,* p. 51, 1956.
15. CAMPBELL, M., AND KAUNTZE, R. Congenital valvular stenosis. Brit. Heart J., **15:** 179, 1953.
16. GRUENWALD, P. Subaortic stenosis of the left ventricle. J. Tech. Meth., **27:** 173, 1947.
17. MONIE, J. W., AND DE PAPE, A. D. J. Congenital aortic atresia. Amer. Heart J., **40:** 595, 1950.
18. LICHTMAN, S. S. Isolated congenital dextrocardia. Arch. Int. Med., **48:** 683, 1931.
19. BYRON, F. Ectopia cordis. J. Thor. Surg., **7:** 717, 1948.
20. GREGG, N. M. Congenital cataract following German measles in the mother. Trans. Ophthal. Soc. Aust., **3:** 35, 1941.
21. WARKANY, J. Etiologic factors of congenital heart disease. In *Congenital Heart Disease*, edited by H. W. Kaplan and S. J. Robinson, p. 83. American Association for the Advancement of Science, Washington, D. C., 1960.
22. CAMPBELL, M. Place of maternal rubella in the aetiology of congenital heart disease. Brit. Med. J., **1:** 5227, 1961.
23. BELL, J. On rubella in pregnancy. Brit. Med. J., **1:** 1302, 1959.
24. McKEOWN, T., MACMAHON, B., AND PARSONS, C. G. The familial incidence of congenital malformations of the heart. Brit. Heart J., **15:** 273, 1953.
25. POLANI, P. E., AND CAMPBELL, M. An etiological study of congenital heart disease. Ann. Hum. Genet., **19:** 209, 1955.
26. UCHIDA, J. A., AND ROWE, R. D. Discordant heart anomalies in twins. Amer. J. Hum. Genet., **9:** 133, 1957.
27. BÖÖK, J. A. Heredity and heart disease. Amer. J. Public Health, **50:** 1, 1960.
28. FOX, M. H., AND GOSS, C. M. Experimentally produced malformations of the heart and great vessels in rat fetuses; transposition complexes and aortic arch abnormalities. Amer. J. Anat., **102:** 65, 1958.
29. RICHMAN, S., THOMAS, W., AND KONIKOV, N. Survival of rats with induced congenital cardiovascular anomalies. A. M. A. Arch. Path., **63:** 43, 1957.

Special Embryology

30. WILSON, J. G., AND WARKANY, J. Aortic arch and cardiac anomalies in offspring of vitamin A deficient rats. Amer. J. Anat., **85:** 113, 1949.
31. WILSON, J. G., JORDON, H. C., AND BRENT, R. L. Effects of irradiation on embryonic development. II. X-rays on the ninth day of gestation in the rat. Amer. J. Anat., **92:** 153, 1953.
32. INGALLS, T. H., CURLEY, F. J., AND PRINDLE, R. Experimental production of congenital anomalies. New Engl. J. Med., **247:** 758, 1952.
33. BAIRD, C. D. C., NELSON, M. M., MONIE, T. W., AND EVANS, H. M. Congenital cardiovascular anomalies by pteroylglutamic acid deficiency during gestation in the rat. Circulat. Rec., **2:** 544, 1954.
34. MONIE, T. W., NELSON, M. M., BAIRD, C. D. C., AND EVANS, H. M. Pathogenesis of cardiovascular abnormalities in fetal rats following transitory maternal pteroylglutamic acid deficiency. Circulation, **12:** 750, 1955.

# ARTERIAL SYSTEM

NORMAL DEVELOPMENT
•AORTIC ARCHES
•VITELLINE AND UMBILICAL ARTERIES
ABNORMALITIES OF THE GREAT VESSELS
•*Patent ductus arteriosus; coarctation of the aorta; abnormal right subclavian artery; double aortic arch; interrupted aortic arch; right aortic arch; abnormal left common carotid artery*

## Normal Development

### Aortic Arches

The first major intra-embryonic vessels are represented by the *dorsal aortas*, which run along the axis of the embryo (fig. 12-29). Initially these arteries form continuations of the endocardial heart tubes. As a result of the rotation of the cardiogenic plate, and the subsequent fusion of the endocardial heart tubes, the cranial portions of the dorsal aortas become arched. They then run on either side of the foregut, embedded in the mesenchyme of the first pharyngeal arch, and are known as the *first* or *mandibular aortic arches* (fig. 12-29). The junction of the arches with the truncus arteriosus is somewhat dilated and known as the *aortic sac* (fig. 12-14).[1] With the formation of the other pharyngeal arches, the aortic sac contributes a branch to each new arch, giving rise to a total of six pairs of arteries. All these arteries curve around the pharyngeal gut and are only present as such in early embryonic life. During further development they become greatly modified or retrogress altogether.

Although in human development the six aortic arches never exist all at the same time, the basic vascular pattern represented in Figure 12-30 may be useful in understanding the transformation into the adult arterial system (fig. 12-30*B*, *C*).

In a 4 mm. embryo the first aortic arch has largely disappeared (fig. 12-31*A*). A small portion, however, persists to form the *maxillary artery*. The second arch similarly will disappear soon. The remaining portions of this arch are the *hyoid* and *stapedial arteries*.[2] The third arch is large; the fourth and sixth arches are in the process of formation. Even though the sixth arch is not completed, the *primitive pulmonary artery* is already present as a major branch (fig. 12-31*A*).

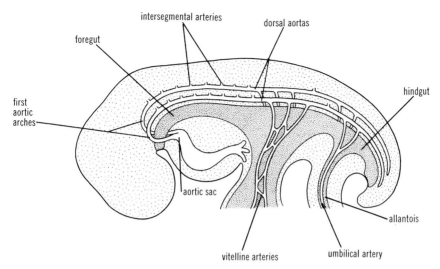

Figure 12-29. *Drawing of the arterial system in a 3-week old embryo. Note the position of the heart tube and the first aortic arches curving around the foregut.*

In a 10 mm. embryo the first two aortic arches have disappeared (fig. 12-31*B*). The third, fourth and sixth arches are large. The trunco-aortic sac has been divided so that the sixth arches are now continuous with the pulmonary trunk.

In the 14 mm. embryo the aortic arch system has largely lost its original symmetrical form and the definitive pattern becomes recognizable (fig. 12-32). The third aortic arch forms the *common carotid artery* and the first part of the *internal carotid artery*. The remainder of the internal carotid is formed by the cranial portion of the dorsal aorta. The origin of the *external carotid artery* is controversial, but in later stages it is found as a sprout of the third aortic arch, which joins with the remaining portions of the first and second aortic arches.

The *fourth aortic arch* persists on both sides, but its ultimate fate is different on the right and left sides. On the left it forms part of the arch of the aorta, between the left common carotid and the left subclavian arteries. On the right it forms the most proximal segment of the right subclavian artery, the distal part of which is formed by a portion of the right dorsal aorta and the seventh intersegmental artery (fig. 12-30*B*).

The *fifth aortic arch* is transient, and is never well developed. The *sixth aortic arch*, also known as the pulmonary arch, gives off an important branch which grows toward the developing lung bud. On the right side the proximal part becomes the proximal segment of the right pulmonary artery. The distal portion of this arch

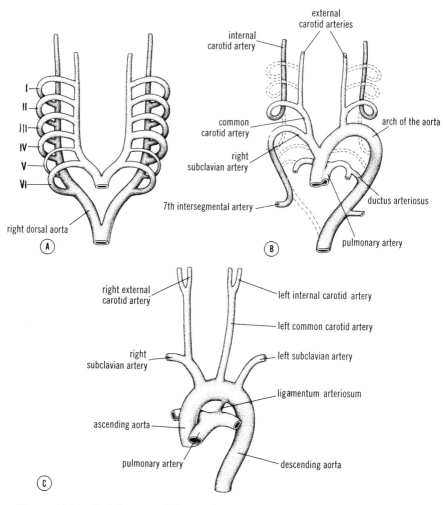

Figure 12-30. *A, Diagram of the aortic arches and dorsal aortas before transformation into the definitive vascular pattern. B, Diagram of the aortic arches and dorsal aortas after the transformation. The obliterated components are indicated by broken lines. Note the patent ductus arteriosus and the position of the seventh intersegmental artery on the left. C, The great arteries in the adult. Compare the distance between the place of origin of the left common carotid artery and the left subclavian in B and C.*

loses its connection with the dorsal aorta and disappears. On the left, the distal part persists during intra-uterine life as the *ductus arteriosus.*

Simultaneously with the alterations in the aortic arch system, a number of other changes occur. (1) The dorsal aorta located be-

Special Embryology

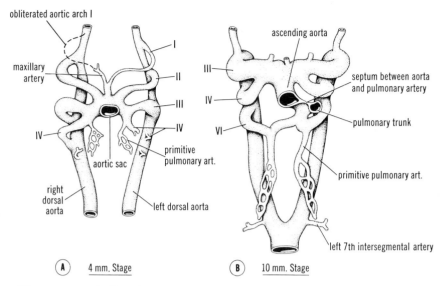

Figure 12-31. *A, Drawing of the aortic arches at the 4 mm. stage. The first aortic arch is obliterated before the sixth arch has fully developed. B, Aortic arch system at the 10 mm. stage. Note the aortico-pulmonary septum and the large primitive pulmonary arteries.*

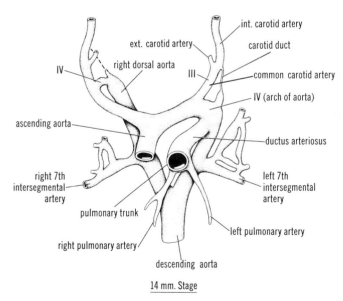

14 mm. Stage

Figure 12-32. *Drawing of the aortic arches at the 14 mm. stage. Note the carotid duct and the ductus arteriosus. Compare the origin of the subclavian artery on the right and left side.*

Cardiovascular System                                                              217

tween the entrance of the third and fourth arches, known as the *carotid duct*, is obliterated early in development (fig. 12-32). (2) The right dorsal aorta disappears between the origin of the right seventh intersegmental artery and the junction of the left dorsal aorta (fig. 12-30*B*). (3) The formation of the neck causes the heart to descend from its initial cervical position into the thoracic cavity. Hence, the carotid and innominate arteries elongate considerably. As a further result of this caudal shift, the left subclavian artery, distally fixed in the arm bud, shifts its point of origin from the aorta at the level of the seventh intersegmental artery to an increasingly higher point, until it comes close to the origin of the left common carotid artery.[3]

### Vitelline and Umbilical Arteries

The *vitelline arteries*, initially a number of paired vessels supplying the yolk sac (fig. 12-3), gradually fuse and form the arteries located in the dorsal mesentery of the gut. In the adult they are represented by the *coeliac, superior mesenteric,* and *inferior mesenteric arteries*. These vessels supply the derivatives of the foregut, midgut, and hindgut, respectively (see fig. 14-6).

The *umbilical arteries*, initially paired ventral branches of the dorsal aortas, course to the placenta in close association with the allantois (fig. 12-29). During the fourth week, however, each artery acquires a secondary connection with the dorsal branch of the aorta, the *common iliac artery*, and loses its original origin. After birth the proximal portions of the umbilical arteries persist as the *internal iliac* and the *superior vesical arteries*, while the distal parts are obliterated to form the *lateral vesico-umbilical ligaments*.

# Abnormalities of the Great Arteries

*Patent Ductus Arteriosus*

Under normal conditions the ductus arteriosus is functionally closed through contraction of its muscular wall shortly after birth.[4] Anatomical closure, however, by means of intima proliferation takes from 1 to 3 months.[5] A patent ductus arteriosus is one of the most frequently seen abnormalities of the great vessels and may occur either as an isolated abnormality or in combination with other heart defects (figs. 12-25*A* and 12-27).

*Coarctation of the Aorta*

Coarctation of the aorta (fig. 12-33*A, B*) is a condition in which the aortic lumen below the origin of the left subclavian artery is

Special Embryology

significantly narrowed. Since the constriction may be located above or below the entrance of the ductus arteriosus, two types of coarctation may be distinguished: the *preductal* and *postductal* types. The cause of the aortic narrowing is primarily an abnormality in the media of the aorta followed by intima proliferations.[6] In the preductal type the ductus arteriosus persists, whereas in the postductal type this channel usually is obliterated. In the latter case, a collateral circulation between the proximal and distal parts of the aorta is established by way of large intercostal and internal mammary arteries.[7]

### Abnormal Origin of the Right Subclavian Artery

In this abnormality (fig. 12-34A, B) the right subclavian artery is formed by the distal portion of the right dorsal aorta and the seventh intersegmental artery. The right fourth aortic arch and the proximal part of the right dorsal aorta have been obliterated. With shortening of the aorta between the left common carotid and the left subclavian arteries, the origin of the abnormal right subclavian artery is finally found just below that of the left subclavian artery.[3] Since its stem is derived from the right dorsal aorta, it must cross the midline behind the esophagus to reach the right arm. This abnormality, which is frequently seen, may occasionally cause difficulties in swallowing.[8, 9] In such instances, the recurrent laryngeal nerve does not hook around

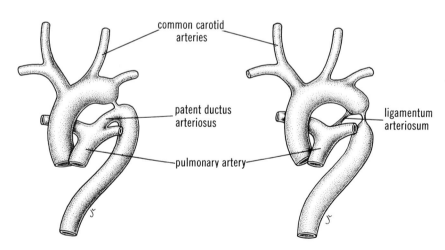

(A) Preductal Coarctation of the Aorta      (B) Postductal Coarctation of the Aorta

Figure 12-33. *Coarctation of the aorta. A, Preductal type; B, postductal type. The caudal part of the body is supplied by large, hypertrophied intercostal and internal mammary arteries.*

Cardiovascular System

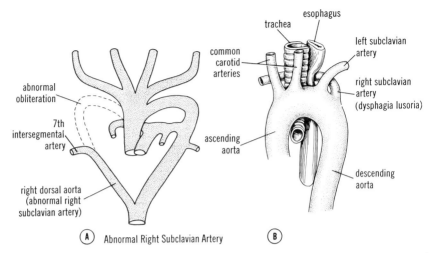

abnormal
obliteration

7th
intersegmental
artery

right dorsal aorta
(abnormal right
subclavian artery)

common
carotid
arteries

ascending
aorta

trachea

esophagus

left subclavian
artery

right subclavian
artery
(dysphagia lusoria)

descending
aorta

(A)  Abnormal Right Subclavian Artery        (B)

Figure 12-34. *Abnormal origin of the right subclavian artery (dysphagia lusoria). A, Scheme to show the obliteration of the right fourth aortic arch and the proximal portion of the right dorsal aorta, and the persistence of the distal portion of the right dorsal aorta. B, The abnormal right subclavian artery crosses the midline behind the esophagus and may compress the latter.*

the right subclavian artery, but passes directly from the vagus to the larynx musculature.

## Double Aortic Arch

Under normal conditions the right dorsal aorta disappears between the origin of the seventh intersegmental artery and its junction with the left dorsal aorta. If, however, this fails to occur, a double aortic arch results (fig. 12-35A, B). A *vascular ring* is thus formed which surrounds the trachea and esophagus and frequently compresses these structures, causing difficulties in breathing and swallowing.[10, 11]

## Interrupted Aortic Arch

This interesting anomaly, which is more serious than the abnormalities previously described, is caused by obliteration of the fourth aortic arch on the left side (fig. 12-36A, B). It is frequently combined with an abnormal origin of the right subclavian artery. The ductus arteriosus remains wide open and the descending aorta and subclavian arteries are supplied with blood of low oxygen content. The aortic trunk supplies the two common carotid arteries.[12]

Special Embryology

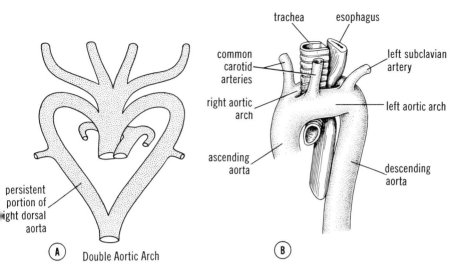

trachea    esophagus

common
carotid
arteries

left subclavian
artery

right aortic
arch

left aortic arch

ascending
aorta

descending
aorta

persistent
portion of
right dorsal
aorta

(A) Double Aortic Arch    (B)

Figure 12-35. *Double aortic arch. A, Scheme showing the persistence of the distal portion of the right dorsal aorta. B, The double aortic arch forms a vascular ring around the trachea and the esophagus.*

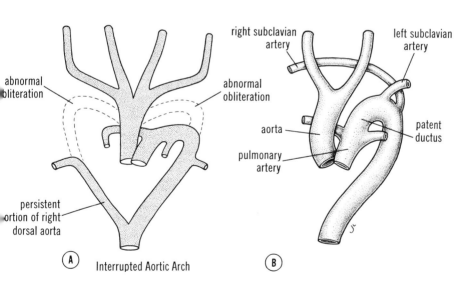

right subclavian
artery

left subclavian
artery

abnormal
obliteration

abnormal
obliteration

aorta

patent
ductus

pulmonary
artery

persistent
portion of right
dorsal aorta

(A) Interrupted Aortic Arch    (B)

Figure 12-36. *A, Scheme showing the obliteration of the fourth aortic arch on the right as well as on the left and persistence of the distal portion of the right dorsal aorta. B, Case of interrupted aortic arch. The aorta supplies the head; the pulmonary artery by way of the ductus arteriosus supplies the remaining parts of the body.*

Cardiovascular System

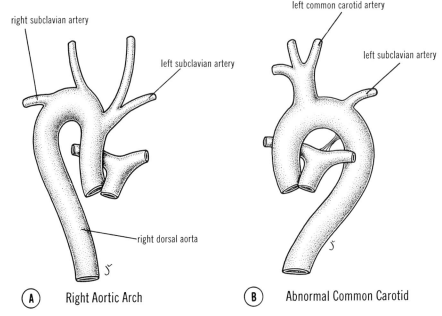

right subclavian artery

left common carotid artery

left subclavian artery

left subclavian artery

right dorsal aorta

(A) Right Aortic Arch

(B) Abnormal Common Carotid

Figure 12-37. *A Right aortic arch. B, Abnormal origin of left common carotid artery.*

### Right Aortic Arch

In such a case the left fourth aortic arch and left dorsal aorta have been completely obliterated and are replaced by the corresponding vessels on the right side (fig. 12-37A). Occasionally, when the ligamentum arteriosum is situated on the left side and passes behind the esophagus, it may cause complaints with swallowing.[13]

### Abnormal Origin of the Left Common Carotid Artery

In such a case the left common carotid artery arises from the innominate artery (fig. 11-37B). It then winds around the anterior surface of the trachea in a cranial direction. This anomaly is frequently accompained by an abnormal vertebral artery.[14]

### References—Arterial System

1. CONGDON, E. D. Transformation of the aortic arch system during development of the human embryo. Contrib. Embryol., **14:** 47, 1922.
2. PADGET, D. H. The development of the cranial arteries in the human embryo. Contrib. Embryol., **32:** 205, 1948.
3. BARRY, A. The aortic arch derivatives in the human adult. Anat. Rec., **111:** 221, 1951.

Special Embryology

4. ADAMS, F. H., AND LIND, J. Physiologic studies on the cardiovascular status of the normal newborn infant (with special reference to the ductus arteriosus). A. M. A. J. Dis. Child., **93:** 13, 1957.
5. JAGER, B. V., AND WOLLENMAN, O. J. An anatomical study of the closure of the ductus arteriosus. Amer. J. Path., **18:** 595, 1942.
6. WIELENGA, G. The relationship between coarctation of the aorta and the ligamentum arteriosum. Thesis, University of Leyden, 1959.
7. EDWARDS, J. E., CHRISTENSEN, N. A., CLADGETT, O. T., AND McDONALD, J. R. Pathologic considerations in coarctation of the aorta. Proc. Mayo Clin., **23:** 324, 1948.
8. PATTINSON, J. N. Anomalous right subclavian artery. Brit. Heart J., **15:** 150, 1953.
9. LANGMAN, J. Esophagus atresia accompained by a remarkable vessel anomaly. Arch. Chir. Neerl., **4:** 39, 1952.
10. GRISWOLD, H. E., AND YOUNG, M. D. Double aortic arch. Pediatrics, **4:** 751, 1949.
11. EKSTROM, G., AND SANDBLOM, P. Double aortic arch; embryonic development. Acta Chir. Scand., **102:** 183, 1951.
12. KLEINERMAN, J., YANG, W., HACKEL, D. B., AND KAUFMAN, N. Absence of the transverse aortic arch. A. M. A. Arch. Path., **65:** 490, 1958.
13. BEDFORD, D. E., AND PARKINSON, J. Right sided aortic arch. Brit. J. Radiol., **9:** 776, 1936.
14. MAISEL, H. Some anomalies of the origin of the left vertebral artery. S. Afr. Med. J., **32:** 1141, 1958.

# VENOUS SYSTEM

NORMAL DEVELOPMENT
•VITELLINE VEINS
•UMBILICAL VEINS
•CARDINAL VEINS: *inferior vena cava; azygos vein; superior vena cava*
•PULMONARY VEINS
ABNORMAL VENOUS DRAINAGE
•*Double inferior vena cava; absent hepatic portion of the inferior vena cava; left superior vena cava; double superior vena cava; abnormal pulmonary venous drainage*

## Normal Development

In a 4 mm. embryo three pairs of major veins can be distinguished: (1) the *vitelline* or *omphalomesenteric veins*, carrying blood from the yolk sac to the sinus venosus; (2) *the umbilical veins*, originating in the chorionic villi and carrying oxygenated blood to the embryo; and (3) the *cardinal veins*, draining the body of the embryo proper (fig. 12-3). The cardinal system consists of the *anterior cardinal veins*, which drain the cephalic part of the embryo, and the *posterior cardinal veins*, draining the remaining part of the body of the embryo including the mesenephroi. The anterior and posterior cardinal veins join before entering the heart and form the short *common cardinal veins*. These veins enter the right and left sinus horn just lateral to the umbilical veins (fig. 12-11).

### Vitelline Veins

Before entering the sinus venosus, the vitelline veins form a plexus around the duodenum and then enter the liver (fig. 12-38*A*, *B*). The growing liver cords interrupt the course of the veins and an extensive vascular network is formed, known as the *hepatic sinusoids*. The vascular connections between the hepatic sinusoids and the heart are often referred to as the *hepato-cardiac channels*.

In subsequent development the anastomotic network around the duodenum develops into a single vessel, the *portal vein* (fig. 12-38*C*, *D*). The *superior mesenteric vein*, which drains the primitive intestinal loop, is considered as the successor of the distal portion of the right vitelline vein. The distal portion of the left vitelline vein disappears.

With the reduction of the left sinus horn, blood from the left side

Special Embryology

of the liver is rechanneled toward the right, resulting in an en-largment of the right vitelline vein (right hepato-cardiac channel). Ultimately the right hepato-cardiac channel forms the *post-hepatic portion of the inferior vena cava*. The proximal part of the left vitelline vein disappears.

## Umbilical Veins

The umbilical veins pass initially on each side of the liver, but soon become connected to the hepatic sinusoids (fig. 12-38A, B). The

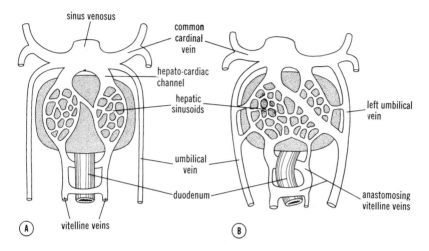

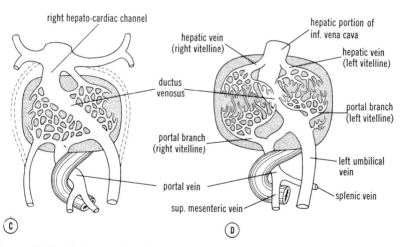

Figure 12-38. *Schemes showing the development of the umbilical and vitelline veins. A, At the end of the fourth week; B, in the fifth week; C, in the sixth week; D, in the third month. Note the formation of the ductus venosus between the left umbilical vein and the inferior vena cava.*

Cardiovascular System

proximal part of both umbilical veins as well as the remainder of the right umbilical vein then disappear, so that the left vein is the only one to carry blood from the placenta to the liver. With the increase of the placental circulation, a direct communication is formed between the left umbilical vein and the right hepato-cardiac channel, the *ductus venosus* (fig. 12-38B, C). This vessel bypasses the sinusoidal plexus of the liver. After birth the left umbilical vein and ductus venosus are obliterated and form the *ligamentum teres hepatis* and *ligamentum venosum*, respectively (see "Circulatory Changes at Birth").

## Cardinal Veins

Shortly after the posterior cardinal veins have been established as two longitudinal vessels draining the dorsal body wall, a new venous system develops, the *subcardinal veins* (fig. 12-39A). These veins arise along the medial aspect of the mesonephroi and gradually take over the drainage of these organs from the posterior cardinal veins. Cranially, they empty into the posterior cardinal veins. As a result of the enormous growth of the mesonephroi, the subcardinal veins enlarge, come closer together, and form an anastomosing plexus between them (fig. 12-39B). A new connection between the right subcardinal vein and the right hepato-cardiac channel is then formed. At first this connection is plexiform, but soon it develops into a large channel, the *hepato-subcardinal anastomosis* (*hepatic segment of the inferior vena cava*) (fig. 12-39C). When this communication has been established, the left subcardinal vein disappears, and only its distal portion remains as the *left gonadal vein*. Blood from the left side is channeled to the right by the *left renal vein* which is derived from a subcardinal anastomosis. Hence the right subcardinal vein becomes the main drainage channel and develops into the *renal segment of the inferior vena cava* (fig. 12-39C).

With continuous growth of the embryo and formation of the lower extremities, a third venous system, the *sacro-cardinal veins*, appears (fig. 12-39C). These veins initially empty into the posterior cardinal veins, but with the disappearance of these veins, they become connected with the subcardinal system. Simultaneously an anastomosis develops between the right and left sacro-cardinal veins. The right sacro-cardinal vein finally becomes the *sacro-cardinal segment of the inferior vena cava*, and the communicating channel between the two sacro-cardinal veins forms the *left common iliac vein* (fig. 12-40B). The left sacro-cardinal vein proximal to this anastomosis eventually disappears.

With the obliteration of the posterior cardinal veins, a fourth venous system, the *supracardinal veins*, begins to develop (figs. 12-39 and 12-40). These veins drain the body wall by way of the intercostal veins, thereby taking over the function from the posterior cardinal veins. Cranially, the supracardinal veins empty into the terminal portion of the posterior cardinal veins. The fourth to eleventh right intercostal veins empty into the right supracardinal vein, which together with the terminal portion of the posterior cardinal vein, forms the *azygos vein* (fig. 12-40). On the left, the fourth to seventh intercostal veins enter into the left supracardinal vein. After development of a communicating vessel between the two supracardinals, the left supracardinal empties mainly by way of the azygos vein. The left supracardinal vein is then known as the *hemiazygos vein* (fig. 12-40).

The formation of anastomoses between the right and left veins is not restricted to the caudal part of the body, but also occurs between the *anterior cardinal veins* (fig. 12-40). A large communicating vessel, the *left branchiocephalic vein*, appears between the right and left anterior cardinal veins. Most of the blood from the left side of the head and left upper extremity is then channeled to the right.

The terminal portion of the left posterior cardinal vein and a part of the anterior cardinal vein entering into the left branchiocephalic vein are retained as a small vessel, the *left superior intercostal vein*

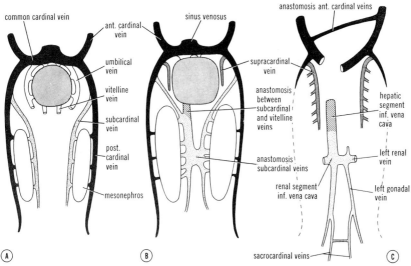

Figure 12-39. *Diagrams showing the development of the inferior vena cava, the azygos vein, and the superior vena cava. A, In the fourth week; B, in the sixth week; C, in the seventh week; anastomoses are formed between the subcardinals, the sacrocardinals, and the anterior cardinals.*

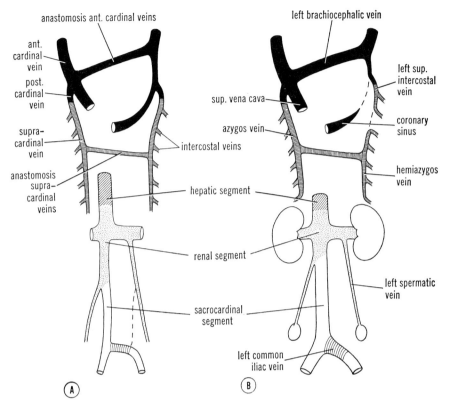

anastomosis ant. cardinal veins

ant. cardinal vein

post. cardinal vein

supra- cardinal vein

anastomosis supra- cardinal veins

left brachiocephalic vein

left sup. intercostal vein

sup. vena cava

coronary sinus

azygos vein

intercostal veins

hemiazygos vein

hepatic segment

renal segment

left spermatic vein

sacrocardinal segment

left common iliac vein

Ⓐ

Ⓑ

Figure 12-40. *Diagrams showing the further development of the inferior vena cava. A, At 9 weeks; B, full term. Note the anastomosis between the two supra- cardinal veins (adapted from Gruenwald, McClure and Butler).*

(fig. 12-40*B*). This vessel receives blood from the second and third intercostal spaces. A similar vessel on the right, the *right superior intercostal vein*, empties into the azygos vein. The *superior vena cava* is formed by the right common cardinal vein and the proximal portion of the right anterior cardinal vein.[1-3]

## Pulmonary Veins

At approximately the 4 mm. stage the common pulmonary vein can be recognized as an evagination of the dorsal wall of the atrium,[4-6] This bud subsequently grows out into the dorsal meso- cardium in the direction of the primitive foregut, which gives rise to the lung buds. With further development of the atrial cavity the stem of the pulmonary vein is progressively incorporated into the wall of the left atrium. Hence, whereas on the right side the smooth- walled part of the atrium originates from the right sinus horn, on

Special Embryology

the left it develops from the wall of the pulmonary veins. The incorporation of the pulmonary veins continues until two right and two left branches of the pulmonary stem enter the atrial cavity.

## Abnormal Venous Drainage

The complicated development of the venae cavae accounts for the fact that deviations from the normal pattern are frequently seen.

### Double Inferior Vena Cava at the Lumbar Level

In this abnormality (fig. 12-41A), the left sacrocardinal vein has failed to lose its connection with the left subcardinal, and the left common iliac vein may or may not be present. The left gonadal vein, however, is present as in normal conditions.

### Absence of the Inferior Vena Cava

In this case (fig. 12-41B) the right subcardinal vein has failed to make its connection with the liver and shunts its blood directly into the right supracardinal vein (fig. 12-39B). Hence, the blood stream from the caudal part of the body reaches the heart by way of the

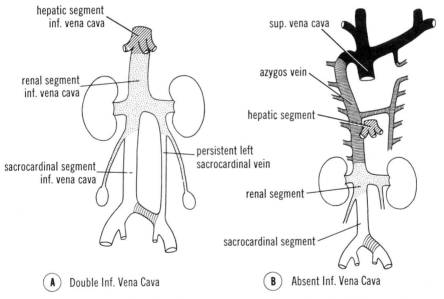

(A) Double Inf. Vena Cava     (B) Absent Inf. Vena Cava

Figure 12-41. A, *Double inferior vena cava at the lumbar level due to the persistence of the left sacrocardinal vein. B, Absent inferior vena cava. The lower half of the body is drained by the azygos vein, which enters the superior vena cava. The hepatic vein enters the heart at the site of the inferior vena cava.*

Cardiovascular System                                                        229

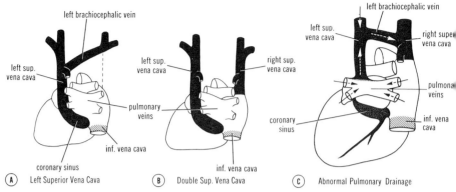

Figure 12-42. *A, Left superior vena cava draining into the right atrium by way of the coronary sinus (dorsal view). B, Double superior vena cava. The communicating vein between the two anterior cardinals has failed to develop (dorsal view). C, Total abnormal pulmonary venous drainage. The pulmonary veins enter the left superior vena cava, which enters the right superior vena cava by way of the brachiocephalic vein (dorsal view).*

azygos and superior vena cava. The hepatic vein enters into the right atrium at the site of the inferior vena cava.[7] Usually this abnormality is associated with other heart malformations.

### Left Superior Vena Cava

This abnormality (fig. 12-42A) is caused by the persistence of the left anterior cardinal vein and the obliteration of the common cardinal and proximal part of the anterior cardinal vein on the right. In such a case, the blood from the right is channeled toward the left by way of the branchiocephalic vein.[8]

### Double Superior Vena Cava

This condition (fig. 12-42B) is characterized by the persistence of the left anterior cardinal vein and the failure of the left branchiocephalic vein to form. The persistent left anterior cardinal, which is called *left superior vena cava*, drains into the right atrium by way of the coronary sinus.[9]

### Abnormal Pulmonary Venous Drainage

Occasionally some or all the pulmonary veins fail to drain into the left atrium (fig. 12-42C). In the partial form, the abnormal veins usually drain into the right atrium or into the superior vena cava. In

Special Embryology

case of a totally abnormal pulmonary venous drainage, they drain into a persistent left superior vena cava.[5, 9]

## References—Venous System

1. Grünwald, P. Die Entwicklung der Vena Cava Caudalis. Z. Mikroskopischanat. Forsch., **43:** 275, 1938.
2. McClure, F. W., and Butler, E. G. The development of the vena cava inferior in man. Amer. J. Anat., **35:** 331, 1925.
3. Reagan, F. P., and Robinson, A. The later development of the inferior vena cava in man and in carnivora. J. Anat., **61:** 482, 1927.
4. Auer, J. The development of the human pulmonary veins and its major variations. Anat. Rec., **101:** 581, 1948.
5. Neil, C. A. Development of pulmonary veins. Pediatrics, **18:** 880, 1956.
6. Los, J. A. The development of the pulmonary veins and the coronary sinus in the human embryo. Doctoral thesis, University of Leyden, 1958.
7. Anderson, R. C., Heilig, W., Novick, R., and Jarvis, C. Anomalous inferior vena cava with azygos drainage. Amer. Heart J., **49:** 318, 1955.
8. Winter, F. S. Persistent left superior vena cava. Angiology, **5:** 90, 1954.
9. Darling, R. C., Rothneg, W. B., and Craig, J. M. Total pulmonary venous drainage into the right side of the heart. Lab Invest., **6:** 44, 1957.

# CIRCULATORY CHANGES AT BIRTH

•FETAL CIRCULATION
•CHANGES AT BIRTH

## Fetal Circulation

Our present knowledge of the fetal circulation is based largely on angiocardiographic investigations in the fetal lamb and in the human fetus.[1-5]

Before birth, oxygenated blood from the placenta returns to the fetus by way of the umbilical vein. On approaching the liver, the main portion of this blood flows through the ductus venosus directly into the inferior vena cava, thereby short-circuiting the liver. A smaller portion enters the liver sinusoids and mixes here with blood from the portal circulation (fig. 12-43). A sphincter mechanism in the ductus venosus, close to the entrance of the umbilical vein, regulates the flow of umbilical blood through the liver sinusoids. It is thought that this sphincter closes when, because of a uterine contraction, the venous return is too high, thus preventing a sudden overloading of the heart.[6]

After a short course in the inferior vena cava, the blood enters the right atrium. Here it is guided toward the oval foramen by the valve of the inferior vena cava, and the major portion of the blood stream passes directly into the left atrium. A small portion, however, is prevented from so doing by the lower edge of the septum secundum, the *crista dividens*, and remains in the right atrium. Here it mixes with the desaturated blood returning from the head and arms by way of the superior vena cava.

From the left atrium the blood stream enters the left ventricle and ascending aorta. Since the coronary and carotid arteries are the first branches of the ascending aorta, the heart musculature and the brain are supplied with well-oxygenated blood. The desaturated blood from the superior vena cava flows by way of the right ventricle into the pulmonary trunk. Since the resistance in the pulmonary vessels during fetal life is high, the main portion of this blood passes directly through the *ductus arteriosus* into the descending aorta, where it mixes with blood from the proximal aorta. From here on the blood stream flows toward the placenta by way of the two umbilical arteries.

During its course from the placenta to the organs of the fetus,

Special Embryology

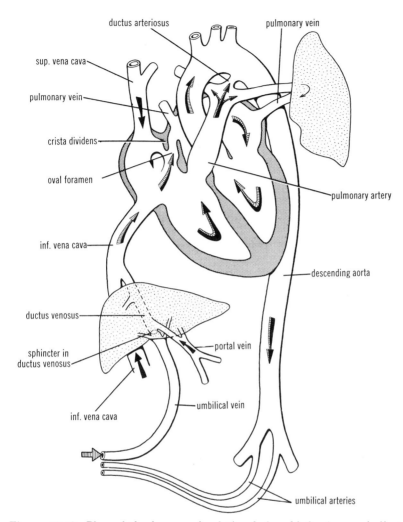

ductus arteriosus          pulmonary vein

sup. vena cava

pulmonary vein

crista dividens

oval foramen

                         pulmonary artery

inf. vena cava

                 descending aorta

ductus venosus

sphincter in
ductus venosus        portal vein

             umbilical vein

inf. vena cava

                 umbilical arteries

Figure 12-43. *Plan of the human circulation before birth. Arrows indicate the direction of the blood flow.*

the high oxygen content of the blood in the umbilical vein gradually decreases by mixing with varying amounts of desaturated blood. Theoretically this may occur to a greater or lesser extent in the following places: (1) in the liver by mixture with a small amount of blood returning from the portal system; (2) in the inferior vena cava, which carries deoxygenated blood returning from the lower extremities, pelvis, and kidneys; (3) in the left atrium by mixture with blood returning from the lungs; and (4) at the entrance of the ductus arteriosus into the descending aorta.

## Changes at Birth

The sudden changes occurring in the vascular system at birth are caused by the cessation of the placental blood flow and the beginning of the lung respiration. As a result of the compression of the chest at birth, the amnion fluid in the bronchial tree is replaced by air, and the lungs suddenly become aerated. Since, at the same time, the ductus arteriosus closes by muscular contraction of its wall, the amount of blood flowing through the lung vessels increases rapidly. This in turn results in a rise in pressure in the left atrium. Simultaneously with these changes on the left, the pressure in the right atrium decreases as a result of interruption of the placental blood flow. The septum primum is then apposed to the septum secundum, and the oval foramen closes functionally.

Summarizing, the following changes occur in the vascular system after birth (fig. 12-44):

1. *Closure of the umbilical arteries* is accomplished by contraction of the smooth musculature in the wall of the vessels and is probably caused by thermal and mechanical stimuli and a change in oxygen tension.[7] Functionally, the arteries are closed a few minutes after birth. The actual obliteration of the lumen by fibrous proliferation, however, may take from 2 to 3 months.[8, 9] The distal parts of the umbilical arteries then form the *lateral vesico-umbilical ligaments*, while the proximal portions remain open as the *superior vesical arteries*.

2. *Closure of the umbilical vein and ductus venosus* occurs shortly after that of the umbilical arteries. Hence, blood from the placenta may enter the newborn for some time after birth and an additional quantity equal to 1 to 4.5 per cent of the child's blood weight may be added before the placental flow completely ceases. After obliteration, the umbilical vein forms the *ligamentum teres hepatis* in the lower margin of the falciform ligament. The ductus venosus, which courses from the ligamentum teres to the inferior vena cava, is also obliterated and forms the *ligamentum venosum*.

3. *Closure of the ductus arteriosus* by contraction of its muscular wall occurs almost immediately after birth. Angiocardiography and cardiac catheterization, however, have revealed that during the first days after birth a left-to-right shunt is not unusual.[7, 10] Complete anatomical obliteration by proliferation of the intima is thought to take from 1 to 3 months.[8] In the adult, the obliterated ductus arteriosus forms the *ligamentum arteriosum*.

4. *Closure of the oval foramen* is caused by an increased pressure in the left atrium combined with a decrease in pressure on the right

Special Embryology

side. With the first good breath the septum primum is pressed against the septum secundum. During the first days of life, however, this closure is reversible. Crying of the baby creates a shunt from right to left, thus accounting for the cyanotic periods in the newborn. Constant apposition gradually leads to fusion of the two septa

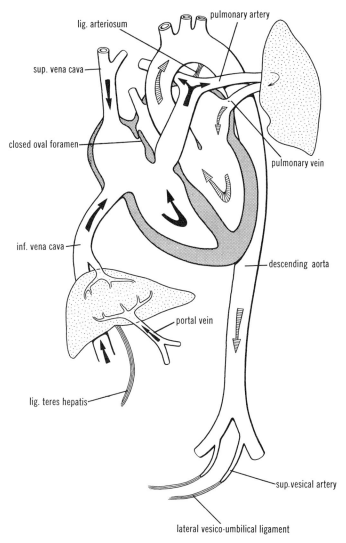

Figure 12-44. *Plan of the human circulation after birth. Note the changes occurring as a result of the beginning of respiration and the interruption of the placental blood flow.*

Cardiovascular System

in about 1 year. In 20 to 25 per cent of all individuals, however, perfect anatomical closure may never be obtained.[9]

## References—Circulatory Changes at Birth

1. BARCLAY, Q. E., FRANKLIN, K. L., AND PRICHARD, M. M. L. *The Fetal Circulation.* Blackwell Scientific Publications, Oxford, 1944.
2. BARCROFT, J. *Researches on Prenatal Life.* Blackwell Scientific Publications, Oxford, 1946.
3. LIND, J., AND WEGELIUS, C. Human fetal circulation in: the mammalian fetus; physiological aspects of development. Symposia Quant. Biol., **19:** 109, 1954.
4. BARCROFT, J. Foetal and neonatal physiology. Brit. Med. Bull., **17:** 247, 1961.
5. DAWES, J. S. Changes in the circulation at birth and the effects of asphyxia. In *Recent Advances in Pediatrics,* edited by D. Gairdner. Little, Brown & Co., Boston, 1958.
6. GRIBBE, G., HIRVONEN, L., LIND, J., AND WEGELIUS, C. Cineangiocardiographic recordings of the cyclic changes in volume of the left ventricle. Cardiologia, **34:** 348, 1959.
7. ADAMS, F. H., AND LIND, J. Physiologic studies on the cardiovascular status of normal newborn infants with special reference to the ductus arteriosus. Pediatrics, **19:** 431, 1957.
8. ODE, E. De ductus arteriosus. Doctoral thesis, University of Leyden, 1951.
9. PATTEN, B. M. The development of the heart. In *Pathology of the Heart,* 1st ed., edited by S. E. Gould, p. 20. Charles C Thomas, Springfield, Ill., 1953.
10. LIND, J., BOESEN, T., AND WEGELIUS, C. Selective angiocardiography in congenital heart disease. Progr. Cardiov. Dis., **2:** 293, 1959-60.

Special Embryology

CHAPTER **13**

# Digestive Tube and Its Derivatives

As a result of the cephalo-caudal folding of the embryo, the ento-derm-lined cavity is divided into an intra-embryonic portion, the *primitive gut*, and two extra-embryonic portions, the *yolk sac* and the *allantois* (fig. 13-1A–D). In the cephalic as well as the caudal part of the embryo the primitive gut forms a blind ending tube, the *foregut* and *hindgut*, respectively. The middle part, the *midgut*, re-mains temporarily connected to the yolk sac by means of the *vitelline* or *omphalomesenteric duct* (fig. 13-1D) (see Chapter 5).

In this chapter, the development of the primitive gut and its de-rivatives is discussed in four sections: (1) the *pharyngeal gut* or *pharynx*, which forms the cranial part of the foregut, and extends from the buccopharyngeal membrane to the tracheobronchial di-verticulum (figs. 13-1D and 13-3); (2) the *caudal part of the foregut*, lying caudal to the tracheobronchial diverticulum and extending as far caudally as the liver outgrowth; (3) the *midgut*, beginning caudal to the liver bud (the anterior intestinal portal) and extending to a point where, in the adult, the junction of the right two-thirds and left one-third of the transverse colon is found (known, in the embryo, as the posterior intestinal portal); (4) the *hindgut*, extending from the posterior intestinal portal to the cloacal membrane (figs. 13-1 and 13-3).

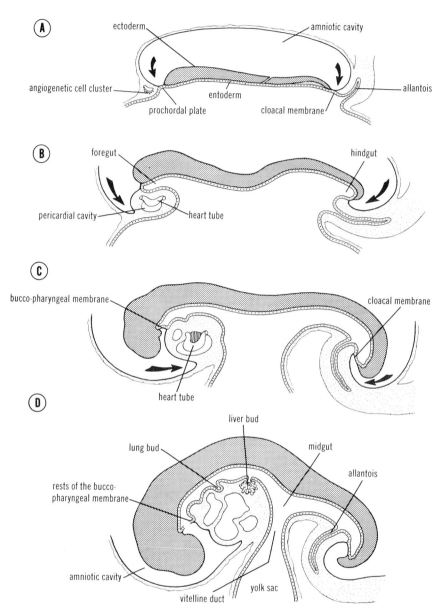

Figure 13-1. *Schematic drawings of sagittal sections through embryos at various stages of development to demonstrate the effect of the cephalocaudal flexion on the position of the entoderm-lined cavity. Note the formation of the foregut, midgut and hindgut. A, Presomite embryo; B, seven-somite embryo; C, 14-somite embryo; D, at the end of the first month.*

238                                                        Special Embryology

# PHARYNGEAL GUT

## NORMAL DEVELOPMENT
- **PHARYNGEAL ARCHES**: *Meckel's cartilage; ossicles; styloid process; hyoid bone; laryngeal cartilages*
- **PHARYNGEAL POUCHES**: *tympanic cavity; Eustachian tube; palatine tonsil; parathyroid glands; thymus; ultimobranchial body*
- **PHARYNGEAL CLEFTS**: *external auditory meatus; cervical sinus*
- **FLOOR OF THE PHARYNX**: *tongue; thyroid gland*
- **RESPIRATORY SYSTEM**: *trachea; bronchi; lungs; alveoli*

## CONGENITAL MALFORMATIONS
- **LATERAL CYSTS OF THE NECK (BRANCHIAL CYSTS)**
- **THYROGLOSSAL CYST AND FISTULA**
- **ESOPHAGOTRACHEAL FISTULA AND ATRESIA OF THE ESOPHAGUS**
- **ABNORMALITIES OF THE LUNGS**

## *Normal Development*

At its cephalic end the *pharyngeal gut* or *pharynx* is in direct contact with the ectoderm at the floor of the stomodeum, and the entoderm-ectoderm membrane so formed is known as the *buccopharyngeal membrane* (figs. 13-1*C* and 13-2*A*). At the end of the third week this membrane ruptures, thereby establishing an open connection between the stomodeum and the foregut (fig. 13-2*B*).

During the fourth and fifth weeks of development the pharynx forms a number of outpocketings, the *pharyngeal pouches* (fig. 13-3*B*). These pouches appear along the lateral walls and gradually penetrate the surrounding mesenchyme. By the end of the fifth week the openings of the pharyngeal pouches into the pharynx have the appearance of grooves (fig. 13-4*A*). Simultaneous with the formation of the pouches, four grooves become visible on the surface of the embryo (fig. 13-4*B*). These grooves, known as the *pharyngeal clefts*, penetrate the underlying mesenchyme. Although the clefts approach the pharyngeal pouches closely, they rarely communicate with each other in the form of open gills.

As a result of the formation of the ectodermal clefts and the entodermal outpocketings, the mesodermal tissue surrounding the pharyngeal gut is pushed aside and a number of mesodermal bars, the *branchial* or *pharyngeal arches*, make their appearance (fig. 13-4*B*). The lower vertebrates may have six or more pharyngeal arches; the human embryo, however, has only five, the tailmost one being poorly defined.

Digestive Tube and Its Derivatives                                      239

As the formation of the pharyngeal arches is intimately associated with that of the entodermal pouches and the ectodermal clefts, the further development of all three components is discussed in the following sections.

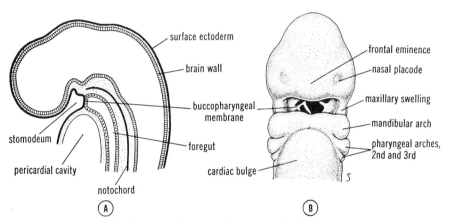

Figure 13-2. A, *Sagittal section through the cephalic end of an embryo of approximately 25 days. The buccopharyngeal membrane is formed by the epithelial entodermal lining of the foregut and the ectodermal lining at the bottom of the stomodeum. B, Frontal view of a slightly older embryo, showing the rupture of the buccopharyngeal membrane.*

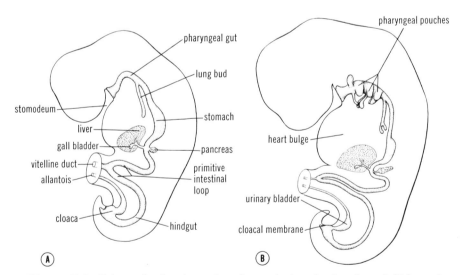

Figure 13-3. *Schematic drawings of embryos during the fourth and fifth weeks of development to show the formation of the gastrointestinal tract and the various derivatives originating from the entodermal germ layer.*

Special Embryology

## Pharyngeal Arches

When the embryo is four to five weeks old the pharyngeal arches, separated by deep clefts, contribute greatly to the characteristic external appearance of the embryo (figs. 5-4, 5-12 and 13-4B). During further development each arch forms its own cartilaginous and muscular components, while in addition it has its own artery and nerve (fig. 13-5A, B). While some of the cartilaginous parts eventually vanish, others persist throughout life as bony or cartilaginous structures (fig. 13-6). The muscles of the different arches do not always attach to the bony or cartilaginous components of their own arch, but sometimes migrate into surrounding regions. The origin of these muscles, however, can always be traced, since their nerve supply comes from the arch of origin.

*First Pharyngeal Arch*

The cartilage of the *first* or *mandibular arch* consists of a small dorsal portion, known as the *maxillary process*, extending forward beneath the region of the eye, and a much larger ventral portion, the *mandibular process* or *Meckel's cartilage* (fig. 13-5B). During further development both the maxillary process and Meckel's carti-

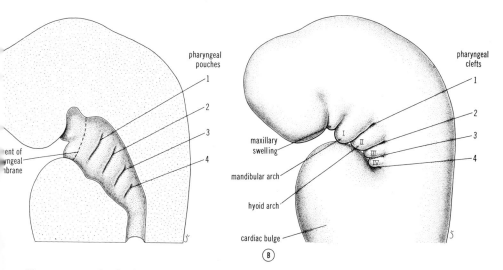

Figure 13-4. *A, Sagittal section through the cephalic end of a 5-week embryo (approximately 6 mm.), showing the openings of the pharyngeal pouches along the lateral wall of the pharyngeal gut. Broken line represents the approximate site of attachment of the buccopharyngeal membrane. B, The pharyngeal arches and clefts in a 5-week embryo.*

Digestive Tube and Its Derivatives

lage retrogress and disappear, except for two small portions at their dorsal ends which persist and form the *incus* and *malleus*, respectively (fig. 13-6).[1] The *mandible* is formed secondarily by intramembranous ossification of the mesodermal tissue surrounding Meckel's cartilage. A portion of Meckel's cartilage undergoes a fibrous transformation and forms the *sphenomandibular ligament*.

The musculature of the mandibular arch (that is, the *muscles of mastication*, the *anterior belly of the digastric*, and the *tensor tympani*) is innervated by the *mandibular branch of the trigeminal nerve*, the nerve of the first arch (fig. 13-5A). In addition, this nerve innervates the skin over the mandible and the anterior two-thirds of the mucosa of the tongue.

*Second Pharyngeal Arch*

The cartilage of the *second* or *hyoid arch* is known as *Reichert's cartilage* (fig. 13-5B). It gives rise to the *stapes*, the *styloid process of the temporal bone*, the *stylohyoid ligament*, and, in its ventral portion, to the *lesser horn* and the *upper part of the body of the hyoid bone* (fig. 13-6).

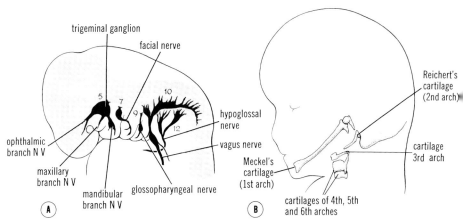

Figure 13-5. *A, The musculature of each pharyngeal arch is supplied by its own cranial nerve. The trigeminal nerve supplying the first arch has three branches; the nerve of the second arch is the facial nerve, that of the third the glossopharyngeal nerve. The musculature of the fourth arch is supplied by a superior laryngeal branch of the vagus nerve, and that of the sixth arch by the recurrent laryngeal branch of the vagus nerve. The hypoglossal nerve supplies the tongue musculature. B, Drawing showing the cartilaginous components of the pharyngeal arches in the human embryo. Some of the components ossify, while others disappear or become ligamentous. The maxillary process and Meckel's cartilage are replaced by the definitive maxilla and mandible, which both develop by membranous ossification.*

Special Embryology

The muscles of the hyoid arch (the *stapedius*, the *stylohyoid*, the *posterior belly of the digastric*, and the *muscles of facial expression*) are supplied by the *facial nerve*, the nerve of the second arch (fig. 13-5A).

### Third Pharyngeal Arch

The cartilage of this arch produces the *lower part of the body* and the *greater horn of the hyoid bone* (fig. 13-6).

The musculature of this arch is limited to the *stylopharyngeal muscle*, which is innervated by the *glossopharyngeal nerve*, the nerve of the third arch (fig. 13-5A). Since part of the tongue is also derived from the third arch, its sensory innervation is partly supplied by the glossopharyngeal nerve.

### Fourth and Sixth Pharyngeal Arches

The cartilaginous components of these arches fuse to form the *thyroid, cricoid*, and *arytenoid cartilages* of the larynx (figs. 13-5B and 13-6).

The muscles of the fourth arch (the *cricothyroid* and the *constrictors of the pharynx*) are innervated by the *superior laryngeal branch of the vagus*, the nerve of the fourth arch. The intrinsic muscles of

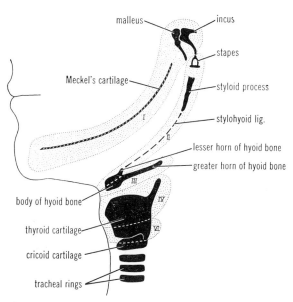

Figure 13-6. *Drawing showing the definitive structures formed by the cartilaginous components of the various pharyngeal arches (modified after Giroud).*

Digestive Tube and Its Derivatives

the larynx, however, are supplied by the *recurrent laryngeal branch of the vagus*, the nerve of the sixth arch (fig. 13-5A).

## Pharyngeal Pouches

The human embryo has five pairs of pharyngeal pouches (figs. 13-3B and 13-4A). The last one of these is atypical and often considered as part of the fourth. Since the epithelial entodermal lining of the pouches gives rise to a number of important organs, the fate of each pouch is discussed separately.

### First Pharyngeal Pouch

The first pharyngeal pouch forms a stalk-like diverticulum, the *tubotympanic recess*, which comes in contact with the epithelial

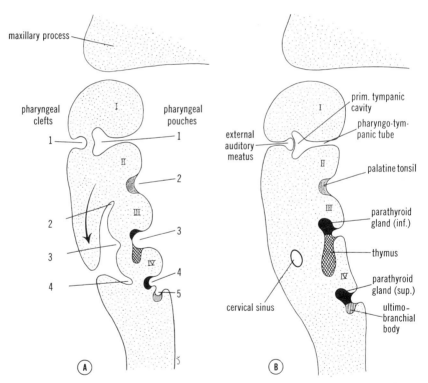

Figure 13-7. A, *Schematic representation of the development of the pharyngeal clefts and pouches. Note how the second arch grows over the third and fourth arches, thereby burying the second, third and fourth pharyngeal clefts. B, The remnants of the second, third and fourth pharyngeal clefts form the cervical sinus. Note also the differentiation of the epithelium in the wall of the entodermal pharyngeal pouches (modified after Starck).*

Special Embryology

lining of the first pharyngeal cleft (fig. 13-7A, B). The distal portion of the outpocketing widens into a saclike structure, the *primitive tympanic* or *middle ear cavity*, whereas the proximal part remains narrow, forming the *pharyngotympanic* or *Eustachian tube*. The entodermal lining of the tympanic cavity later aids in the formation of the *tympanic membrane* or *eardrum* (see Ear, Chapter 17).

## Second Pharyngeal Pouch

The major portion of this pouch is obliterated. The epithelial lining of the remaining part proliferates and is secondarily invaded by mesodermal tissue, thus forming the primordium of the *palatine tonsil* (fig. 13-7A, B). During the third to fifth months the tonsil is gradually infiltrated by lymphatic tissue.

## Third Pharyngeal Pouch

The third and fourth pouches are characterized at their distal extremity by a so-called dorsal and ventral wing. In the fifth week of development the epithelium of the dorsal wing of the third pouch differentiates into *parathyroid tissue*, while that of the ventral part forms the primordium of the *thymus* (fig. 13-7A, B).

Further growth of the thymus and parathyroid tissues causes obliteration of the lumen of the pouch, and at the sixth week both the gland primordia lose their connection with the pharyngeal wall.[2] The thymus then migrates in a caudal and medial direction, pulling the parathyroid with it (fig. 13-8). While the main portion of the thymus moves rapidly to its final position in the thorax, where it fuses with its counterpart from the opposite side, its tail portion becomes thin and elongated and eventually breaks up into small fragments. These fragments usually disappear but may sometimes persist either embedded in the thyroid gland or as isolated thymic nests.[3, 4]

The parathyroid tissue of the third pouch finally comes to rest on the dorsal surface of the thyroid gland and, in the adult, forms the *inferior parathyroid gland* (fig. 13-8). Occasionally, this parathyroid tissue is pulled down too far and may then be found at the lower pole of the thyroid or even in the thorax close to the thymus.

## Fourth Pharyngeal Pouch

The epithelium of the dorsal wing of this pouch forms the *superior parathyroid gland*. Although the fate of the ventral portion of the pouch is uncertain, it is believed that in man it may give rise to a small amount of thymus tissue which, soon after its formation, dis-

Digestive Tube and Its Derivatives 245

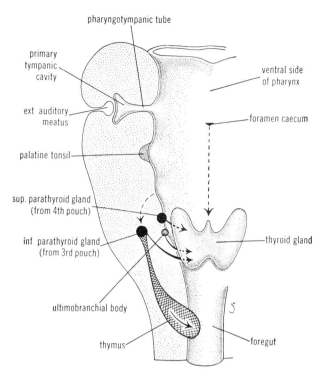

**Figure 13-8.** *Schematic representation of the migration of the thymus, parathyroid glands, and ultimobranchial body (anterior view). The thyroid gland originating in the ventral wall of the pharynx at the level of the foramen caecum descends to the level of the first tracheal rings (modified after Starck).*

appears without contributing to the definitive gland. According to some investigators the fourth pouch also contributes to the thyroid gland by forming the so-called *lateral thyroid*.[3, 5-7] Solid evidence that part of the thyroid gland in the human embryo is derived from the fourth pouch, however, is lacking.

When the parathyroid gland loses its contact with the wall of the pharynx, it attaches itself to the caudally migrating thyroid and finally is found on the dorsal surface of this gland as the *superior parathyroid gland* (fig. 13-8).

*Fifth Pharyngeal Pouch*

This is the last of the pharyngeal pouches to develop and it is usually considered to be a part of the fourth pouch. It gives rise to the *ultimobranchial body*, which is later incorporated in the thyroid gland.[5] In the adult, the cells of the ultimobranchial body can sometimes be distinguished as groups of large pale cells. Although many

Special Embryology

theories have been proposed with regard to the function and ultimate fate of this body, no general agreement has been reached.[4, 6, 8, 9]

## Pharyngeal Clefts

The 5-week embryo is characterized by the presence of four pharyngeal clefts of which only the first one contributes to the definitive structure of the embryo. The dorsal part of this cleft penetrates the underlying mesoderm in the direction of the first pharyngeal pouch and gives rise to the *external auditory meatus* (figs. 13-7 and 13-8). The epithelial lining at the bottom of this meatus participates in the formation of the *eardrum* (see Ear, Chapter 17).

Active proliferation of the mesodermal tissue in the second arch causes it to grow caudally, thereby overlapping the third and fourth arches. Finally, the second arch fuses with the so-called *epicardial ridge* in the lower part of the neck (fig. 13-7A, B). As a result of this overgrowth the second, third and fourth clefts are gradually buried and lose contact with the outside (fig. 13-7B). Temporarily, the clefts form a cavity lined with ectodermal epithelium, the *cervical sinus*, but with further development this sinus usually disappears entirely.

## Floor of the Pharynx

### Tongue

The tongue appears in embryos of approximately 4 weeks in the form of two *lateral lingual swellings* and one medial swelling, the *tuberculum impar* (fig. 13-9A). These three swellings result from proliferation of mesoderm in the ventral parts of the mandibular arch. A second median swelling, the *copula* or *hypobranchial eminence*, is formed by mesoderm of the second, third and part of the fourth arch. Finally, a third median swelling, formed by the posterior part of the fourth arch, marks the development of the *epiglottis*. Immediately behind this swelling is the *tracheobronchial groove* or *laryngeal orifice*, which is flanked by the *arytenoid swellings*.

As a result of the proliferation and ingrowth of surrounding mesoderm into the lateral lingual swellings, these swellings increase greatly in size and fuse with each other, thus forming the anterior two-thirds or the *body of the tongue* (fig. 13-9B). Since the mucosa covering the body of the tongue originates from the first pharyngeal arch, it is innervated by the *mandibular branch of the trigeminal nerve*. The anterior two-thirds or body of the tongue is separated from the posterior third by a V-shaped groove, the *terminal sulcus* (fig. 13-9B).

The posterior part or *root of the tongue* develops from the second,

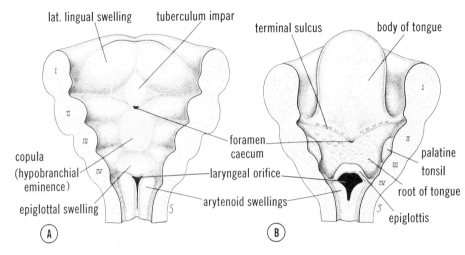

lat. lingual swelling    tuberculum impar

terminal sulcus    body of tongue

copula
(hypobranchial
eminence)

epiglottal swelling

foramen
caecum

laryngeal orifice

arytenoid swellings

palatine
tonsil

root of tongue

epiglottis

A    B

Figure 13-9. *The ventral portions of the pharyngeal arches seen from above, to show development of the tongue. The cut pharyngeal arches are indicated by numbers I to IV, respectively. A, At 5 weeks (approximately 6 mm.). B, At fifth month; note the foramen caecum, the site of origin of the thyroid primordium, and the terminal sulcus which forms the dividing line between the first and second pharyngeal arches.*

third and part of the fourth pharyngeal arch. Since in the adult the sensory innervation of this part of the tongue is supplied by the *glossopharyngeal nerve*, it seems likely that tissue of the third arch has overgrown that of the second. The extreme posterior part of the tongue as well as the epiglottis are innervated by the *superior laryngeal nerve*, indicating their development from the fourth arch.

Some of the tongue muscles probably differentiate *in situ*, but others are believed to be derived from mesoderm originating in the occipital somites. The latter theory is supported by the fact that the tongue musculature is innervated by the hypoglossal nerve.

*Thyroid Gland*

The thyroid gland appears in the third week of development as an epithelial proliferation in the floor of the pharyngeal gut between the tuberculum impar and the copula, at a point later indicated by the *foramen caecum* (figs. 13-9 and 13-10).[10] Subsequently the thyroid primordium penetrates the underlying mesoderm and descends in front of the pharyngeal gut as a bilobed diverticulum (fig. 13-10). During this migration the gland remains connected to the floor of the pharyngeal gut by means of a narrow canal, the *thyroglossal duct*. This duct later becomes solid and finally disappears.

With further development, the thyroid gland descends in front of the hyoid bone and the laryngeal cartilages. It reaches its final position in front of the trachea in the seventh week (fig. 13-13). By then it has acquired a small median isthmus and two lateral lobes. Whether or not part of the thyroid gland is formed by epithelial proliferation of the fourth pharyngeal pouch is still a point of discussion.[3, 5-7]

The thyroid begins to function at approximately the end of the third month, at which time the first follicles containing colloid become visible.

From the above description it is evident that the pharyngeal gut in the embryo gives rise to the major part of the oral cavity, the tongue, the thyroid gland and the various organs developing from the epithelial lining of the pharyngeal pouches. Only then does it become comparable to the definitive pharynx, which is divided into the naso- and oropharynx. The laryngeal division of the definitive pharynx is situated immediately dorsal to the cartilaginous components of the larynx.

## Respiratory System

When the embryo is approximately 3 weeks old (crown-rump length, 3 mm.) the primordium of the respiratory system appears as an entodermal outgrowth from the ventral wall of the foregut immediately caudal to the hypobranchial eminence (figs. 13-3 and 13-11). Hence, the respiratory system is of entodermal origin.

Initially the *respiratory diverticulum* is in wide open connection with the foregut, but is soon separated from it by the *esophagotracheal septum* (fig. 13-11), except at the entrance to the larynx, where the respiratory primordium maintains its communication with the

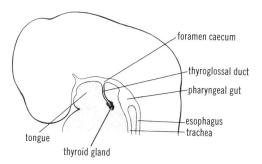

Figure 13-10. *The thyroid primordium arises as an epithelial diverticulum in the midline of the pharynx immediately caudal of the tuberculum impar. It then descends in the loose mesenchyme surrounding the foregut, but remains temporarily connected to the lumen of the foregut by the thyroglossal duct.*

Digestive Tube and Its Derivatives

foregut through the *laryngeal orifice* (fig. 13-9B). Hence, the foregut is divided into a ventral portion, the *respiratory primordium*, and a dorsal portion, the *esophagus*.

## Trachea, Bronchi, and Lungs

During its separation from the foregut, the respiratory primordium begins to grow in a caudal direction, thereby forming a midline structure, the *trachea*, and two lateral outpocketings, the *lung buds* (fig. 13-11B, C). The right lung bud subsequently divides into three branches, the *main bronchi*, and the left into two main bronchi (fig. 13-11C), thus foreshadowing the presence of three lobes on the right side and two on the left (fig. 13-11D).

During further development the main bronchi divide repeatedly in a dichotomous fashion, and by the end of the sixth month approximately 17 generations of subdivisions have been formed. Before the bronchial tree has reached its final shape, however, an additional six divisions are formed. These appear during postnatal life.[11-12] During their development the lungs migrate caudally and by the time of birth the bifurcation of the trachea is found opposite the fourth thoracic vertebra. The mesoderm surrounding the bronchial tree differentiates into cartilage, muscle tissue and blood vessels, thus forming a mesoderm framework around the entodermal bronchial tree.

## Alveoli

With the onset of respiration the distal end of the terminal bronchioli expands into the alveoli, which are lined with flat epithelial

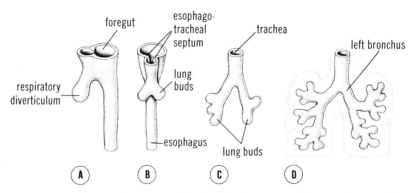

Figure 13-11. *Successive stages in the development of the trachea and lungs. A, At 3 weeks, lateral view; B, 4 weeks, ventral view; C, 5 weeks; D, 6 weeks (adapted from several sources).*

Special Embryology

cells of entodermal origin.[11] Although it was believed that the epithelial cells of the alveoli disappear, thus leaving the endothelial wall of the capillaries in direct contact with the alveolar air,[13, 14] it is now generally accepted that the epithelial alveolar cells persist and are in intimate contact with the endothelial wall of the surrounding capillaries.[15, 16]

Although respiratory-like chest movements may occur *in utero*, in stillborn infants the alveoli are collapsed and the bronchial tree is filled with amniotic fluid. Under normal conditions the amniotic fluid is rapidly absorbed shortly after birth, and by the third postnatal day all alveoli have expanded.

# Congenital Malformations

## Lateral Cysts of the Neck (Branchial Cysts)

In the sixth week of development, the second pharyngeal arch grows caudally over the third and fourth arches and fuses with the epipericardial ridge in the lower part of the neck. The second, third and fourth pharyngeal clefts are thus covered by the second arch (figs. 13-7*B* and 13-12*A*). When this fails to occur, the remnants of

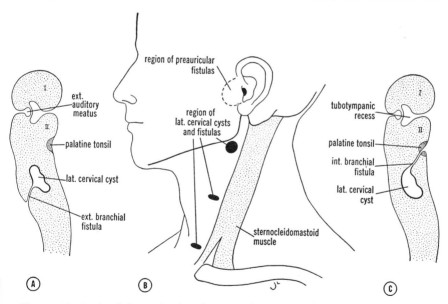

Figure 13-12. A, *Schematic drawing of a lateral cervical cyst opening at the lateral side of the neck by way of a fistula. B, Localization of lateral cervical cysts and fistulas in front of the sternomastoid muscle. Note also the region of localization of the preauricular fistulas. C, A lateral cervical cyst opening into the pharynx at the level of the palatine tonsil.*

the clefts, known as the *cervical sinus*, remain in contact with the surface by a narrow canal, known as the *branchial fistula* (fig. 13-12A). Such a fistula, found on the lateral aspect of the neck directly anterior to the sternomastoid muscle, usually provides drainage for a *lateral cervical cyst*. These cysts are remnants of the cervical sinus and are most often located just below the angle of the jaw (fig. 13-12B).[17] They may, however, be found anywhere along the anterior border of the sternomastoid muscle.[18] Frequently, a lateral cervical cyst is not visible at birth, but becomes evident as the result of enlargement later in life. The lateral cervical cysts frequently contain cholesterol crystals and have a tendency to develop into an epidermoid carcinoma.

A rare anomaly is the *internal branchial fistula*. The cervical sinus is then connected to the lumen of the pharynx by a small canal, which usually opens in the tonsillar region (fig. 13-12C). Such a fistula seems to indicate a rupture of the membrane between the second pharyngeal cleft and pouch at some time during development.[19]

Sometimes a branchial fistula is confused with a *pre-auricular fis-*

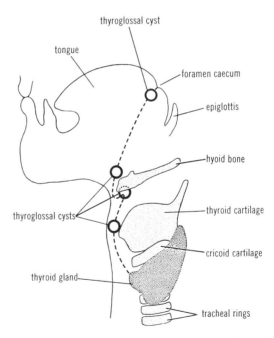

Figure 13-13. *Schematic drawing indicating the localization of the thyroglossal cysts. These cysts, most frequently found in the hyoid region, are always located close to the midline. Broken line indicates the migratory path followed by the thyroid gland during its descent from the foramen caecum to its definitive position in front of the trachea.*

Special Embryology

*tula.* These fistulas, found in front of the ear, have probably no re-lationship to the branchial fistulas (fig. 13-12*B*). It is thought that they result from an incomplete disappearance of one of the sulci be-tween the auricular hillocks (see Ear, Chapter 17).[20]

## Thyroglossal Cyst and Fistula

A thyroglossal cyst may be found at any point along the migratory path followed by the thyroid gland, but is always located close to or in the midline of the neck. As indicated by its name, it is a cystic remnant of the thyroglossal duct, which in the embryo connects the thyroid gland with the floor of the pharynx. Although approximately 50 per cent of these cysts are located close to or even behind the hy-oid bone (fig. 13-13), they may also be found at the base of the tongue, or close to the thyroid cartilage.[21, 22]

Sometimes a thyroglossal cyst is connected to the outside by a fis-tulous canal, the *thyroglossal fistula.* Such a fistula usually arises secondarily after rupture of a cyst, but may be present at birth.

*Aberrant thyroid tissue* may be found anywhere along the path of the descent of the thyroid gland. It is most commonly found in the base of the tongue, just behind the foramen caecum, and is subject to the same diseases as the gland itself.[23, 24]

Congenital *hypoplasia* or *aplasia of the thyroid* is rarely observed. Recently, it has been suggested that antibodies circulating in the maternal blood stream during pregnancy may be the cause of thy-roid hypoplasia in the embryo.[25, 26] Evidence for this auto-immuni-zation theory, however, is insufficient.

## Esophagotracheal Fistula and Atresia of the Esophagus

In the most common form of this abnormality the proximal part of the esophagus ends as a blind sac, whereas the distal part is con-nected to the trachea by a narrow canal at a point just above the bi-furcation (fig. 13-14*A*).[27] This abnormality is thought to result either from a spontaneous deviation of the esophagotracheal septum in a posterior direction, or from some mechanical factor pushing the dor-sal wall of the foregut anteriorly.[28, 29] Occasionally, the fistulous canal between the trachea and the distal portion of the esophagus is replaced by a ligamentous cord (fig. 13-14*B*). Rarely do both the proximal and distal portions of the esophagus open into the trachea (fig. 13-14*C*).[30]

Atresia of the esophagus prevents the normal passage of amniotic fluid into the intestinal tract; this results in the accumulation of ex-cess fluid in the amniotic sac and consequently an enlarged uterus. Although a newborn child with atresia of the esophagus may appear

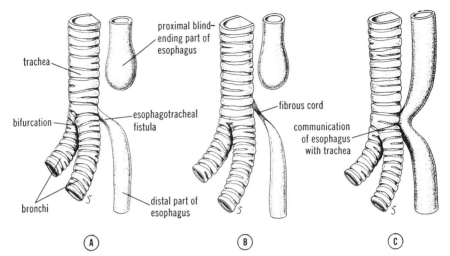

Figure 13-14. *A, Atresia of the esophagus and esophagotracheal fistula. B, Atresia of esophagus. The connection between the distal part of the esophagus and trachea is formed by a fibrous cord. C, The proximal and distal parts of the esophagus are both connected to the trachea by a narrow canal.*

normal, at its first attempt to drink the proximal portion of the esophagus will fill rapidly and milk will flow over into the trachea and lungs. Such a condition will usually lead to aspiration pneumonia. If recognized early, the defect may be repaired successfully.

**Abnormalities of the Lungs**

Although many abnormalities of the lung and bronchial tree have been described, *e.g.*, blind-ending trachea with absence of lungs and agenesis of one lung, most of these gross abnormalities are rare.[31] More frequently seen are abnormal divisions of the bronchial tree, sometimes resulting in the presence of supernumary lobules. These variations of the bronchial tree are of little functional significance, but may cause unexpected difficulties in bronchoscopy.

More interesting are *ectopic lung lobes* which arise from the trachea or esophagus. It is believed that these lobes are formed from additional respiratory buds of the foregut which develop independently of the main respiratory system.

Most important clinically are the *congenital cysts of the lung.* Such cysts, formed by dilatation of the terminal or larger bronchi, may be multiple, giving the lung a honeycomb appearance on x-ray, or they may be restricted to one or more larger ones. Since cystic structures of the lung usually drain poorly, they frequently cause chronic infections. With the increased knowledge of thoracic surgery,

Special Embryology

however, many of the cystic conditions of the lungs have now become operable.

## References—Pharyngeal Gut

1. HANSON, J. R., ANSON, B. J., AND BEST, T. H. The early embryology of the auditory vesicles in man. Quart. Bull. Northw. Univ. Med. Sch., **33**: 350, 1959.
2. NORRIS, E. H. The parathyroid glands and the lateral thyroid in man; their morphogenesis, histogenesis, topographic anatomy and prenatal growth. Contrib. Embryol., **26**: 247, 1937.
3. NORRIS, E. H. The morphogenesis and histogenesis of the thymus gland in man; in which the origin of the Hassall's corpuscles of the human thymus is discovered. Contrib. Embryol., **27**: 193, 1938.
4. GILMOUR, J. R. The embryology of the parathyroid glands, the thymus and certain associated rudiments. J. Path. Bact., **45**: 507, 1937.
5. KINGSBURY, B. F. The question of a lateral thyroid in mammals, with special reference to man. Amer. J. Anat., **65**: 333, 1939.
6. VAN DYKE, J. H. Behavior of the ultimobranchial tissue in the postnatal thyroid gland. Amer. J. Path., **76**: 201, 1945.
7. WATZKA, H. Vergleichende Untersuchungen über den Ultimobranchialen Körper. Z. Mikroskopischanat. Forsch., **34**: 485, 1933.
8. WELLER, G. L. Development of the thyroid, parathyroid and thymus glands in man. Contrib. Embryol., **24**: 93, 1933.
9. BOYD, J. D. Development of the thyroid and parathyroid glands and the thymus. Ann. Roy. Coll. Surg. Engl., **7**: 455, 1950.
10. SGALITZER, K. E. Contribution to the study of the morphogenesis of the thyroid gland. J. Anat., **75**: 389, 1941.
11. BROMAN, T. Zur Kenntnis der Lungenentwicklung. Anat. Anz., **57**: 83, 1923.
12. WILSON, H. G. Postnatal development of the lung. Amer. J. Anat., **41**: 97, 1928.
13. CLEMENTS, L. P. Embryonic development of the respiratory portion of the pig's lung. Anat. Rec., **70**: 575, 1938.
14. LOOSLI, C. G., AND POTTER, E. L. The prenatal development of the human being. Anat. Rec., **109**: 320, 1951.
15. LOW, F. N. The pulmonary alveolar epithelium of laboratory mammals and man. Anat. Rec., **117**: 241, 1951.
16. BERTALANFFY, F. D., AND LEBLOND, C. P. Structure of respiratory tissue. Lancet, **2**: 1365, 1955.
17. GROSS, R. E., AND LADD, W. E. *Abdominal Surgery of Infancy and Childhood*. W. B. Saunders Co., Philadelphia, 1953.
18. NEEL, H. B., AND PEMBERTON, J. DEJ. Lateral cervical (branchial) cysts and fistulas. Surgery, **18**: 267, 1945.
19. DOUGLAS, J. Branchiogenetic cyst with sinus leading into pharynx. Ann. Surg., **67**: 240, 1918.
20. MARTINS, A. G. Lateral cervical and pre-auricular sinuses. Brit. Med. J., **5**: 255, 1961.
21. MARSHALL, S. F., AND BEEKER, W. F. Thyroglossal cysts and sinuses. Ann. Surg., **129**: 642, 1949.
22. McCLINTOCK, J. C., AND MAHAFFEY, D. E. Thyroglossal tract lesions. In *Transactions of the American Goiter Association*, Charles C Thomas, Springfield, Ill., 1950.
23. GOETSCH, E. Lingual goiter. Ann. Surg., **127**: 291, 1948.
24. MONTGOMERY, M. L. Lingual thyroid; a comprehensive review. Western J. Surg., **44**: 54, 1936.

25. BLIZZARD, R. M., CHANDLER, R. W., LANDING, B. H., PETIT, M. D., AND WEST, C. D. Maternal auto-immunization to thyroid as probable cause of athyrotic cretinism. New Engl. J. Med., **263**: 336, 1960.
26. SUTHERLAND, J. M., ESSELBORN, V. M., BURKET, R. L., SHILLMAN, T. B., AND BENSON, J. T. Familial non-goiterous cretinism apparently due to maternal antithyroid antibody. New Engl. J. Med., **263**: 336, 1960.
27. LADD, W. E. Congenital anomalies of the esophagus. Pediatrics, **6**: 9, 1950.
28. GRUENWALD, P. A case of atresia of the esophagus combined with tracheo-esophageal fistula in a 9 mm. human embryo, and its embryological explanation. Anat. Rec., **78**: 293, 1940.
29. LANGMAN, J. Esophagus atresia accompained by vessel anomalies. Arch. Chir. Neerl., **4**: 39, 1952.
30. HERWEG, J. C., AND OGURA, J. H. Congenital tracheo-esophageal fistula without esophageal atresia; endoscopic diagnostic technique. J. Pediat., **47**: 293, 1955.
31. THOMAS, L. B., AND BOYDEN, E. A. Agenesis of the right lung. Surgery, **31**: 429, 1952.

# CAUDAL PART OF THE FOREGUT

NORMAL DEVELOPMENT
- ESOPHAGUS
- STOMACH
- DUODENUM
- LIVER AND GALL BLADDER
- PANCREAS

CONGENITAL MALFORMATIONS
- PYLORIC STENOSIS
- ATRESIA OF THE GALL BLADDER AND BILE DUCTS
- ANNULAR PANCREAS
- HETEROTOPIC PANCREATIC TISSUE

## *Normal Development*

### Esophagus

The esophagus extends from the respiratory diverticulum to the fusiform dilation which forms the stomach (figs. 13-3 and 13-15). Initially the esophagus is very short, but with the descent of the heart and lungs, it lengthens rapidly. The muscular coat, which is formed by the surrounding mesenchyme, is striated in its upper two-thirds and smooth in the lower one-third.

### Stomach

The stomach appears as a fusiform dilation of the foregut in the fifth week of development (fig. 13-15). During the following weeks its appearance and position change greatly as a result of the different rate of growth in various regions of its wall, and the changes in position of the surrounding organs.[1] The positional changes of the stomach are most easily explained by assuming that it rotates around a longitudinal and an anteroposterior axis (fig. 13-16).

Around its longitudinal axis, the stomach carries out a 90° clockwise rotation, causing its left side to face anteriorly and its right side, posteriorly (fig. 13-16A, B, C). Hence, the left vagus nerve, initially innervating the left side of the stomach, now innervates the anterior wall; similarly the right vagus then innervates the posterior wall. During this rotation the original posterior part of the stomach grows faster than the anterior portion and this results in the formation of the *greater* and *lesser curvatures* (fig. 13-16C).

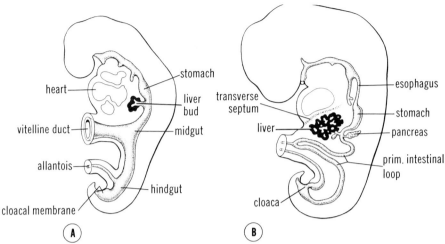

Figure 13-15. *A, Drawing of a 3-mm. embryo (approximately 25 days) to show the primitive gastro-intestinal tract. Note the formation of the hepatic diverticulum. The hepatic diverticulum is formed by the entodermal epithelial lining of the terminal part of the foregut. B, Drawing of a 5-mm. embryo (approximately 32 days). The epithelial liver cords penetrate the mesenchyme of the transverse septum. Note the primary intestinal loop.*

Since at this stage of development the stomach is attached to the posterior and anterior body wall by the dorsal and ventral mesogastrium, respectively (see Chapter 14), rotation around the longitudinal axis is thought to pull the dorsal mesogastrium to the left, thus helping in the formation of the *omental bursa*, a pouch of the peritoneum located behind the stomach (fig. 13-16*D, E, F*).

The cephalic and caudal ends of the stomach are originally located in the midline, but during further growth the caudal or *pyloric part* moves to the right and upward, and the cephalic or *cardiac portion* to the left and slightly downward (fig. 13-16*G, H*). The stomach thus assumes its final position, and its length axis runs from above left to below right. The greater curvature faces downward and the lesser curvature upward and to the right (figs. 13-16 and 14-11).

## Duodenum

This portion of the intestinal tract is formed by the terminal part of the foregut and the cephalic part of the midgut. The junction of the two parts is located directly distal to the origin of the liver bud (fig. 13-15). As the stomach rotates, the duodenum takes on the form of a U-shaped loop, rotates to the right, and finally comes to lie retroperitoneally (see Chapter 14). During the second month the

Special Embryology

lumen of the duodenum may temporarily be obliterated. Under normal conditions, however, the lumen is re-established shortly afterward.

## Liver and Gall Bladder

The liver primordium appears in the middle of the third week as an outgrowth of the entodermal epithelium at the distal end of the foregut (fig. 13-15A, B). This outgrowth, known as the *hepatic diverticulum*, consists of rapidly proliferating cell strands which penetrate the *septum transversum*, that is, the mesodermal plate between the pericardial cavity and the stalk of the yolk sac (fig. 13-15A, B). While the hepatic cell strands continue to penetrate in

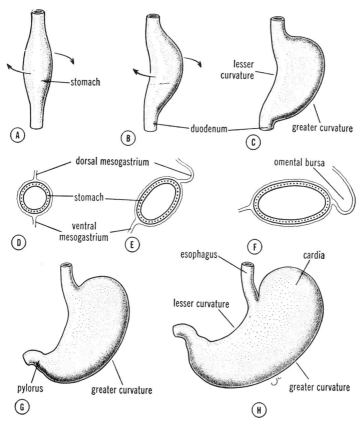

Figure 13-16. *Schematic representation of the positional changes of the stomach. A, B, and C show the rotation of the stomach along its longitudinal axis as seen from anterior; D, E and F show, in transverse section, the effect of rotation on the peritoneal attachments; G and H show the rotation of the stomach around the anteroposterior axis (seen from anterior).*

Digestive Tube and Its Derivatives

the septum, the connection between the hepatic diverticulum and the foregut (duodenum) narrows, thus forming the *bile duct*. A small ventral outgrowth is formed by the bile duct and this outgrowth gives rise to the gall bladder and the cystic duct (figs. 13-15*B*, 13-17, 13-18). During further development the epithelial liver cords intermingle with the blood sinuses of the vitelline and umbilical veins in the septum transversum, thus forming the parenchymatous tissue of the liver. The connective tissue components of the liver are formed by the mesoderm of the septum transversum.

As a result of its continuous rapid growth, the liver becomes too large for the confines of the septum transversum and begins gradually to protrude into the abdominal cavity. The mesoderm of the septum between the ventral abdominal wall of the liver becomes stretched and very thin, thus forming a thin membrane, known as the *falciform ligament* (fig. 13-17*A*, *B*). The umbilical vein, originally found in the mesoderm of the septum, now occupies a position in the free, caudal margin of the falciform ligament. Similarly the septum mesoderm between the liver and the foregut (stomach and duodenum) becomes stretched and membranous, thereby forming

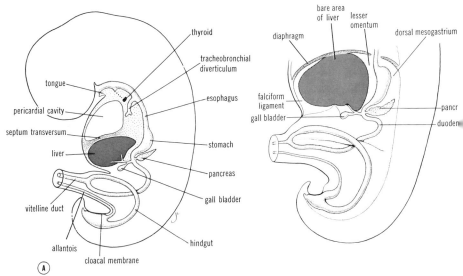

Figure 13-17. A, *Drawing of a 9-mm. embryo (approximately 36 days). The liver expands caudally into the abdominal cavity. Note the condensation of mesenchyme in the area between the liver and the pericardial cavity, foreshadowing the formation of the diaphragm. B, Drawing of a slightly older embryo. Note the falciform ligament extending between the liver and the anterior abdominal wall, and the lesser omentum between the liver and the foregut (stomach and duodenum). The liver is entirely surrounded by peritoneum, except in its contact area with the diaphragm. This area is known as the bare area of the liver.*

Special Embryology

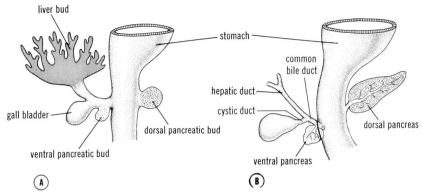

liver bud

stomach

common
bile duct

hepatic duct

cystic duct

dorsal pancreas

gall bladder

dorsal pancreatic bud

ventral pancreatic bud

ventral pancreas

A

B

Figure 13-18. *Successive stages in the development of the pancreas. A, At 30 days (approximately 5 mm.); B, 35 days (approximately 7 mm.). The ventral pancreatic bud is initially located close to the hepatic diverticulum, but later migrates posteriorly around the duodenum in the direction of the dorsal pancreatic bud.*

the *lesser omentum*. In the caudal or free margin of the lesser omentum are found the bile duct, the portal vein and the hepatic artery. Hence, when the liver bulges caudally into the abdominal cavity, the mesoderm of the septum transversum located between the liver and the foregut, and the liver and the ventral abdominal wall, becomes membranous, thus forming the *lesser omentum* and *falciform ligament*, respectively. Together they form the peritoneal connection between the foregut and the ventral abdominal wall and are known as the *ventral mesogastrium*. The mesoderm on the surface of the liver likewise differentiates into peritoneum except on its cranial surface (fig. 13-17B). In this region the liver remains in contact with the most cranial portion of the septum transversum. This portion of the septum consists of densely packed mesoderm and will form an important portion of the diaphragm. The surface of the liver, which is in contact with the future diaphragm, is never covered by peritoneum and is known as the *bare area of the liver*.

In the 10th week of development the weight of the liver is approximately 10 per cent of the total body weight. Though this may be attributed partly to the presence of a large number of sinusoids from the vitelline and umbilical veins, another important factor contributing to the weight of the liver at this stage of development is its *hematopoietic function*. Large nests of proliferating cells, which produce red and white blood cells, are found between the hepatic cells and the walls of the vessels. This activity subsides gradually during the last 2 months of intra-uterine life and only small hematopoietic islands remain at birth. The weight of the liver is then only 5 per cent of the total body weight.

Digestive Tube and Its Derivatives

261

Meanwhile, the *gall bladder* and *cystic duct* have fully developed and the cystic duct has joined the hepatic duct to form the *common bile duct* (fig. 13-17B). As a result of the positional changes of the duodenum, the entrance of the common bile duct gradually shifts from its initial anterior position to a posterior one, and consequently the common bile duct is found passing behind the duodenum (figs. 13-18 and 13-19).

## Pancreas

The pancreas is formed by two buds originating from the entodermal epithelium of the duodenum (fig. 13-18A). While the *dorsal pancreatic bud* is located opposite and slightly above the hepatic diverticulum, the *ventral pancreatic bud* is found in the angle below the hepatic rudiment and is closely related to the common bile duct.

The ventral pancreatic bud subsequently migrates dorsally, in a manner similar to the shifting of the entrance of the common bile duct, and finally comes to lie immediately below and behind the dorsal pancreas (figs. 13-18B and 13-19).

Later the parenchyme as well as the duct systems of the dorsal and ventral pancreatic buds fuse (fig. 13-19B). The *common pancreatic duct* (*duct of Wirsung*) is formed by the distal part of the dorsal pancreatic duct and the entire ventral pancreatic duct (fig. 13-19B). As this duct becomes the main drainage channel of the pancreas,

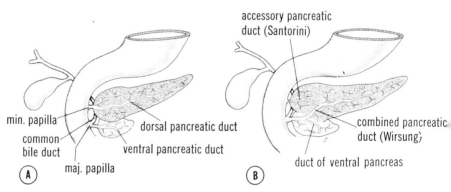

Figure 13-19. *A, The pancreas during the sixth week of development (approximately 10 mm.). The ventral pancreatic bud is in close contact with the dorsal pancreatic bud. The dorsal pancreatic duct enters the duodenum at the minor papilla and the ventral pancreatic duct at the major papilla. B, Drawing showing the fusion of the pancreatic ducts. The common pancreatic duct (Wirsung) now enters the duodenum in combination with the common bile duct at the major papilla. The accessory pancreatic duct (Santorini) enters the duodenum at the minor papilla (modified after Starck).*

Special Embryology

the proximal part of the dorsal pancreatic duct either is obliterated or persists as a small channel, the *accessory pancreatic duct* (*duct of Santorini*). The common pancreatic duct enters the duodenum at the site of the major papilla; the entrance of the accessory duct is at the site of the minor papilla. In about 10 per cent of all cases the duct system fails to fuse and the original double system persists.[2]

The *pancreatic islets* develop from the parenchymatous pancreatic tissue in the third month of fetal life and are scattered throughout the gland. Insulin secretion begins at approximately the fifth month.

# Congenital Malformations

### Pyloric Stenosis

This abnormality is characterized by a hypertrophy of the circular and, to a lesser degree, the longitudinal musculature of the stomach in the region of the pylorus. It is one of the most common abnormalities of the stomach in infants and is believed to develop during fetal life. There is an extreme narrowing of the pyloric lumen, and the passage of food is obstructed, resulting in severe progressive vomiting. A few cases have been described in which the pylorus was atretic.[3]

Other malformations of the stomach, such as duplications and the presence of a prepyloric septum, are rare.[4, 5]

### Atresia of the Gall Bladder and Bile Ducts

Initially the gall bladder is a hollow organ, but as a result of proliferation of its epithelial lining it becomes temporarily solid. The definitive lumen develops by vacuolization of the epithelial cords. When this fails to occur the gall bladder remains atretic and does not develop.[6]

The intra- and extrahepatic ducts also go through a solid stage in their development. If the lumen fails to reopen the ducts will appear as narrow, fibrous cords.[7] Occasionally, such an atresia is limited to a small portion of the common bile duct only (fig. 13-20A). The gall bladder and the hepatic duct proximal to the atresia are then considerably distended, and severe, steadily increasing jaundice will become obvious after birth.

In addition to atresia of the gall bladder, duplication, partial subdivision, and diverticula of the gall bladder have frequently been described (fig. 13-20B).[8]

## Annular Pancreas

Under normal conditions, the ventral pancreatic bud rotates around the duodenum in such a manner that it comes to lie below the dorsal pancreatic bud. Occasionally, however, this fails to occur. A portion of the ventral bud then migrates along its normal route, but another part migrates in an opposite direction. In this manner the duodenum is completely surrounded by pancreatic tis-

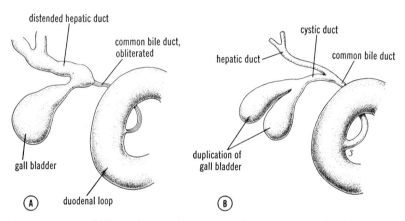

Figure 13-20. *A, Obliteration of the common bile duct, resulting in a distention of the gall bladder and hepatic ducts distal to the obliteration. B, Bifid gall bladder.*

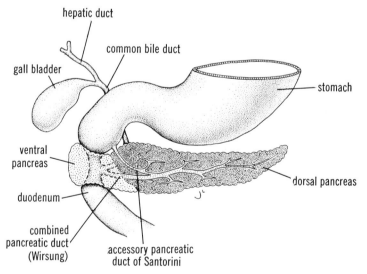

Figure 13-21. *Annular pancreas. The ventral pancreas forms a ring around the duodenum, occasionally resulting in duodenal stenosis.*

sue, and an *annular pancreas* is formed (fig. 13-21).[9] Although this malformation usually does not cause any symptoms, sometimes it may constrict the duodenum and cause complete obstruction.

## Heterotopic Pancreatic Tissue

Heterotopic pancreatic tissue may be found anywhere from the distal end of the esophagus to the tip of the primary intestinal loop. Most frequently it is found in the mucosa of the stomach and in Meckel's diverticulum.[10] Here it may show all the pathological changes characteristic of the pancreas itself.[11] Occasionally, a major part of the ventral pancreatic bud grows out with the liver bud and forms a pancreatic nodule or *pancreatic bladder*, located close to the gall bladder.[12]

## References—Caudal Part of the Foregut

1. DANKMEYER, J., AND MIETE, M. Le développement précoce de l'estomac chez l'embryon humain. C. R. Ass. Anat., **103:** 341, 1958.
2. DAWSON, W., AND LANGMAN, J. An anatomical-radiological study on the pancreatic duct pattern in man. Anat. Rec., **139:** 59, 1961.
3. SALEBURY, A. M., AND COLLINS, R. E. Congenital pyloric atresia. M. A. Arch. Surg., **80:** 501, 1960.
4. BOTHA MULLER, G. S. Intrathoracic duplications of the foregut. II. S. Afr. Med. J., **34:** 259, 1960.
5. RAWLING, J. T. A prepyloric septum. Brit. J. Surg., **47:** 162, 1960.
6. HOULE, M. P., AND HILL, P. S. Congenital absence of the gallbladder. J. Maine Med. Assn., **51:** 108, 1960.
7. AHRENS, E. H., HARRIS, R. C., AND MACMAHAN, M. E. Atresia of the intrahepatic bile ducts. Pediatrics, **8:** 628, 1951.
8. POPPER, H., AND SHAFFNER, F. *Liver, Structure and Function.* McGraw-Hill Book Co., New York, 1957.
9. WEATHERILL, D., FORGRAVE, E. G., AND CARPENTER, W. S. Annular pancreas producing duodenal obstruction in the newborn. A. M. A. J. Dis. Child., **95:** 202, 1958.
10. MARTINEZ, N. S., MORLACH, C. G., DOCKERTY, B., WAUGH, J. M., AND WEBER, H. Heterotopic pancreatic tissue involving the stomach. Ann. Surg., **147:** 1, 1958.
11. BARBOSA, J., DOCKERTY, M. B., AND WAUGH, J. Pancreatic heterotopia. Surg. Gynec. Obstet., **82:** 527, 1946.
12. BOYDEN, E. A. The problem of the pancreatic bladder. Amer. J. Anat., **36:** 151, 1925.

# MIDGUT

## NORMAL DEVELOPMENT
• *Distal part of the duodenum; jejunum; ileum; caecum and appendix; colon ascendens; proximal two-thirds of the transverse colon*

## CONGENITAL MALFORMATIONS
• REMNANTS OF THE VITELLINE DUCT: *Meckel's diverticulum, vitelline fistula, enterocystoma*
• OMPHALOCELE: *congenital hernia into the umbilical cord*
• ABNORMAL ROTATION OF THE INTESTINAL LOOP
• DUPLICATIONS OF THE GASTROINTESTINAL TRACT
• ATRESIA AND STENOSIS OF THE GUT

## *Normal Development*

In the 5-mm. embryo the midgut extends from the *anterior* to the *posterior intestinal portal* and communicates widely with the yolk sac by way of the vitelline duct (figs. 13-1 and 13-15). Although in the embryo the cranial and caudal borders of the midgut are vaguely defined, it is generally accepted that, in the adult, the midgut begins immediately distal to the entrance of the bile duct into the duodenum, and terminates at the junction of the proximal two-thirds of the transverse colon with the distal one-third.

The development of the midgut is characterized by a rapid elongation, resulting in the formation of the *primary intestinal loop* (figs. 13-15*B*, 13-17 and 13-22). At its apex, the loop remains in open connection with the yolk sac by way of the narrow *vitelline* or *omphalomesenteric duct.* The cephalic limb of the loop develops into the distal part of the duodenum, the jejunum, and part of the ileum. The caudal limb becomes the lower portion of the ileum, the caecum and the appendix, the ascending colon, and the proximal two-thirds of the transverse colon. The junction of the cranial and caudal limbs can in the adult only be recognized if a portion of the vitelline duct persists as *Meckel's diverticulum* (figs. 13-23 and 13-26).

Further development of the primary intestinal loop is characterized by rapid elongation, particularly of the cephalic limb. As a result of the rapid growth, the abdominal cavity temporarily becomes too small to contain all the intestinal loops and they enter the extra-embryonic coelom in the umbilical cord during the sixth week of development (*physiological umbilical herniation*) (fig. 13-24).

266                                                                    Special Embryology

Coincident with the growth in length, the primitive intestinal loop rotates around an axis formed by the *superior mesenteric artery* (fig. 13-22A). When viewed from the front this rotation occurs in a counterclockwise direction and amounts to approximately 270° when it is completed (figs. 13-22 and 13-23). Even during the rotation movement, the elongation of the small intestinal loop continues

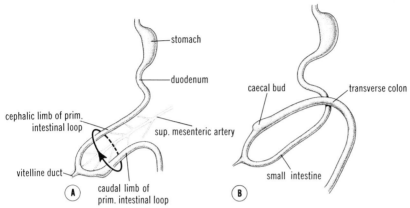

Figure 13-22. *A, Schematic drawing of the primitive intestinal loop before rotation (lateral view). The superior mesenteric artery forms the axis of the loop. Arrow indicates the direction of the anticlockwise rotation. B, Similar view as in A, showing the primitive intestinal loop after 180° anticlockwise rotation. The transverse colon passes in front of the duodenum (modified after Giroud).*

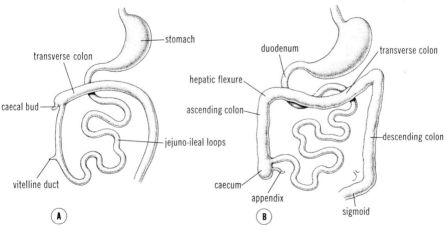

Figure 13-23. *A, Anterior view of the intestinal loops after 270° anticlockwise rotation. Note the coiling of the small intestinal loops and the position of the caecal bud in the right upper quadrant of the abdomen. B, Similar view as in A, with the intestinal loops in the final position. Caecum and appendix are located in the right lower quadrant of the abdomen (modified after Giroud).*

Digestive Tube and Its Derivatives

and the jejunum and ileum form a number of coiled loops. The large intestine likewise grows considerably in length, but fails to participate in the coiling phenomenon.

At about the end of the third month the herniated intestinal loops begin to return to the abdominal cavity. Though the factors responsible for this return are not precisely known, it is thought that the regression of the mesonephroi, the reduced growth of the liver and the actual expansion of the abdominal cavity play important roles.

The proximal part of the jejunum is the first part to re-enter the abdominal cavity and it comes to lie on the left side. The later re-

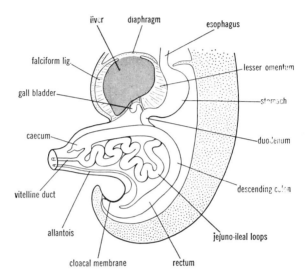

Figure 13-24. *Umbilical herniation of the intestinal loops in an embryo of approximately 8 weeks (crown-rump length, 35 mm.). Coiling of the small intestinal loops and formation of the caecum occur during the herniation.*

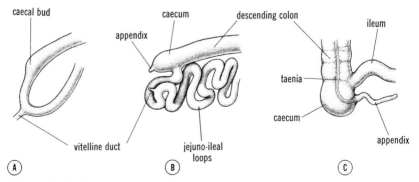

Figure 13-25. *Successive stages in the development of the caecum and appendix. A, At 7 weeks; B, 8 weeks; C, newborn.*

Special Embryology

turning loops gradually settle more and more to the right. The *caecal swelling*, which appears at about the 12-mm. stage as a small conical dilatation of the caudal limb of the primitive intestinal loop, is the last part of the gut to re-enter the abdominal cavity. It is temporarily located in the right upper quadrant directly below the right lobe of the liver (fig. 13-23A). From here it descends into the right iliac fossa, thereby forming the *ascending colon* and the *hepatic flexure* (fig. 13-23B). During this process the distal end of the caecal swelling forms a narrow diverticulum, the *primitive appendix* (fig. 13-25).

# Congenital Malformations

## Remnants of the Vitelline Duct

*Meckel's Diverticulum, Vitelline Fistula, Enterocystoma*

Normally, the vitelline or omphalomesenteric duct disappears when the embryo is approximately 6 weeks old. Sometimes, a small portion of the duct persists, forming an outpocketing of the ileum, known as *Meckel's diverticulum* (fig. 13-26A). In the adult, this diverticulum is located about 2 to 3 feet from the ileocaecal valve and does not usually cause any complaints.[1, 2] When it contains heterotopic pancreatic tissue or gastric mucosa, however, a Meckel's diverticulum may show ulceration, cause bleeding, or may even perforate.[3, 4]

Sometimes the vitelline duct remains patent over its entire length, thus forming a direct communication between the umbilicus and the intestinal tract. This abnormality is known as *umbilical* or *vitelline fistula* (fig. 13-26C).[5] A fecal discharge may then be found at the umbilicus, and occasionally the ileum may prolapse through

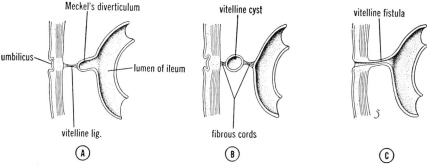

Figure 13-26. *Remnants of the vitelline duct. A, Meckel's diverticulum combined with fibrous cord (vitelline ligament). B, Vitelline cyst attached to the umbilicus and the wall of the ileum by vitelline ligaments. C, Vitelline fistula connecting the lumen of the ileum with the umbilicus.*

Digestive Tube and Its Derivatives

the fistula.[6] In another variation, both ends of the vitelline duct are transformed into fibrous cords, while the middle portion forms a large cyst, the *enterocystoma* or *vitelline cyst* (fig. 13-26B). Since the fibrous cords transverse the peritoneal cavity, they may easily cause intestinal strangulation or volvulus.

## Omphalocele

Sometimes the intestinal loops fail to return from the umbilical cord into the abdominal cavity. When this occurs the loops remain in the extra-embryonic coelom of the umbilical cord. At birth the herniated loops cause a large swelling in the umbilical cord and are covered only by the amnion. This defect is known as an *omphalocele* (fig. 13-27A).[7, 8]

*Congenital Hernia into the Umbilical Cord*

This abnormality is caused by incomplete closure of the central part of the abdominal wall. The muscular layers and skin in the region surrounding the umbilicus are absent and the surface layer is formed by the amnion. The viscera protruding outside the abdominal cavity are covered by peritoneum and amnion, but not by skin. The sac thus formed is extremely thin and often ruptures during birth.

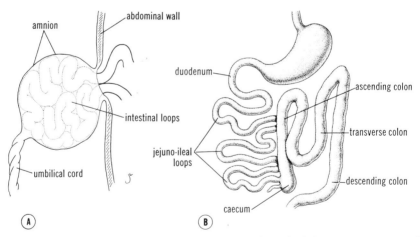

Figure 13-27. A, *Omphalocele—failure of the intestinal loops to return to the abdominal cavity. The herniated loops are surrounded by a membranous sac formed by the amnion. B, Abnormal rotation of the primitive intestinal loop. The colon is located on the left side of the abdomen, and the small intestinal loops on the right. Note that the ileum enters the caecum from the right.*

Special Embryology

In more severe cases, all the viscera, including the liver, may be found outside the abdominal cavity. This abnormality, known as *eventration of the abdominal viscera*, is caused by failure of the anterior abdominal wall to close. The defect is usually associated with abnormalities of the urogenital system (see Chapter 11).

## Abnormal Rotation of the Intestinal Loop

The primitive intestinal loop normally rotates 270° anticlockwise. Occasionally, however, rotation amounts to 90° only. When this occurs, the colon and caecum are the first portions of the gut to return from the umbilical cord and they settle on the left side of the abdominal cavity (fig. 13-27B). The later returning loops then become located more and more to the right.[9, 10]

In some cases, known as *reversed rotation of the intestinal loop*, the primitive loop rotates 90° in a clockwise direction. In such an abnormality the transverse colon passes behind the duodenum.

## Duplications of the Gastrointestinal Tract

Duplications of intestinal loops may occur anywhere along the length of the alimentary canal, from the base of the tongue to the anus.[11, 12] Duplications are most frequently located in the region of the ileum, where they may vary in form and size from a small diverticulum to a large cyst. Although duplications of the gut always remain attached to the segment of origin, their mucosa may be greatly different. A duplication of the rectum has been found to be lined with gastric mucosa.[13] With regard to the development of intestinal duplications, Bremer[14] suggests that parts of the alimentary canal go through a transient solid state, which is followed by re-establishment of the lumen by means of vacuolization. If, however, some isolated vacuoles do not properly fuse with those forming the main lumen, a duplication may arise.

## Atresia and Stenosis of the Gut

Atresia and stenosis may likewise occur anywhere along the length of the primitive intestinal loop. In case of atresia, a thin diaphragm is usually found across the lumen of the gut. This diaphragm is thought to result from an incomplete vacuolization of the lumen. The duodenum is particularly known for the presence of a *stenosis*.[15] Such a stenosis frequently results in a distention of the proximal part and a marked narrowing of the intestinal loops below the level of the stenosis. The proximal part of the duodenum may exceed the stomach in size.

# References—Midgut

1. BROOKES, V. B. Meckel's diverticulum in children. Brit. J. Surg., **42:** 57, 1954.
2. HOWELL, L. M. Meckel's diverticulum. Amer. J. Dis. Child., **71:** 365, 1946.
3. ASCHNER, P. W., AND KARELITZ, S. Peptic ulcer of Meckel's diverticulum and ileum. Ann. Surg., **91:** 583, 1930.
4. CARD, W. I., AND MIMPRISS, T. W. Peptic ulcer of Meckel's diverticulum. Lancet, **2:** 963, 1937.
5. SMITH, J. R. Accessory enteric formations; a classification and nomenclature. Arch. Dis. Child., **35:** 87, 1960.
6. HOWARD, S., MOSS, P. D., AND O'DOMHNAILL, S. Patent vitello-intestinal duct with associated fistula and prolapse. Lancet, **2:** 968, 1953.
7. McKEOWN, T., MACMAHON, B., AND RECORD, R. G. An investigation of 69 cases of exomphalos. Amer. J. Hum. Genet., **5:** 168, 1953.
8. FERGUSON, J. A. Omphalocoele, persistent omphalomesenteric duct, and Meckel's diverticulum. Univ. Hosp. Bull., Ann Arbor, **14:** 47, 1948.
9. ESTRADA, R. L. *Anomalies of Intestinal Rotation and Fixation*. Charles C Thomas, Springfield, Ill., 1958.
10. DOTT, N. M. Anomalies of intestinal rotation. Brit. J. Surg., **11:** 251, 1923.
11. CHRISTENSEN, C. R. Duplications in the gastro-intestinal tract in children. Danish Med. Bull.. **5–6:** 281, 1959.
12. GROSS, R. E., HOLCOMB, G. W., AND FARBER, S. Duplications of the alimentary tract. Pediatrics, **9:** 449, 1952.
13. CLIFT, M. M. Duplication of the small intestine. J. Amer. Med. Wom. Assn. **9:** 396, 1954.
14. BREMER, J. L. *Congenital Anomalies of the Viscera*, p. 67. Harvard University Press, Cambridge, Mass., 1957.
15. SAUNDERS, J. B. DE C. M., AND LINDNER, H. H. Congenital anomalies of the duodenum. Ann. Surg., **112:** 321, 1940.

# HINDGUT

## NORMAL DEVELOPMENT
• *Distal third of the transverse colon; descending colon; sigmoid; rectum; upper portion of the anal canal*

## CONGENITAL MALFORMATIONS
• IMPERFORATE ANUS, RECTAL ATRESIA
• RECTAL FISTULAS

## *Normal Development*

The hindgut, which in the embryo extends from the *posterior intestinal portal* to the *cloacal membrane*, gives rise to the distal third of the transverse colon, the descending colon, the sigmoid, the rectum, and the upper part of the anal canal.

The terminal portion of the hindgut enters into the cloaca, an entoderm-lined cavity which is in direct contact with the surface ectoderm. In the contact area between the entoderm and ectoderm, the *cloacal membrane* is formed (fig. 13-28A, B).

During further development a transverse ridge, the *urorectal septum*, arises in the angle between the allantois and the hindgut (fig. 13-28). This septum gradually grows caudad, thereby dividing the cloaca into an anterior portion, the *primitive urogenital sinus*, and a posterior part, the *anorectal canal* (fig. 13-28).[1] When the embryo is 7 weeks old the urorectal septum reaches the cloacal mem-

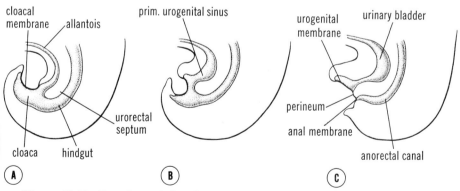

Figure 13-28. *Drawings of the cloacal region in embryos at successive stages of development. Arrow indicates the route of descent followed by the urorectal septum. Note the formation of the anorectal canal and the perineum.*

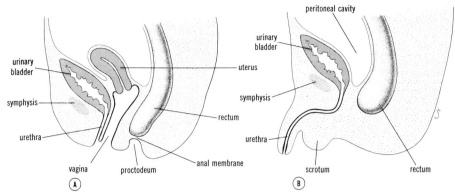

Figure 13-29. A, *Imperforate anus. The anal membrane persists as a diaphragm between the upper and lower portions of the anal canal. B, Rectal atresia. The ampulla of the rectum has failed to develop, while in addition the proctodeum is absent.*

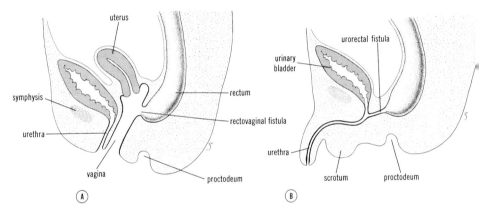

Figure 13-30. A, *Rectovaginal fistula combined with rectal atresia, due to a defect in the formation of the urorectal septum. B, Urorectal fistula combined with rectal atresia.*

brane, at which point the *primitive perineum* is formed. The cloacal membrane is then divided into the posterior *anal membrane*, and the anterior *urogenital membrane* (for discussion of further development of the urogenital sinus, see Chapter 11).

In the meantime, the anal membrane is surrounded by mesenchymal swellings, and in the ninth week it is found at the bottom of an ectodermal depression, known as *proctodeum* (fig. 13-29A).[2] The surrounding swellings are known as the *anal folds*. Soon thereafter the anal membrane ruptures and an open pathway is formed between the rectum and the outside. The upper part of the anal canal is thus entodermal in origin and is vascularized by the artery of the

Special Embryology

hindgut, the *inferior mesenteric artery*. The lower third of the anal canal, however, is of ectodermal origin and is supplied by the systemic rectal arteries, branches of the *internal iliac artery*.

# Congenital Malformations

## Imperforate Anus, Rectal Atresia

Imperforate anus is one of the more common abnormalities of the hindgut.[3] In simple cases, the anal canal ends blind at the anal membrane, which then forms a diaphragm between the entodermal and ectodermal portions of the anal canal (fig. 13-29A). In more serious cases, a thick layer of connective tissue may be found between the terminal end of the rectum and the surface, either due to a failure of the proctodeum to develop, or due to an atresia of the ampullar part of the rectum, *rectal atresia* (fig. 13-29B).[4]

## Rectal Fistulas

Rectal fistulas are frequently observed in association with an imperforate anus, and may be found between the rectum and the vagina, the urinary bladder, or the urethra (fig. 13-30). Occasionally, such a fistula may open to the surface in the anal region.

## References—Hindgut

1. POLITZER, G. Über die Entwicklung des Dammes beim Menschen. Z. Anat. Entwicklungsgesch., **95:** 734, 1931.
2. TENCH, E. M. Development of the anus in the human embryo. Amer. J. Anat., **59:** 333, 1936.
3. MOORE, T. C., AND LAWRENCE, C. A. Congenital malformations of the rectum and anus. Surgery, **32:** 352, 1952.
4. BACON, H. E., AND SHERMAN, S. F. Surgical management of congenital malformations of the anus and rectum. A. M. A. Arch. Surg., **64:** 331, 1952.

# CHAPTER 14

# Coelomic Cavity and Mesenteries

---

NORMAL DEVELOPMENT
- FORMATION AND PARTITIONING OF THE COELOMIC CAVITY: *diaphragm; pleuroperitoneal and pleuropericardial membranes*
- MESENTERIES: *ventral mesentery, falciform ligament and lesser omentum; dorsal mesentery; lesser peritoneal sac; dorsal mesoduodenum; mesentery of the primitive intestinal loop*

CONGENITAL MALFORMATIONS
- DIAPHRAGMATIC HERNIA
- MOBILE CAECUM AND COLON

---

## *Normal Development*

### Formation and Partitioning of the Coelomic Cavity

At the end of the third week the intra-embryonic mesoderm on each side of the midline differentiates into a paraxial portion, an intermediate portion, and a lateral plate (fig. 14-1*A*). When subsequently numerous intercellular clefts appear in the lateral mesoderm, the plates are divided into two layers: the *somatic mesoderm layer*, which is continuous with the extra-embryonic mesoderm covering the wall of the amniotic cavity; and the *splanchnic mesoderm layer*, which is continuous with the mesoderm of the wall of the yolk sac (fig. 14-1*B*). The space bordered by these layers forms the *intra-embryonic coelom*.

At first the right and left intra-embryonic coelomic cavities are in wide open connection with the extra-embryonic coelom. With fur-

Special Embryology

ther development, however, when the body of the embryo folds in cephalo-caudal and lateral directions, they lose this connection (fig. 14-2A, B), and the coelomic cavity then forms a large intra-embryonic space extending from the thoracic to the pelvic region. The connection between the thoracic and abdominal portions of the coelomic

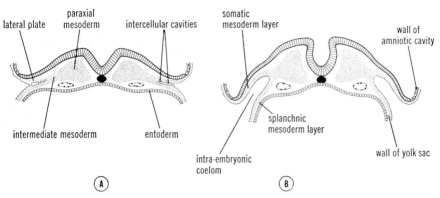

Figure 14-1. *A, Schematic transverse section through an embryo of approximately 19 days showing the differentiation of the mesoderm into the paraxial, intermediate, and lateral plate components. The first intercellular cavities are visible in the lateral plate. B, Similar section as in A, through an embryo of approximately 20 days. The lateral plate is divided into the somatic and splanchnic mesoderm layers which line the intra-embryonic coelomic cavities.*

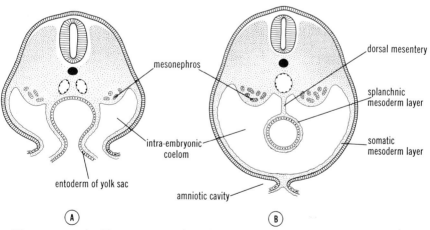

Figure 14-2. *A, Transverse section through a 21-day embryo in the region of the mesonephros. The intra-embryonic coelomic cavities communicate with the extra-embryonic coelom. B, Similar section as in A, at the end of the fourth week. The splanchnic mesoderm layers are fused in the midline and form a double-layered membrane between the right and left intra-embryonic coelom.*

cavity temporarily is formed by the *pericardioperitoneal canals*, located on each side of the foregut (fig. 14-3A).

In the adult, the intra-embryonic coelom is divided into three well defined compartments: (1) the pericardial cavity containing the heart; (2) the pleural cavities containing the lungs; and (3) the peritoneal cavity containing the viscera caudal to the diaphragm. The septum between the thoracic and abdominal cavities is formed by the *diaphragm*, and that between the pericardial and pleural cavities by the *pleuropericardial membranes*.

*Diaphragm*

The most important component of the diaphragm is formed by the *septum transversum*, a thick plate of mesodermal tissue occupying the space between the pericardial cavity and the stalk of the yolk sac (figs. 13-15 and 13-17). Contrary to the diaphragm in the adult, this septum does not separate the thoracic and abdominal cavities entirely but leaves a large opening on each side of the foregut connecting the two (fig. 14-3A). The canals thus formed are known as the *pericardioperitoneal canals*, and are of fundamental importance for

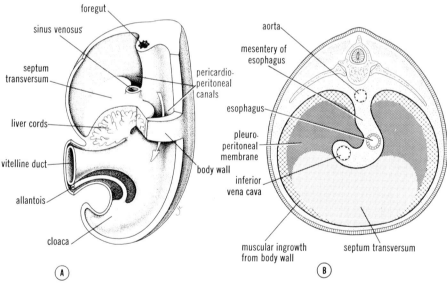

Figure 14-3. *A, Model of a portion of an embryo of approximately 5 weeks. Parts of the body wall and the septum transversum have been removed to show the pericardioperitoneal canals. Note the size and thickness of the septum transversum and the liver cords penetrating the mesenchyme. B, Schematic representation of the definitive diaphragm, indicating the origin of the various components.*

Special Embryology

the development of the lungs. Shortly after their formation the lung buds expand in caudolateral direction within the pericardioperitoneal canals. As a result of the rapid growth of the lung buds, however, the pericardioperitoneal canals soon become too small, and they begin to expand into the mesenchyme of the body wall in dorsal, lateral and ventral directions (fig. 14-4). This expansion into the mesenchyme of the body wall occurs by vacuolization, a process comparable with the formation of the coelomic cavity in the mesoderm of the lateral plate. The expansion of the canals in dorsal direction causes the formation of a short mesentery for the esophagus (fig. 14-3B).

The expansion in ventral and lateral directions occurs in a plane lateral to the *pleuropericardial ridge*, formed by the common cardinal vein and the phrenic nerve (fig. 14-4A, B). The pericardioperitoneal canals, which gradually contain the major portion of the lungs, are now referred to as the *primitive pleural cavities*.

Caudally the expansion of the pericardioperitoneal canals is delimited by a crescent-shaped fold, the *pleuroperitoneal fold*.[1, 2] This fold (caused by the original cranial ligament of the mesoneph-

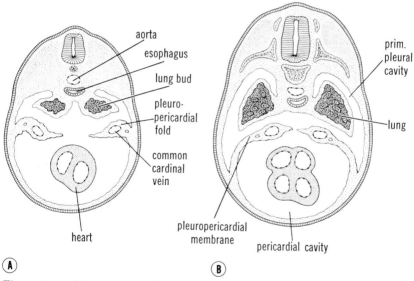

aorta
esophagus
lung bud
pleuro-pericardial fold
common cardinal vein
prim. pleural cavity
lung
pleuropericardial membrane
heart
pericardial cavity

A          B

Figure 14-4. *Schematic drawings at two successive stages of development showing the transformation of the pericardioperitoneal canals into the primitive pleural cavities and the formation of the pleuropericardial membranes. A, Note the relationship of the common cardinal vein to the pleuropericardial ridge. B, As a result of the expansion of the pericardioperitoneal canals the mesenchyme of the body wall is split into the pleuropericardial membranes and the definitive body wall.*

ros) projects into the abdominal end of the pericardioperitoneal canal. With further development the fold extends in medial and anterior directions and by the seventh week fuses with the mesentery of the esophagus and with the septum transversum. Hence, the connection between the thoracic and abdominal portions of the coelomic cavity is closed by the *pleuroperitoneal membranes* (fig. 14-3B). Further expansion of the pleural cavities into the mesenchyme of the body wall results in the addition of a peripheral rim to the pleuroperitoneal membranes. Once this rim is established, myoblasts originating in the body wall penetrate the membranes to form the muscular part of the diaphragm. As the myoblasts are probably derived from the third, fourth and fifth cervical segments, the diaphragm is innervated by the *phrenic nerve*, which likewise originates from the third to the fifth cervical segment.

The diaphragm in the adult is thus derived from the following structures: (1) the septum transversum, which forms the *central tendon*; (2) the two pleuroperitoneal membranes, which peripherally are enforced by components from the lateral and dorsal body walls; and (3) the mesentery of the esophagus, in which the *crura of the diaphragm* develop (fig. 14-3B).

### Pleuropericardial Membranes

The thoracic portion of the coelomic cavity is divided into the pericardial and pleural cavities by the *pleuropericardial membranes.* At first these membranes appear as small ridges projecting into the primitive undivided thoracic cavity (fig. 14-4A). With the expansion of the primitive pleural cavities the mesoderm of the body wall is split into two components (fig. 14-4A, B): (1) the definitive wall of the thorax; and (2) a thin mesodermal membrane, the *pleuropericardial membrane*, which contains the common cardinal vein and phrenic nerve. When subsequently, as a result of the descent of the heart and the positional changes of the sinus venosus, the common cardinal veins shift toward the midline, the pleuropericardial folds are drawn out in mesentery-like fashion. They finally fuse with the dorsal mesocardium and with the root of the lungs, and the thoracic cavity is then divided into the definitive *pericardial cavity* and two *pleural cavities* (fig. 14-4B). In the adult the pleuropericardial membranes form the *fibrous pericardium*. Since the right common cardinal vein is much larger than the left one, the partitioning between the pleural cavity and pericardial cavity is first completed on the right side. Persistent connection between the pleural and pericardial cavities is almost always found on the left side.

# Mesenteries

Initially the foregut, midgut and hindgut are in broad contact with the mesenchyme of the posterior abdominal wall (figs. 14-2*A* and 14-3*A*). In the 8 mm. embryo, however, the connecting tissue bridge has become membranous and the caudal part of the foregut, the midgut and the major part of the hindgut are suspended from the abdominal wall by the so-called *dorsal mesentery* (figs. 14-2*B* and 13-17*B*). This mesentery extends from the terminal part of the esophagus to the cloacal region of the hindgut. A ventral mesentery does not exist, except in the region of the terminal part of the esophagus, the stomach and the upper part of the duodenum.

## *Formation of the Ventral Mesentery*

The stomach and upper part of the duodenum are initially in direct contact with the septum transversum, thus facilitating the growth of the liver cords into the mesenchyme of the septum (figs. 14-3 and 13-15). As a result of the enormous growth of the liver, the septum cannot contain the liver which then begins to expand caudally into the abdominal cavity. This is possible since simultaneously with the growth of the liver the abdominal cavity increases considerably in width and depth. The mesenchyme of the septum transversum between the ventral abdominal wall and the liver becomes stretched and membranous, thus forming the *falciform ligament* (figs. 14-5 and 13-17*B*). In a similar manner the mesenchyme of the septum, extending between the liver and the ventral border of the stomach and duodenum, forms a membrane, known as the *lesser omentum*. The free margin of the falciform ligament contains the umbilical vein, which after birth is obliterated to form the *round ligament of the liver* (*ligamentum teres hepatis*). The free margin of the lesser omentum contains the common bile duct, the portal vein and the hepatic artery. In the adult the lower border of the lesser omentum forms the upper margin of the *epiploic foramen of Winslow*. Through this foramen, entrance is gained into the lesser peritoneal sac behind the stomach (see below).

The liver, suspended between the falciform ligament and the lesser omentum, is completely covered by peritoneum except for an area on its upper surface, where it remains in contact with the condensed cranial portion of the septum, the future central tendon of the diaphragm (fig. 14-5). This uncovered area is known as the *bare area of the liver*. At the lines of reflection, where the peritoneal covering of the liver becomes continuous with the peritoneum on the underside of the diaphragm, the *coronary ligaments* are formed.

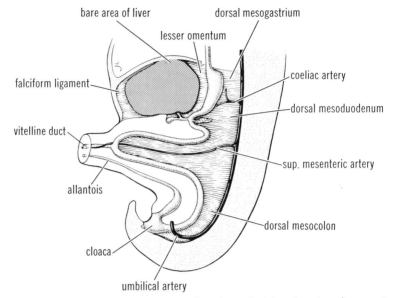

Figure 14-5. *Schematic drawing showing the primitive dorsal and ventral mesenteries. Note how the liver is connected to the ventral abdominal wall and to the stomach by the falciform ligament and lesser omentum, respectively. The superior mesenteric artery runs through the mesentery proper and continues toward the yolk sac as the vitelline artery.*

### Dorsal Mesentery

The dorsal mesentery extends from the lower end of the esophagus to the cloacal region of the hindgut. In the region of the stomach it is known as the *dorsal mesogastrium* or *greater omentum;* in the region of the duodenum, as the *dorsal mesoduodenum;* and in the region of the colon, as the *dorsal mesocolon*. The dorsal mesentery of the jejunal and ileal loops is known as the *mesentery proper*. Throughout its length the mesentery serves as a pathway for the blood vessels, nerves, and lymphatics supplying the intestinal tract (fig. 14-5).

### Lesser Peritoneal Sac or Omental Bursa

In the fourth week of development, when the caudal part of the foregut is still in broad contact with the posterior abdominal wall, small intercellular clefts appear in the mesenchyme dorsal to the stomach. These clefts fuse rapidly and a cavity, the future *omental bursa*, is formed behind the stomach (fig. 14-6). On the right side this cavity extends in cranial direction until it reaches the right lung bud.[4] The so-called recess is known as the *pneumato-enteric recess*

Special Embryology

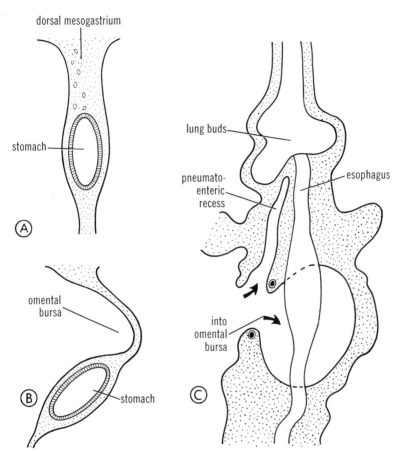

Figure 14-6. *A, Schematic transverse section through a four-week embryo to show the intercellular clefts appearing in the dorsal mesogastrium. B, The clefts have fused and the omental bursa is formed as an extension of the right side of the coelomic cavity behind the stomach. C, Note the pneumatoenteric recess.*

and is a cranial extension of the primitive omental bursa. With development of the pleuroperitoneal membranes, the recess becomes isolated and forms a small supradiaphragmatic bursa, the *infracardiac bursa.*[5, 6] In the adult remnants of this bursa are sometimes found as small cysts, located posterior to the root of the right lung.

In the meantime the omental bursa extends further dorsal to the stomach and causes a bulge of the left surface of the dorsal mesogastrium (fig. 14-7A). Continuous expansion of the omental bursa, which in effect is an extension of the right half of the peritoneal cavity, has a profound effect on the stomach, the spleen and the pancreas (fig. 14-7B).[7] The primordium of the spleen appears in the fifth week of development as a mesodermal proliferation between

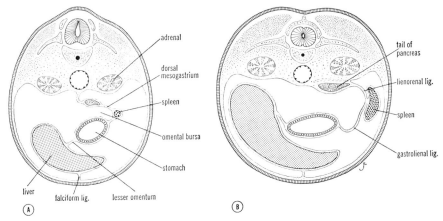

Figure 14-7. *Diagrammatic transverse sections through the region of the stomach, liver, and spleen, showing the formation of the lesser peritoneal sac, the rotation of the stomach, and the position of the spleen and tail of the pancreas between the two leaves of the dorsal mesogastrium. With further development, the pancreas obtains a retroperitoneal position (adapted from several sources).*

the two leaves of the dorsal mesogastrium. With the formation of the omental bursa, a portion of the dorsal mesogastrium located between the spleen and dorsal midline fuses with the posterior abdominal wall (fig. 14-7*B*). The spleen, which always maintains an intraperitoneal position, is then connected to the dorsal body wall in the region of the left kidney by the *lienorenal ligament* and to the stomach by the *gastrolienal ligament*.

The formation of the omental bursa also influences the position of the pancreas. This organ initially grows into the dorsal mesoduodenum, but with time its tail expands into the dorsal mesogastrium (fig. 14-7*A*). Since the left leaf of this portion of the dorsal mesogastrium fuses with the peritoneum of the dorsal body wall, the tail of the pancreas comes to lie in retroperitoneal position (figs. 14-7*B* and 14-9*A*).

As a result of the positional changes of the stomach, the dorsal mesogastrium, forming the left wall of the omental bursa, now bulges in a downward direction (fig. 14-8*A*). The dorsal mesogastrium continues to grow and forms a duplicature, extending over the transverse colon and small intestinal loops like an apron (figs. 14-8*B* and 14-9). This double-leaved apron is the *greater omentum*. Later its leaves fuse to form a single sheet hanging from the greater curvature of the stomach. The upper part of the posterior leaf of the greater omentum fuses with the mesentery of the transverse colon (fig. 14-9*B*).

Special Embryology

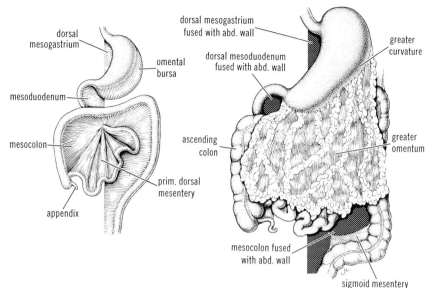

Figure 14-8. A, *Schematic drawing of the dorsal mesentery at the end of the third month. The dorsal mesogastrium bulges out on the left side of the stomach, where it forms the omental bursa. B, In the adult, the greater omentum hangs down from the greater curvature of the stomach in front of the transverse colon and the small intestinal loops. The cross-hatched areas indicate those parts of the primitive dorsal mesentery which have fused with the abdominal wall (adapted from several sources).*

### Dorsal Mesoduodenum

Rotation of the stomach and the duodenum, together with the rapid growth of the head of the pancreas, causes the duodenum to swing from its initial midline position to the right side of the peritoneal cavity (fig. 14-10). The duodenum and the head of the pancreas are pressed against the dorsal body wall, and the right surface of the dorsal mesoduodenum fuses with the adjacent peritoneum. Both layers subsequently disappear, and the duodenum and head of the pancreas become fixed in a *retroperitoneal position*. The dorsal mesoduodenum disappears entirely except in the region of the pylorus of the stomach, where a small portion of the duodenum remains intraperitoneal.

### Mesentery of the Primitive Intestinal Loop, or Mesentery Proper

The mesentery of the primitive intestinal loop undergoes profound changes with rotation and coiling of the loops (figs. 13-22, 13-23 and

Coelomic Cavity and Mesenteries

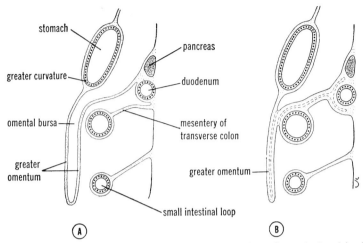

Figure 14-9. *A, Schematic sagittal section showing the relationship between the greater omentum, stomach, transverse colon, and small intestinal loops at 4 months. The pancreas and duodenum have already acquired a retroperitoneal position. B, Similar section as in A, in the newborn. The leaves of the greater omentum have fused with each other and with the transverse mesocolon. The transverse mesocolon covers the already retroperitoneally located duodenum.*

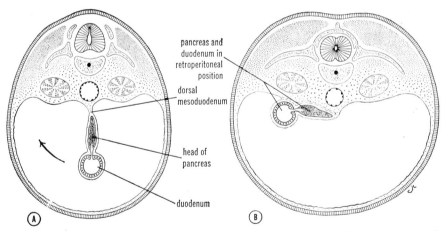

Figure 14-10. *Transverse sections through the region of the duodenum at various stages of development. At first, the duodenum and the head of the pancreas are located in the median plane (A), but later they swing to the right and acquire a retroperitoneal position (B).*

13-24). When the caudal limb moves to the right side of the abdominal cavity, the dorsal mesentery twists around the origin of the superior mesenteric artery (figs. 14-5 and 14-11). Later, when the ascending and descending portions of the colon obtain their definitive

Special Embryology

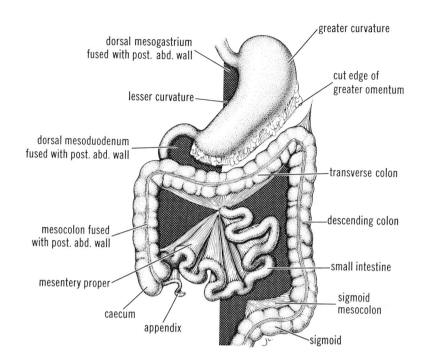

Figure 14-11. *Frontal view of the intestinal loops after removal of the greater omentum. The cross-hatched areas indicate the parts of the dorsal mesentery which fuse with the posterior abdominal wall. Note the line of attachment of the mesentery proper.*

positions, their mesenteries are pressed against the peritoneum of the abdominal wall (fig. 14-11). After fusion of these layers, the ascending and descending colons are permanently anchored in a retroperitoneal position. The appendix and lower end of the caecum, however, retain their free mesentery.

The fate of the transverse mesocolon is different. First, it covers the duodenum with an additional peritoneal layer (fig. 14-9A, B); later, it fuses with the posterior wall of the omental bursa (fig. 14-9B). Its line of attachment finally extends from the hepatic flexure of the ascending colon to the splenic flexure of the descending colon (fig. 14-11).

The mesentery of the jejuno-ileal loops is at first continuous with that of the ascending colon (fig. 14-9A). When the mesentery of the ascending mesocolon fuses with the posterior abdominal wall, the mesentery of the jejuno-ileal loops obtains a new line of attachment which extends from the area where the duodenum becomes intraperitoneal to the ileocaecal junction (fig. 14-11).

Coelomic Cavity and Mesenteries                    287

# Congenital Malformations

## Diaphragmatic Hernia

A diaphragmatic hernia is one of the more common malformations in the newborn and is most frequently caused by failure of the pleuroperitoneal membranes to close the pericardioperitoneal canals. The peritoneum and parietal pleura are then continuous with one another along the posterior body wall, with no line of demarcation between the two. Such a defect, known as the *congenital diaphragmatic hernia of Bochdalek*, allows the abdominal viscera to enter the pleural cavity.[8, 9] Usually the hernia is on the left side, and the stomach, spleen and part of the liver may enter the thoracic cavity (fig. 14-12*A*, *B*). Because of the presence of the abdominal viscera in the chest, the heart is pushed anteriorly, while the lungs are compressed and often hypoplastic. Hence, respiration is difficult and the newborn usually dies shortly after birth. Sometimes, the defective portion of the diaphragm is covered by a membrane composed of pleura and peritoneum. In such cases the intestinal contents penetrating the thoracic cavity are surrounded by the serous membranes.

Occasionally, a small part of the muscular fibers of the diaphragm fails to develop and a hernia may then remain undiscovered until the child is several years old. Although such a defect may be located in the posterior portion of the diaphragm, more frequently it is seen in the anterior portion and is then known as the *parasternal hernia of Morgagni*. Such a hernia is located between the sternal and sternocostal portions of the diaphragm, and a small peritoneal sac containing the intestinal loops may enter the chest.

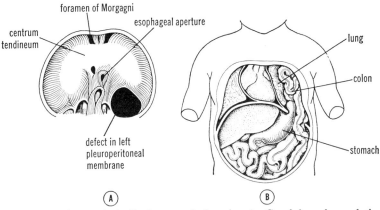

Figure 14-12. *Congenital diaphragmatic hernia. A, Caudal surface of the diaphragm, showing a large defect of the pleuroperitoneal membrane on the left side. B, Hernia of the intestinal loops and part of the stomach into the left pleural cavity. The heart and mediastinum are frequently pushed to the right, while the left lung is compressed.*

Special Embryology

Another type of diaphragmatic hernia, the *esophageal hernia*, is thought to be due to a congenital shortness of the esophagus. The cardia and upper part of the stomach are retained in the thorax and the stomach is then constricted at the level of the diaphragm.

Although the cause of a diaphragmatic hernia is unknown, it has been shown that the offspring of rats fed a vitamin A-deficient diet has a high percentage of diaphragmatic defects.[10]

## Mobile Caecum and Colon

Normally the ascending colon, except for its most caudal part (approximately 1 inch), is fused to the posterior abdominal wall and covered by peritoneum on its anterior surface and sides. Persistence of a portion of the mesocolon gives rise to what is usually termed a *mobile caecum*. In its most extreme form, the mesentery of the ascending colon has failed to fuse with the posterior body wall, so that the root of the common mesentery is limited to a small area around the origin of the superior mesenteric artery. Such an unusually long mesentery allows for abnormal movements of the gut or even volvulus of the caecum and colon.[11] Similarly, retrocolic pockets may occur behind the ascending mesocolon, and a *retrocolic hernia* represents the entrapment of portions of the small intestinal loops behind the mesocolon.

## References

1. BREMER, J. L. The diaphragm and diaphragmatic hernia. Arch. Path., **36:** 539, 1943.
2. WELLS, L. J. Observations on the development of the diaphragm in the human embryo. Anat. Rec., **100:** 778, 1948.
3. WELLS, L. J. Development of the human diaphragm and pleural sacs. Contrib. Embryol., **35:** 107, 1954.
4. KANAGASUNTHERAM, R. Development of the human lesser sac. J. Anat., **91:** 188, 1957.
5. BROMAN, I. *Die Entwicklungsgeschichte der Bursa Omentalis und ähnlicher Recessbildungen bei den Wirbeltieren.* J. F. Bergmann, Wiesbaden, 1904.
6. BROMAN, I. Warum wird die Entwicklung der Bursa Omentalis in Lehrbüchern fortwährend unrichtig beschrieben? Anat. Anz., **86:** 195, 1938.
7. PERNKOPF, E. Die Entwicklung der Form des Magendarmkanales beim Menschen. Z. Anat. Entwicklungsgesch., **64:** 136, 1922.
8. HARRINGTON, S. W. Clinical manifestations and surgical treatment of congenital types of diaphragmatic hernia. Rev. Gastroent., **18:** 243, 1951.
9. HARRINGTON, S. W. Esophageal hiatal diaphragmatic hernia. Surg. Gynec. Obstet., **100:** 277, 1955.
10. ANDERSEN, D. M. Effect of diet during pregnancy on incidence of congenital hereditary diaphragmatic hernia in the rat. Amer. J. Path., **25:** 163, 1949.
11. WOLFER, J. A., BEATON, H. E., AND ANSON, B. J. Volvulus of the caecum: anatomical factors in its etiology; report of a case. Surg. Gynec. Obstet., **74:** 882, 1942.

CHAPTER **15**

# Central Nervous System

The central nervous system of the human embryo appears at the beginning of the third week of development as an elongated, slipper-shaped plate of thickened ectoderm, the *neural plate*. This plate is located in the mid-dorsal region in front of the *node of Hensen*. The lateral edges of the plate soon become elevated to form the *neural folds;* the depressed region between the folds is then known as the *neural groove* (fig. 15-1).

With further development the neural folds become more elevated, approach each other in the midline, and finally fuse, resulting in the formation of the *neural tube* (figs. 15-2 and 15-3). This fusion begins in the region of the fourth somite and simultaneously proceeds in cephalic and caudal directions (fig. 15-3A). At the cranial and caudal ends of the embryo, however, fusion is somewhat delayed, and the *anterior* and *posterior neuropores* temporarily form open connections between the lumen of the neural tube and the surrounding amniotic cavity (fig. 15-3B). Closure of the anterior neuropore occurs at the 18- to 20-somite stage (23rd day), and that of the posterior neuropore at the 25-somite stage (25th day). The central nervous system then forms a closed tubular structure with a long caudal portion, the future *spinal cord*, and a broader cephalic portion which becomes the *brain*.

The cephalic end of the. neural tube soon shows three distinct dilatations, the *primary brain vesicles*. From anterior to posterior, these vesicles are known as: (1) the *prosencephalon* or *forebrain*; (2) the *mesencephalon* or *midbrain*; and (3) the *rhombencephalon* or *hindbrain* (fig. 15-4). Coincident with the appearance of these vesicles the neural tube bends in ventral direction, forming two flexures: the *cervical flexure* at the junction of the hindbrain and the spinal cord; and the *cephalic flexure* located in the midbrain region (fig. 15-4A).

When the embryo is 5 weeks old the development of the brain has made considerable progress, and five components can be distin-

290                                                    Special Embryology

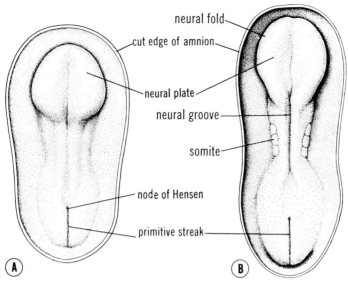

Figure 15-1. *A, Dorsal view of a late presomite embryo (approximately 1.4 mm. and 18 days) (modified after Davis). The amnion has been removed. The neural plate is clearly visible. B, Dorsal view of a human embryo at approximately 20 days (modified after Ingalls). Note the appearance of the somites and the formation of the neural groove and neural folds.*

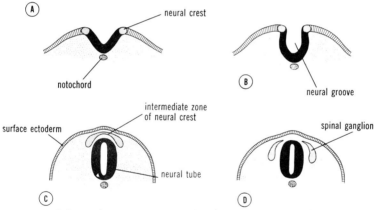

Figure 15-2. *Schematic drawing of a number of transverse sections through successively older embryos, showing the formation of the neural folds, neural groove, neural tube and neural crest. The cells of the neural crest, initially forming an intermediate zone between the neural tube and surface ectoderm (C), develop into the spinal and cranial sensory ganglia (D).*

guished. The prosencephalon consists now of two parts: (1) an anterior portion, the *telencephalon* or *endbrain,* formed by a mid-portion and two lateral outpocketings, the *primitive cerebral hemispheres*; and (2) a posterior part, the *diencephalon,* characterized

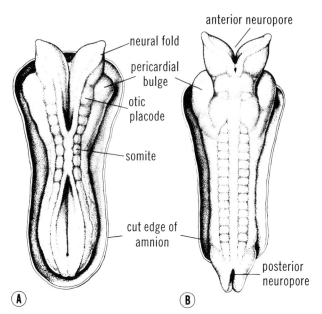

Figure 15-3. *A, Dorsal view of a human embryo at approximately day 22 (modified after Payne). Seven distinct somites are visible on each side of the neural tube. B, Dorsal view of a human embryo at approximately day 23 (modified after Corner). Note the pericardial bulge on each side of the midline in the cephalic part of the embryo. The nervous system is in connection with the amniotic cavity by means of the anterior and posterior neuropores.*

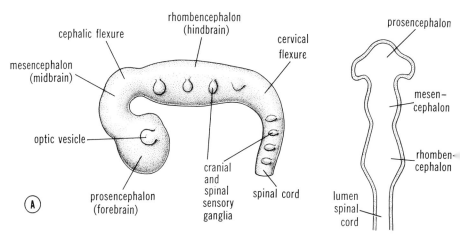

Figure 15-4. *A, Lateral view of the brain vesicles and part of the spinal cord in a 4-week embryo (modified after Hochstetter). Note the sensory ganglia formed by the neural crest on each side of the rhombencephalon and spinal cord. B, Diagram to show the lumina of the three brain vesicles and spinal cord.*

Special Embryology

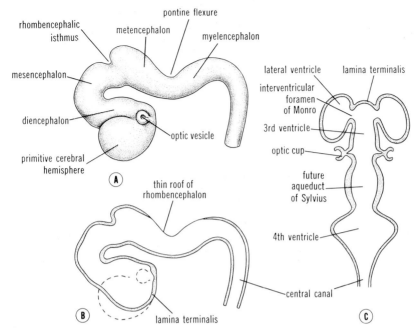

Figure 15-5. *A, Lateral view of the brain vesicles of the human embryo in the beginning of the sixth week (modified after Hochstetter). B, Midline section through the brain vesicles and spinal cord of an embryo of the same age as shown in A. Note the thin roof of the rhombencephalon. C, Diagram to show the lumina of the spinal cord and brain vesicles.*

by the outgrowth of the optic vesicles (fig. 15-5A). The mesencephalon undergoes little change and is separated from the rhombencephalon by a deep furrow, the *rhombencephalic isthmus*. The rhombencephalon now consists also of two parts: (1) an anterior portion, the *metencephalon*, which later forms the *pons* and *cerebellum*; and (2) a posterior portion, the *myelencephalon*, destined to become the *medulla oblongata*. The boundary between these two portions is marked by a flexure, known as the *pontine flexure* (fig. 15-5).

The lumen of the spinal cord, the *central canal*, is continous with that of the brain vesicles, thus allowing the cerebrospinal fluid to circulate freely between the cerebral hemispheres and the most caudal end of the spinal cord. The cavity of the rhombencephalon is known as the *fourth ventricle*, that of the diencephalon as the *third ventricle*, and those of the cerebral hemispheres as the *lateral ventricles* (fig. 15-5C). The third and fourth ventricles are initially connected to each other through the wide lumen of the mesencephalon. Later, the mesencephalic lumen becomes very narrow and is then known as the *aqueduct of Sylvius*. The lateral ventricles communicate with the third ventricle through the *interventricular foramina of Monro* (fig. 15-5C).

Central Nervous System

# SPINAL CORD

NORMAL DEVELOPMENT
•GENERAL STRUCTURE: *neuroepithelial, mantle and marginal layers; basal motor plate; alar sensory plate; roof and floor plates*
•HISTOLOGICAL DIFFERENTIATION: *nerve cells; glia cells; neural crest cells; myelination*
•POSITIONAL CHANGES OF THE CORD

CONGENITAL MALFORMATIONS
•SPINA BIFIDA: *spina bifida occulta; meningocele; meningomyelocele; rachischisis*

## Normal Development

### General Structure

*Neuroepithelial, Mantle and Marginal Layers*

According to the classical theory, the wall of a recently closed neural tube was thought to consist of three different zones. Bordering the lumen of the tube was found the *ependymal zone*, which consisted of large round cells and high columnar epithelial cells (fig. 15-6A). The round cells, referred to as the germinal cells, were believed to give rise to neuroblasts, while the columnar epithelial cells were thought to form spongioblasts (prospective glia cells). Both the neuroblasts and the spongioblasts were believed to migrate to a densely packed nuclear zone, the *mantle zone* (fig. 15-6A). The outermost layer of the tube, the *marginal zone*, was thought to consist of the peripheral processes and axons of the neuroblasts.

Although serious criticism against the classical theory has been raised repeatedly,[1, 2] only recently have the results of microspectrophotometric, radioautographic and electron microscopic observations been widely accepted and have the classical concepts been changed.[3-8] According to the new data, the wall of a recently closed neural tube consists of only one cell type, the *neuroepithelial cells.* These cells extend over the entire thickness of the wall and form a thick pseudostratified epithelium (fig. 15-6B). They are connected to each other by terminal bars at the lumen. During the interphase, when DNA synthesis occurs, the cells are wedge-shaped with the broader portion containing the nucleus in the outer zone of the wall

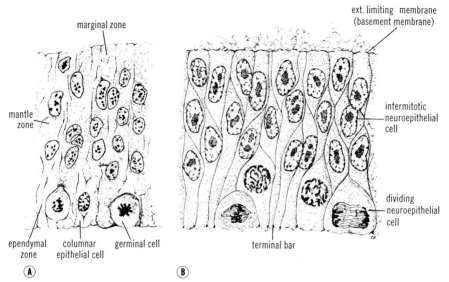

marginal zone

ext. limiting membrane
(basement membrane)

mantle
zone

intermitotic
neuroepithelial
cell

dividing
neuroepithelial
cell

ependymal     columnar      germinal cell                    terminal bar
zone          epithelial cell

Ⓐ                              Ⓑ

Figure 15-6. *A, Drawing of a cross-section through the wall of the recently closed neural tube, representing the classical theory. The germinal cells were believed to give rise to neuroblasts and the columnar epithelial cells to the primitive glia cells. The wall of the tube at this stage of development was thought to consist of the ependymal, mantle and marginal zones. B, According to modern theories, the wall of the recently closed neural tube consists of only one cell type, the neuroepithelial cells, which form a pseudostratified epithelium extending over the full width of the wall. Only later do the mantle and marginal zones appear.*

and a slender cytoplasmic portion extending towards the lumen. Immediately after DNA synthesis, the nucleus begins to move toward the lumen, while the cell contracts toward the terminal bars. During metaphase the cells are round and in broad contact with the lumen, thereby often squeezing the slender cytoplasmic processes of the neighboring nondividing cells. During the neural groove stage and immediately after closure of the tube, the neuroepithelial cells divide rapidly resulting in the production of more neuroepithelial cells. The thick pseudo-stratified epithelium found in the recently closed neural tube is referred to as the *neuroepithelial layer* or *neuroepithelium.*

Once the neural tube is closed, the neuroepithelial cells begin to give rise to another cell type, which is characterized by a large round nucleus with pale nucleoplasm and a dark-staining nucleolus. These cells, which are produced in ever-increasing numbers, are the primitive nerve cells or *neuroblasts* (fig. 15-7). They form a zone which surrounds the neuroepithelial layer and is known as the *man-*

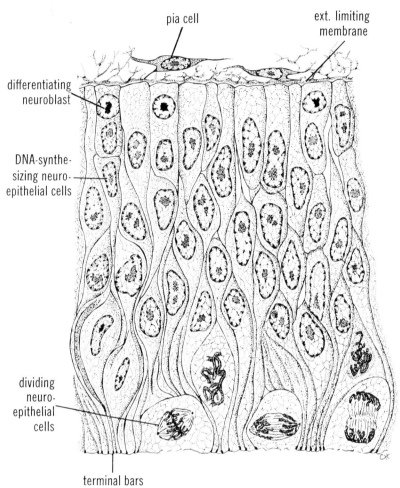

pia cell

ext. limiting membrane

differentiating neuroblast

DNA-synthe-sizing neuro-epithelial cells

dividing neuro-epithelial cells

terminal bars

Figure 15-7. *Drawing of a cross-section through the wall of the neural tube at a slightly more advanced stage than represented in Figure 15-6. The major portion of the wall consists of neuroepithelial cells, either in mitosis or in the DNA synthetic phase. On the periphery, however, immediately adjacent to the external limiting membrane are found differentiating neuroblasts. These cells, which are produced by the neuroepithelial cells in ever-increasing numbers, will form the mantle zone.*

*tle layer* (fig. 15-8). The mantle zone later forms the *gray matter of the spinal cord*.

The outermost layer of the spinal cord contains the nerve fibers emerging from the neuroblasts in the mantle layer and is known as the *marginal layer*. As a result of the myelination of the nerve fibers, this layer obtains a white appearance and is therefore referred to as the *white matter of the spinal cord* (fig. 15-8).

Special Embryology

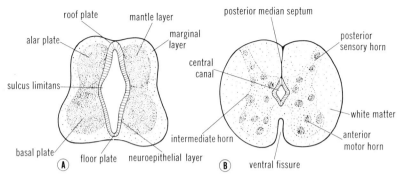

Figure 15-8. *Diagrams to show two successive stages in the development of the spinal cord. Note the formation of the anterior motor and posterior sensory horns, the intermediate column, the ventral fissure, and the posterior median septum.*

### Basal, Alar, Roof and Floor Plates

As a result of the continuous addition of neuroblasts to the mantle layer, each side of the neural tube shows a ventral and dorsal thickening. The ventral thickenings, the *basal plates*, contain the anterior motor horn cells and form the motor areas of the spinal cord, whereas the dorsal thickenings, the *alar plates*, form the sensory areas (fig. 15-8A). A longitudinal groove, the *sulcus limitans*, found bilaterally on the inner surface of the tube, marks the boundary between the anterior motor and posterior sensory areas (fig. 15-8A). The thin dorsal and ventral midline portions of the neural tube, known as the *roof* and *floor plates*, respectively, do not contain neuroblasts and serve primarily as pathways for nerve fibers crossing from one side of the spinal cord to the other.

As a result of the continuous enlargement of the neuroblasts, the basal plates bulge forward on each side of the midline, thus causing a deep longitudinal groove on the ventral aspect of the spinal cord (fig. 15-8B). This groove, the *ventral fissure*, later contains the anterior spinal artery. The alar plates expand mainly in a medial direction, thereby compressing the dorsal portion of the lumen of the neural tube. When finally the two alar plates fuse in the midline, the *posterior median septum* is formed at the plane of fusion. The spinal cord has then acquired its definitive form with motor horns anteriorly, sensory horns posteriorly, and a small lumen known as the *central canal*.

## Histological Differentiation

While the above-described gross organization of the spinal cord occurs, two distinct cell types, the *nerve* and *glia cells*, become visible.

Central Nervous System                                          297

## Nerve Cells

The *neuroblasts* or primitive nerve cells arise exclusively by division of the neuroepithelial cells. The neuroblasts of the anterior horn are formed first, and only when most of these have migrated to the mantle layer does the formation of nerve cells for the alar plate begin.[9, 10] Initially the neuroblasts have a central process extending to the lumen (*transient dendrite*),[7, 11] but when they migrate into the mantle zone this process disappears and the neuroblasts are temporarily round, *apolar neuroblasts* (fig. 15-9A). With further differentiation two new cytoplasmic processes appear on opposite sides of the cell body, thus forming the *bipolar neuroblasts* (fig. 15-9B). The process at one end of the cell elongates rapidly to form the *primitive axon*, while the process at the other end shows a number of cytoplasmic arborizations, known as the *primitive dendrites* (fig. 15-9C). The cell is then known as a *multipolar neuroblast* and with further development becomes the adult nerve cell or *neuron*. Once the neuroblasts are formed, they lose their ability to divide.

The axons of the neurons in the posterior sensory horn behave differently from those in the anterior motor horn. The former penetrate the marginal layer of the cord, where they either ascend or descend to a higher or lower level (*association neurons*); the latter, on the other hand, break through the marginal zone and become visible on the ventral aspect of the cord, where they are known collectively as the *anterior motor root of the spinal nerve*. These fibers conduct motor impulses from the spinal cord to the muscles (fig. 15-10).

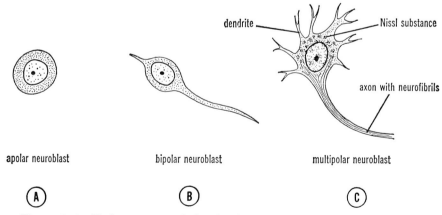

apolar neuroblast      bipolar neuroblast      multipolar neuroblast

(A)      (B)      (C)

Figure 15-9. *Various stages of the development of a neuroblast. A neuron is a structural and functional unit, consisting of the cell body and all its processes.*

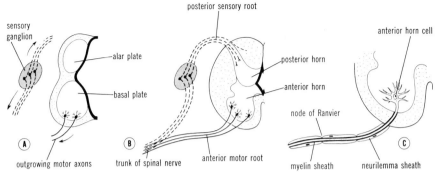

Figure 15-10. *A, Drawing showing the motor axons growing out from the neurons in the basal plate, and the centrally and peripherally growing fibers of the nerve cells in the sensory ganglion. B, The nerve fibers of the ventral motor and dorsal sensory roots join to form the trunk of the spinal nerve. C, Drawing of an anterior horn cell and its axons surrounded by the neurilemma and myelin sheath.*

*Glia Cells*

The majority of the primitive supporting cells, referred to as the *gliablasts*, are formed by the neuroepithelial cells after the production of neuroblasts has ceased. From the neuroepithelial layer the gliablasts migrate to the mantle layer, though some are thought to proceed toward the marginal layer. In the mantle layer they differentiate into the *protoplasmic* and *fibrillar astrocytes*.[12, 13]

Another type of supporting cell, possibly derived from the gliablasts, is the *oligodendroglia cell*. This cell, which is mainly found in the marginal layer, forms the myelin sheaths around the ascending and descending axons in the marginal layer. Recently it has been suggested that they may be derived from mesenchyme cells penetrating into the central nervous system and their origin from the neuroepithelial cells is at present in doubt.[14]

In the second half of development a third type of supporting cell, the *microglia cell*, appears in the central nervous system. This cell type is believed to originate from the mesoderm surrounding the neural tube.[15]

When the neuroepithelial cells cease to produce neuroblasts and gliablasts, they finally differentiate into the ependymal cells as seen in the adult.

Recent observations made with radioautographic and electron microscopic techniques have considerably complicated the diverse pathways followed by the various types of glia cells.[16, 17] The complexity of the various controversial theories prevents the discussion in this chapter, but some of the uncertainties are indicated in the flow chart presented in Figure 15-11.

Central Nervous System 299

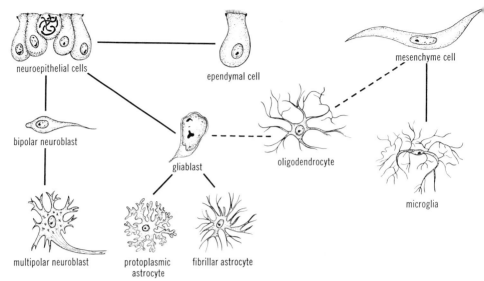

neuroepithelial cells

ependymal cell

mesenchyme cell

bipolar neuroblast

gliablast

oligodendrocyte

microglia

multipolar neuroblast

protoplasmic astrocyte

fibrillar astrocyte

Figure 15-11. *Schematic diagram showing the origin of the nerve cell and the various types of glia cells. The neuroblasts, the fibrillar and protoplasmic astrocytes, and the ependymal cells originate from the neuroepithelial cells. The microglia develops from mesenchyme cells. The origin of the oligodendrocyte remains in doubt.*

### Neural Crest Cells

During the invagination of the neural plate, a distinct group of cells appears along each edge of the neural groove (fig. 15-2A). These cells, ectodermal in origin, and known as the *neural crest cells*, temporarily form an intermediate zone between the tube and the surface ectoderm (fig. 15-2C). This zone extends from the mesencephalon to the level of the caudal somites, and with time divides into two parts, each of which migrates to the dorsolateral aspect of the neural tube.[18-20] Here the cells of the neural crest form a series of cell clusters which give rise to the *sensory ganglia* of the spinal and cranial nerves (5th, 7th, 9th and 10th cranial nerves) (figs. 15-2 and 15-4).

During further development the neuroblasts of the sensory ganglia form two processes (fig. 15-10A). The centrally growing processes penetrate the dorsal portion of the neural tube. In the spinal cord they either end in the posterior horn or ascend through the marginal layer to one of the higher brain centers. These processes are known collectively as the *posterior sensory root of the spinal nerve* (fig. 15-10B). The peripherally growing processes join the fibers of the anterior motor root and thus participate in the formation of the trunk of the spinal nerve. Eventually these processes termi-

Special Embryology

nate in the sensory receptor organs. Hence, the neuroblasts of the sensory ganglia give rise to the *posterior root neurons*.

In addition to forming the sensory ganglia, the cells of the neural crest differentiate into sympathetic neuroblasts, Schwann cells, pigment cells, meninges, and cartilage cells of the branchial arches.[21-26] In recent experiments it was found that extirpation of neural crest cells of the trigeminal region resulted in facial abnormalities, among which were clefts of the primary palate[27] (see Chapter 18).

### Myelination

Myelination of the peripheral nerves is accomplished by the *neurilemma cells* or *cells of Schwann*. These cells originate from the neural crest, migrate peripherally and wrap themselves around the axons, thus forming the *neurilemma sheath* (fig. 15-10C). In this manner axons, varying in number from 1 to 20, may be enwrapped by one neurilemma cell.

Beginning at the fourth month of fetal life, the nerve fibers gradually obtain a whitish appearance as a result of the deposition of *myelin* between the axon and the neurilemma. This substance is formed by repeated coiling of the membrane around the axon.[28, 29] Hence, both the neurilemma and the myelin sheath of the peripheral nerve fibers are formed by the cells of Schwann.

The myelin sheath surrounding the nerve fibers in the spinal cord is of completely different origin, since it is formed by the oligodendroglia cells. Although myelination of the nerve fibers in the spinal cord begins in approximately the fourth month of intra-uterine life, some of the motor fibers descending from the higher brain centers to the spinal cord do not become myelinated until the first year of postnatal life. It seems that the tracts in the nervous system become myelinated at about the time they start to function.[30]

### Positional Changes of the Cord

In the third month of development, when the crown-rump length of the embryo is approximately 30 mm., the spinal cord extends the entire length of the embryo and the spinal nerves pass through the intervertebral foramina at their level of origin (fig. 15-12A). With increasing age, however, the vertebral column lengthens more rapidly than the neural tube and the terminal end of the spinal cord gradually shifts to a higher level. At birth this end is located at the level of the third lumbar vertebra (fig. 15-12C). As a result of this disproportionate growth, the spinal nerves run obliquely from their

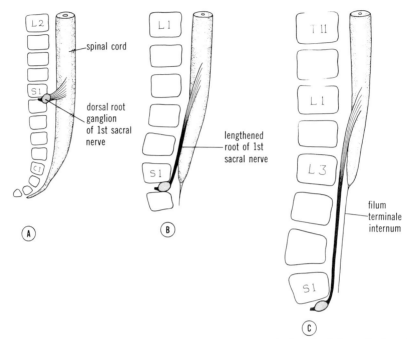

Figure 15-12. *Schematic drawing showing the terminal end of the spinal cord in relation to that of the vertebral column at various stages of development. A, Approximately at third month; B, end of fifth month; C, in the newborn (modified after Streeter).*

segment of origin in the spinal cord to the corresponding level of the vertebral column.

In the adult, the spinal cord terminates at the level of L$_2$. Below this point the central nervous system is represented only by the *filum terminale internum*, which marks the tract of regression of the spinal cord. The nerve fibers below the terminal end of the cord are known collectively as the *cauda equina*.

## Congenital Malformations

By the end of the fourth week the central nervous system forms a closed tubular structure detached from the overlying ectoderm. Occasionally, however, the neural groove fails to close, either because of faulty induction by the underlying chorda mesodermal structures or because of the action of environmental teratogenic factors on the neuroepithelial cells. The neural tissue then remains exposed to the surface. Such a defect may extend the total length of the embryo or may be restricted to a small area only (*complete* or *partial rachischisis*). If localized in the region of the spinal cord, the abnor-

Special Embryology

mality is commonly referred to as *spina bifida*, whereas failure of closure in the cephalic region is known as *anencephalus*.

### Spina Bifida

The term spina bifida is used to cover a wide range of defects. Literally translated, it indicates a bifid spine and in its most simple form is seen as a failure of the dorsal portions of the vertebrae to fuse with one another. Such an abnormality, usually localized in the sacrolumbar region, is usually covered by skin and is not noticeable on the surface except for the presence of a small tuft of hair over the affected area (*spina bifida occulta*) (fig. 15-13A). In such a case the spinal cord and nerves are usually normal.

If more than one or two vertebrae are involved in the defect, the meninges of the spinal cord bulge through the opening and a sac covered with skin is visible on the surface (*meningocele*) (fig. 15-13B). Sometimes this sac is so large that it contains not only the meninges but also the spinal cord and its nerves. The abnormality is then known as *meningomyelocele*, and is usually covered by a thin, easily torn membrane (fig. 15-13C).

Another type of spina bifida results from failure of the neural groove to close, and the nervous tissue is then widely exposed to the surface (*myelocele* or *rachischisis*) (fig. 15-13D, E).[31, 32] Occasionally the neural tissue shows considerable overgrowth; usually, how-

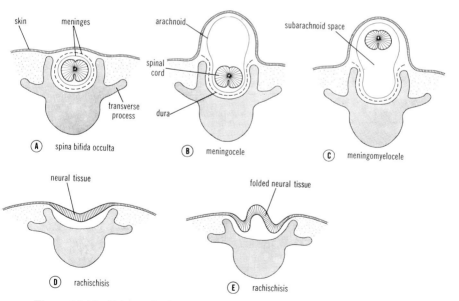

Figure 15-13. *Schematic drawings to show the various types of spina bifida*

ever, the excess tissue becomes necrotic shortly before or after birth.

## References—Spinal Cord

1. SAUER, F. C. Mitosis in the neural tube. J. Comp. Neurol., **62:** 377, 1935.
2. SAUER, F. C. The cellular structure of the neural tube. J. Comp. Neurol., **63:** 13, 1935.
3. SAUER, M. E., AND CHITTENDEN, A. C. Deoxyribonucleic acid content of cell nuclei in the neural tube of the chick embryo: evidence for intermitotic migration of nuclei. Exp. Cell Res., **16:** 1, 1959.
4. SIDMAN, R. L., MIALE, I. L., AND FEDER, N. Cell proliferation and migration in the primitive ependymal zone; an autoradiographic study of histogenesis in the nervous system. Exp. Neurol., **1:** 322, 1959.
5. FUJITA, S. Kinetics of cellular proliferation. Exp. Cell Res., **28:** 52, 1962.
6. LANGMAN, J., GUERRANT, R. L., AND FREEMAN, B. G. Behavior of neuroepithelial cells during closure of the neural tube. J. Comp. Neurol., **127:** 399, 1966.
7. LYSER, K. M. Early differentiation of motor neuroblasts in the chick embryo as studied by electron microscopy. Develop. Biol., **10:** 433, 1964.
8. LYSER, K. M. Early differentiation of motor neuroblasts in the chick embryo as studied by electron microscopy. Develop. Biol., **17:** 117, 1968.
9. FUJITA, H., AND FUJITA, S. Electron microscopic studies on neuroblast differentiation in the central nervous system of domestic fowl. Z. Zellforsch. mikrosk., **60:** 463, 1963.
10. LANGMAN, J., AND HADEN, C. Unpublished data.
11. BARRON, D. H. Observations on the early differentiation of the motor neuroblasts in the spinal cord of the chick. J. Comp. Neurol., **85:** 149, 1946.
12. PENFIELD, W. Neuroglia and microglia. The interstitial tissue of the central nervous system. In *Special Cytology*, Ed. 3, edited by E. V. Cowdry. Paul B. Hoeber, Inc., New York, 1932.
13. GLEES, P. *Neuroglia, Morphology and Function*. Blackwell Scientific Publications, Oxford, 1955.
14. LANGMAN, J., AND SYDNOR, C. S. Unpublished data.
15. KERSHMAN, J. Genesis of microglia in the human brain. Arch. Neurol. Psychiat., **41:** 24, 1939.
16. SMART, J., AND LEBLOND, C. P. Evidence for division and transformations of neuroglia cells in the mouse brain, as derived from radioautography after injection of thymidine-H³. J. Comp. Neurol., **116:** 349, 1961.
17. KRUGER, L., AND MAXWELL, D. S. Electron microscopy of oligodendrocytes in normal rat cerebrum. Am. J. Anat., **118:** 411, 1966.
18. BAXTER, J. S., AND BOYD, J. D. Observations on the neural crest of a ten-somite embryo. J. Anat., **73:** 318, 1939.
19. THEILER, K. Studien zur Entwicklung der Ganglienleiste und doppelter Spinalganglien. Acta Anat. (Basel), **5:** 206, 1948.
20. THEILER, K. Studien zur Entwicklung der Ganglienleiste. II. Frühentwicklung der Ganglienleiste beim Menschen. Acta Anat. (Basel), **8:** 96, 1949.
21. HARRISON, R. G. Die Neuralleiste. Anat. Anz., **85:** 4, 1937.
22. HARVEY, S., AND BURR, H. Development of the meninges. Arch. Neurol. Psychiat., **15:** 545, 1926.
23. HORSTADIUS, S. *The Neural Crest*. Oxford University Press, London, 1950.
24. BOYD, J. D. Argentophil cells in foetal ectodermal epithelia. J. Anat., **83:** 74, 1949.
25. HUMPHREY, T. Primitive neurons in embryonic human central nervous system. J. Comp. Neurol., **81:** 1, 1944.

26. SENSENIG, E. C. The early development of the meninges of the spinal cord in human embryos. Contrib. Embryol., **34:** 147, 1951.

27. JOHNSTON, M. C. A radioautographic study of the migration and fate of cranial neural crest cells in the chick embryo. Anat. Rec., **156:** 143, 1966.

28. UZMAN, B. G., AND NOGUEIRA, G. G. Electron microscope studies of the formation of node of Ranvier in mouse sciatic nerves. J. Biophys. Biochem. Cytol., **3:** 589, 1957.

29. METUZALS, J. Ultrastructure of myelinated nerve fibers and nodes of Ranvier in the central nervous system of the frog. In *Proceedings of the European Regional Conference on Electron Microscopy, Delft, 1960*, Vol. 2, p. 799.

30. LANGWORTHY, H. A correlated study of the development of reflex activity in fetal and young kittens and the myelinization of tracts in the nervous system. J. Comp. Neurol., **81:** 1, 1944.

31. PATTEN, B. M. Overgrowth of the neural tube in young human embryos. Anat. Rec., **113:** 381, 1952.

32. MacCARTHY, D. Problem of spina bifida. Quart. Rev. Pediat., **12:** 167, 1957.

# BRAIN

NORMAL DEVELOPMENT
•MYELENCEPHALON: *basal motor plate; alar sensory plate; roof plate, choroid plexus, and foramina of Luschka and Magendie*
•METENCEPHALON: *basal plate and pons; alar plate and rhombic lip*
   *Cerebellum:* vermis and hemispheres
•MESENCEPHALON: *basal plate and crus cerebri; alar plate and colliculi*
•DIENCEPHALON: *roof plate and epiphysis; thalamus and hypothalamus*
   *Hypophysis:* Rathke's pouch; infundibulum
•TELENCEPHALON
   *Cerebral hemispheres:* caudate nucleus; putamen; globus pallidus
   *Cortex cerebri:* palaeopallium, neopallium
   *Commissures:* anterior and hippocampal commissures; corpus callosum; posterior and habenular commissures; optic chiasma

CONGENITAL MALFORMATIONS
   *Meningocele, meningo-encephalocele and meningohydro-encephalocele*
   *Anencephalus*
   *Hydrocephalus*
   *Environmental and chromosomal factors*

## *Normal Development*

With the appearance of the brain vesicles and the development of the cervical and cephalic flexures the external form of the cephalic portion of the neural tube changes greatly (figs. 15-4, 15-5 and 15-15). Despite these changes a number of morphological characteristics, typical for the spinal cord, can be recognized in most of the brain vesicles. For example, distinct basal and alar plates, representing the motor and sensory areas, respectively, are found on each side of the midline in the majority of the brain vesicles. Even the sulcus limitans, which in the spinal cord forms the boundary line between the alar and basal plates, is present in the rhombencephalon and mesencephalon where it likewise forms the dividing line between motor and sensory areas.

A brief description of the fundamental components of each of the five brain vesicles is given in the following account. A number of structural specializations, however, which are not essential for the understanding of the development of the central nervous system, have been omitted.

### Myelencephalon

The myelencephalon, the most caudal of the brain compartments, extends from the first spinal nerve to the pontine flexure and gives rise to the medulla oblongata (figs. 15-14*A* and 15-15). The medulla differs from the spinal cord in that its lateral walls rotate around an imaginary longitudinal axis in the floor plate, a movement comparable to the opening of a book (fig. 15-14*B*, *C*). As a result of this movement, the roof plate becomes stretched and consists of a single layer of cells. The structure of the lateral walls of the myelencephalon, however, is greatly similar to that of the spinal cord, and the alar and basal plates separated by the sulcus limitans can be clearly distinguished (fig. 15-14*B*, *C*).

*Basal Motor Plate*

The basal plate of the myelencephalon, similar to that of the spinal cord, contains the motor nuclei. In the myelencephalon, however, these nuclei are divided into three groups: (1) a medial *somatic efferent* group; (2) an intermediate *special visceral efferent* group; and (3) a lateral *general visceral efferent* group (fig. 15-14*C*). The first group contains the motor neurons, which innervate the

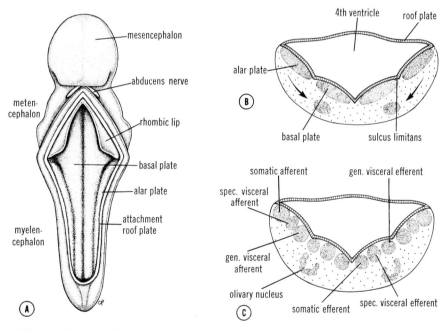

Figure 15-14. *A, Dorsal view of the floor of the fourth ventricle in a 10 mm. embryo after removal of the roof plate. Note the alar and basal plates in the myelencephalon. The rhombic lip is visible in the metencephalon. B and C, Diagrams showing the position and differentiation of the basal and alar plates of the myelencephalon at different stages of development. Note the formation of the nuclear groups in the basal and alar plates. The arrows indicate the path followed by the cells of the alar plate to the olivary nuclear complex.*

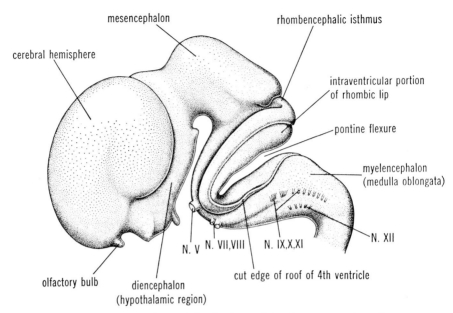

Figure 15-15. *Lateral view of the brain vesicles in an 8-week embryo (crown-rump length approximately 27 mm.) (after Hochstetter). The roof plate of the rhombencephalon has been removed to show the intraventricular portion of the rhombic lip. Note the origin of the cranial nerves.*

striated muscles derived from the myotomes in the cephalic region. As such they form the cephalic continuation of the anterior horn cells. Since the somatic efferent group continues rostrally through the metencephalon into the mesencephalon, this motor group is often referred to as the *somatic efferent motor column.* In the myelencephalon it is represented by the neurons of the *hypoglossal nerve,* which supply the four occipital myotomes (the tongue musculature). In the metencephalon and mesencephalon the column is represented by the neurons of the abducens, trochlear and oculomotor nerves, respectively. These nerves supply the eye musculature, thought to be derived from the preotic myotomes.

The *special visceral efferent* group, which extends into the metencephalon, thus forming the *special visceral efferent motor column,* contains the motor neurons which supply the striated muscles derived from the mesenchyme of the pharyngeal or branchial arches. In the myelencephalon the column is presented by the neurons of the accessory, vagus and glossopharyngeal nerves. In the adult the motor neurons of these nerves are formed by the *nucleus ambiguus* and the *bulbar portion of the accessory nerve.*

The third or *general visceral efferent* group contains the neurons

Special Embryology

whose axons grow out as preganglionic fibers to synapse in the parasympathetic ganglia, which supply the involuntary musculature of the respiratory tract, intestinal tract and heart. In addition they innervate the salivary glands. In the myelencephalon this group is represented by the *dorsal nucleus of the vagus* and the *inferior salivatory nucleus*, which by way of the glossopharyngeal nerve innervates the *parotid gland.*

*Alar Sensory Plate*

The alar plate contains the sensory relay nuclei which, as in the basal plate, are divided into three groups (fig. 15-14C). The most lateral of these, the *somatic afferent* group, receives impulses from the ear and the surface of the head by way of the *stato-acoustic* and the *bulbospinal portion of the trigeminal nerve.* The intermediate or *special visceral afferent* group receives impulses from the taste buds of the tongue and from the palate, oropharynx and epiglottis. These neurons later form the nucleus of the *solitary tract.* The medial or *general visceral afferent* group is represented by the *dorsal sensory nucleus of the vagus.* Its neurons receive interoceptive information from the gastrointestinal tract and the heart.

In addition to the formation of the sensory relay nuclei, other cells of the alar plate migrate downward until they lie ventrolaterally to the basal plate. Here they form a portion of the *olivary nuclear complex* (fig. 15-14B, C).

*Roof Plate, Choroid Plexus, and Foramina of Luschka and Magendie*

The roof plate of the myelencephalon consists of a single layer of ependymal cells. This layer is later covered by vascular mesenchyme, the *pia mater*, and the two combined are known as the *tela choroidea.* Owing to the active proliferation of the vascular mesenchyme, the tela forms a number of saclike invaginations which project into the underlying ventricular cavity in the region of the pontine flexure (fig. 15-19B). These tuftlike invaginations form the *choroid plexus* which produces the cerebrospinal fluid of the central nervous system.

When the embryo is approximately 4 months old, certain areas in the roof plate of the rhombencephalon become extremely thin, bulge outward, and finally disappear. The apertures thus formed— two lateral *foramina of Luschka* and a medial *foramen of Magendie* —allow the cerebrospinal fluid to move freely between the ventricular system inside the brain and the surrounding *subarachnoidal space* (fig. 15-17B).[1]

## Metencephalon

The metencephalon develops from the anterior portion of the rhombencephalon and extends from the pontine flexure to the rhombencephalic isthmus (figs. 15-4, 15-5, 15-14 and 15-15). It differs from the myelencephalon in that two new specialized components are formed: (1) a dorsal portion, the *cerebellum*, which functions as a coordination center for posture and movement; and (2) a ventral portion, the *pons*, which serves as the pathway for nerve fibers between the spinal cord and the cerebral and cerebellar cortices.

### Basal Plate and Pons

Although the lateral walls of the metencephalon reapproach each other, their principal morphological features do not change and the basal motor and alar sensory plates are easily recognizable (fig. 15-16). As in the myelencephalon, each basal plate contains three groups of motor neurons: (1) the medial *somatic efferent* group, which gives rise to the nucleus of the *abducens nerve;* (2) the *special visceral efferent* group containing the nuclei of the *trigeminal* and *facial nerves*, which innervate the musculature of the first and second branchial arches; and (3) the *general visceral efferent* group, which contains the *superior salivatory nucleus*. Axons of this nucleus grow out in the facial nerve and supply the submandibular and sublingual glands as well as the nasal and lacrimal glands.

The marginal layer of the basal plates of the metencephalon ex-

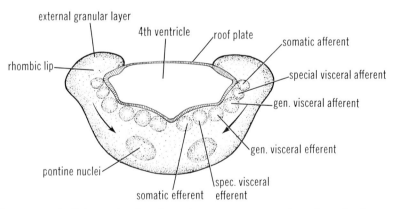

Figure 15-16. *Schematic drawing of a transverse section through the caudal part of the metencephalon. Note the differentiation of the various motor and sensory nuclear areas in the basal and alar plates, respectively. Note the position of the rhombic lips, which project partly into the lumen of the fourth ventricle and partly above the attachment of the roof plate.*

Special Embryology

pands considerably as it serves as a bridge for the nerve fibers connecting the cerebral cortex and the cerebellar cortex with the spinal cord. Hence, this portion of the metencephalon is known as the *pons*. In addition to the nerve fibers, the pons contains the *pontine nuclei*, which originate in the alar plates of the metencephalon and myelencephalon (fig. 15-16). The axons of these nuclei grow toward the cerebellum and give rise to the *middle cerebellar peduncles*.

### Alar Plate and Rhombic Lip

The development of the alar plates of the metencephalon is rather complicated. The ventromedial portion of the plate contains three groups of sensory nuclei: (1) a lateral *somatic afferent* group, which contains the neurons of the *pontine portion of the trigeminal nerve*, and a small portion of the *vestibulocochlear complex*; (2) the *special visceral afferent* group, which is represented by the cranial portion of the nucleus of the *solitary tract*; and (3) the *general visceral afferent* group which is represented by the most cranial portion of the *dorsal sensory nucleus of the vagus* (fig. 15-16).

The dorsolateral parts of the alar plates bend medially and form the *rhombic lips* (figs. 15-15, 15-16, and 15-17). These lips, projecting partly into the lumen of the fourth ventricle and partly above the attachment of the roof plate (the extraventricular portion), give rise to the cerebellum (fig. 15-17).

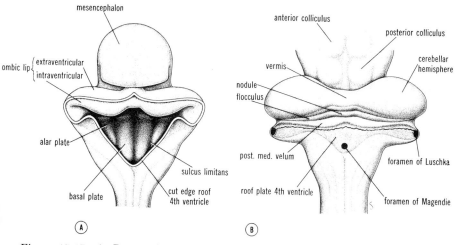

Figure 15-17. A, *Dorsal view of the mesencephalon and rhombencephalon in an 8-week embryo. The roof of the fourth ventricle has been removed, allowing a view of the floor of the fourth ventricle (modified after Hochstetter). B, Similar view in a 4-month embryo. Note the choroidal fissure and the lateral medial apertures in the roof of the fourth ventricle.*

## Cerebellum

In the caudal portion of the metencephalon, the rhombic lips are widely separated, but immediately below the mesencephalon they approach each other in the midline (fig. 15-14A). As a result of a further deepening of the pontine flexure, the rhombic lips become compressed in a cephalocaudal direction and form the *cerebellar plate* (fig. 15-17A, B). In a 12-week embryo this plate shows a small midline portion, the *vermis*, and two lateral portions, the *hemispheres*. A transverse fissure soon separates the *nodule* from the vermis and the lateral *flocculus* from the hemispheres (fig. 15-17B). This *flocculonodular lobe* is phylogenetically the most primitive part of the cerebellum and maintains connections with the vestibular system.[2, 3] Later, many other transverse fissures appear, thus giving the cerebellum its characteristic adult appearance (fig. 15-18).[4]

Initially the *cerebellar plate* consists of a neuroepithelial, a man-

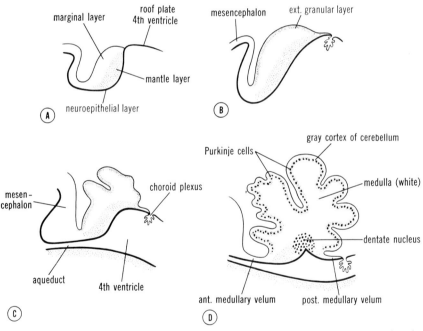

Figure 15-18. *Sagittal sections through the roof of the metencephalon, showing the development of the cerebellum. A, At 8 weeks (approximately 30 mm.); B, 12 weeks (70 mm.); C, 13 weeks; D, 15 weeks (modified after Keibel and Mall). Note the formation of the external granular layer on the external surface of the cerebellar plate (B and C). During later stages the cells of the external granular layer migrate inwards to mingle with the Purkinje cells and thus form the definitive cortex of the cerebellum. The dentate nucleus is one of the deep cerebellar nuclei.*

Special Embryology

tle and a marginal layer (fig. 15-18A). During further development a number of neuroblasts formed by the neuroepithelium migrate through the marginal layer to the surface of the cerebellum to form the *external granular layer*.[5-8] The cells of this layer, unlike neuroblasts elsewhere in the central nervous system, retain their ability to divide and form a proliferative zone on the surface of the cerebellum. The cells produced in the external granular layer migrate inward and develop into the neurons of the *granular layer*. Together with the *Purkinje cells* and *Golgi II neurons* they form the definitive cortex of the cerebellum. Other neuroblasts of the mantle layer, located close to the ventricular surface, differentiate into the *deep cerebellar nuclei* (fig. 15-18D).

The greater part of the original roof plate of the fourth ventricle forms the pia mater on the surface of the cerebellum. Those portions located in front of, and behind, the cerebellum become specialized and form the *anterior* and *posterior medullary velum*, respectively (fig. 15-18D).

## Mesencephalon

### Basal Plate and Crus Cerebri

The mesencephalon is morphologically the most primitive of the brain vesicles (figs. 15-14 and 15-15). In transverse sections the basal and alar plates, separated by the sulcus limitans, are easily recognizable (fig. 15-19A). Each basal plate contains two groups of motor nuclei: (1) a medial *somatic efferent* group represented by the *oculomotor* and *trochlear nerves*, which innervate the preotic myo-

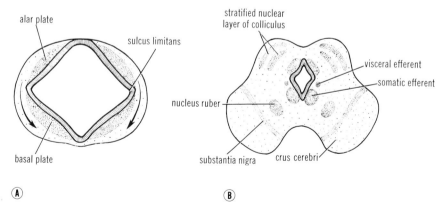

Figure 15-19. *Diagram showing the position and differentiation of the basal and alar plates in the mesencephalon at various stages of development. The arrows in A indicate the path followed by the cells of the alar plate to form the nucleus ruber and substantia nigra. Note the various motor nuclei in the basal plate.*

tomes (the eye musculature), and (2) a small *general visceral efferent* group, represented by the *nucleus of Edinger-Westphal*, which innervates the *sphincter pupillary muscle* (fig. 15-19B).

The marginal layer of each basal plate greatly enlarges and forms the *basis pedunculi* or *crus cerebri*. These crura serve as pathways for the nerve fibers descending from the cerebral cortex to the lower centers in the pons and spinal cord. In the adult these fibers are known as *corticospinal, corticobulbar*, and *corticopontine tracts*.

*Alar Plate and Colliculi*

The alar plates of the mesencephalon initially appear as two longitudinal elevations separated by a shallow midline depression (fig. 15-17A). With further development, a transverse groove divides each longitudinal elevation into an *anterior* (superior) and a *posterior* (inferior) *colliculus* (fig. 15-17B). Whereas the nuclei of the posterior colliculi serve as synaptic relay stations for the auditory reflexes, those of the anterior colliculi function as correlation and reflex centers for the visual impulses.

The colliculi are formed by waves of neuroblasts produced by the neuroepithelial cells and migrating into the overlying marginal zone. Here they become arranged in stratified layers (fig. 15-19B). In addition to the formation of the colliculi, some investigators believe that the cells of the alar plate also give rise to the *nucleus ruber* and the *substantia nigra*. Others, however, are of the opinion that these nuclei differentiate *in situ*.[9]

## Diencephalon

*Roof Plate and Epiphysis*

This part of the brain develops from the median portion of the prosencephalon (figs. 15-5 and 15-15), and is thought to consist of a roof plate and two alar plates, but to lack floor and basal plates.[10] Posteriorly, it is bounded by a plane passing behind the pineal and mammillary bodies, while its anterior boundary is formed by a plane passing just rostral to the optic chiasma and encircling the *foramen of Monro* (fig. 15-20A). The lamina terminalis is considered to be a part of the telencephalon.

The roof plate of the diencephalon consists of a single layer of ependymal cells covered by vascular mesenchyme. The two combined later give rise to the *choroid plexus* of the third ventricle (fig. 15-25). The most caudal part of the roof plate does not participate in the formation of the choroid plexus, but develops into the

Special Embryology

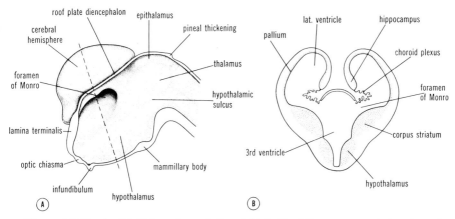

Figure 15-20. *A, Medial surface of the right half of the prosencephalon in a 7-week embryo (modified after Hochstetter). B, Schematic transverse section through the prosencephalon at the level of the broken line in A. The corpus striatum bulges out in the floor of the lateral ventricle and the foramen of Monro.*

*pineal body* or *epiphysis*. This body initially appears as an epithelial thickening in the midline, but by the seventh week begins to evaginate (figs. 15-21 and 15-23). Eventually it becomes a solid organ located on the roof of the mesencephalon (fig. 15-25). Though many theories have been proposed as to its function, no satisfactory answer has yet been found.[11, 12] In the adult, calcium is frequently deposited in the epiphysis and it then serves as a landmark on an x-ray of the skull.

Occasionally the roof plate of the diencephalon forms another evagination close to the interventricular foramen. This evagination is known as the *paraphysis*.[13] This organ sometimes persists into postnatal life and may then give rise to small cysts.[14]

In addition to the formation of the choroid plexus and epiphysis, the roof plate is thought to give rise to the *epithalamus*, a group of nuclei located on each side of the midline close to the pineal gland (fig. 15-20*A*). Whether this theory is correct, or whether the epithalamus is derived from the alar plate, is unknown. The epithalamic region is at first rather large, but later regresses to a small area, where the *habenular nuclei* are found. These nuclei form a link in the olfactory conduction path and are connected to each other across the midline by a group of nerve fibers collectively known as the *habenular commissure*. This commissure is found just rostral to the pineal stalk (figs. 15-23 and 15-25). Another commissure, known as the *posterior commissure*, appears just caudal to the stalk. This commissure likewise connects two nuclear areas on each side of the midline.

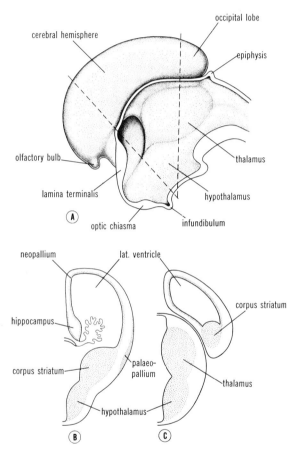

Figure 15-21. A, *Medial surface of the right half of the telencephalon and diencephalon in an 8-week embryo (modified after Hochstetter). B and C, Schematic transverse section through the right half of the telencephalon and diencephalon at the level of the broken lines as indicated in A.*

Special Embryology

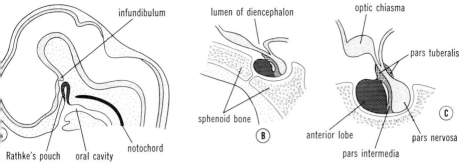

Figure 15-22. *A, Sagittal section through the cephalic part of a 6-week embryo, showing Rathke's pouch as a dorsal outpocketing of the oral cavity, and the infundibulum as a thickening in the floor of the diencephalon. B and C, Sagittal sections through the developing hypophysis in the 11th and 16th weeks of development, respectively. Note the formation of the pars tuberalis, encircling the stalk of the pars nervosa.*

### Thalamus and Hypothalamus

The alar plates form the lateral walls as well as the floor of the diencephalon. On the side facing the lumen a distinct longitudinal groove is visible. This groove, the *hypothalamic sulcus*, divides the alar plate into a dorsal and ventral region, the *thalamus* and *hypothalamus*, respectively (figs. 15–20, 15–21 and 15–23). Although the *hypothalamic sulcus* has been compared to the sulcus limitans, it is of a different nature since it does not form the dividing line between sensory and motor areas.

As a result of a high proliferative activity, the thalamus gradually projects into the lumen of the diencephalon. Frequently, this expansion is so great that the thalamic regions from the right and left sides fuse in the midline, thereby forming the *massa intermedia* or *interthalamic connexus*. The nuclear areas of the thalamus eventually form two distinct nuclear groups: a *dorsal thalamic group* important for the reception and transmission of visual and auditory impulses, and a *ventral thalamic group* serving mainly as a passage and relay station.

The hypothalamus, forming the lower portion of the alar plate, likewise differentiates into a number of separate nuclear groups. These nuclear areas, however, serve as regulation centers of the visceral functions such as sleep, digestion, body temperature, and emotional behavior. One of these groups, the *mammillary body*, becomes conspicuous and forms a round protuberance on the ventral surface of the hypothalamus on each side of the midline (figs. 15-20A and 15-23A).

Central Nervous System

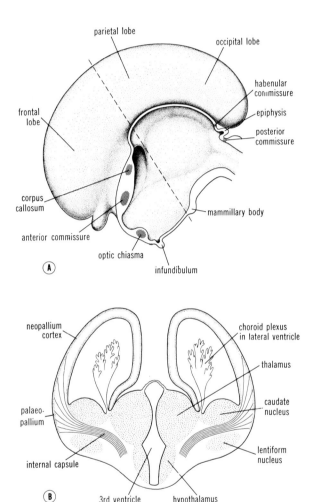

Figure 15-23. A, *Medial surface of the right half of the telencephalon and dien-cephalon in a 10-week embryo (modified after Hochstetter). B, Schematic trans-verse section through the hemisphere and diencephalon at the level of the broken line as indicated in A.*

Special Embryology

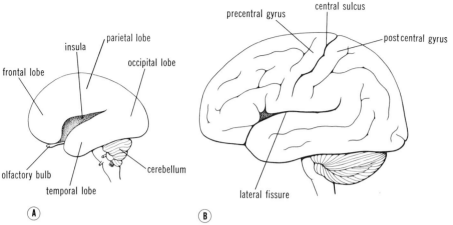

Figure 15-24. *Schematic drawing to show the development of gyri and sulci on the lateral surface of the cerebral hemisphere. A, At seven months; B, nine months (modified after Hochstetter).*

## Hypophysis

The hypophysis or pituitary gland develops from two completely different parts: (1) an ectodermal outpocketing of the stomodeum immediately in front of the buccopharyngeal membrane, known as *Rathke's pouch*; and (2) a downward extension of the diencephalon, the *infundibulum* (fig. 15-22A).

When the embryo is approximately 3 weeks old, Rathke's pouch appears as an evagination of the stomodeum, and subsequently grows dorsally toward the infundibulum. By the end of the second month it loses its connection with the oral cavity and is then in close contact with the infundibulum. Occasionally a small portion of the pouch persists in the wall of the pharynx (*pharyngeal hypophysis*).[15]

During further development the cells in the anterior wall of Rathke's pouch increase rapidly in number and form the *anterior lobe of the hypophysis* (fig. 15-22B). Later, a small extension of this lobe, the *pars tuberalis*, grows along the stalk of the infundibulum and eventually surrounds it (fig. 15-22C). The posterior wall of Rathke's pouch develops into the *pars intermedia*, which in man seems to have little significance. In the adult the lumen of the pouch is obliterated, although occasionally a narrow cleft may remain.

The infundibulum gives rise to the *stalk* and the *pars nervosa* or *posterior lobe of the hypophysis* (fig. 15-22C). It is composed of neuroglia cells which later differentiate into the so-called *pituicytes*.[16]

Central Nervous System

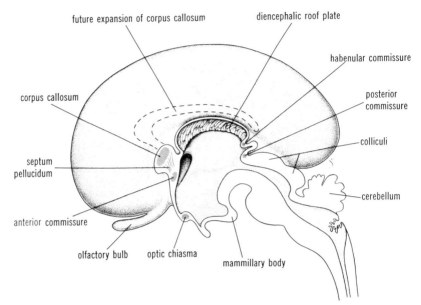

future expansion of corpus callosum

diencephalic roof plate

habenular commissure

corpus callosum

posterior commissure

colliculi

septum pellucidum

cerebellum

anterior commissure

olfactory bulb     optic chiasma

mammillary body

Figure 15-25. *View of the medial surface of the right half of the brain in a 4-month embryo, showing the various commissures. The broken line indicates the future expansion of the corpus callosum. The hippocampal commissure is not indicated (modified after Hochstetter).*

In addition, it contains a number of nerve fibers which come from the hypothalamic area of the diencephalon into the gland.

When in mammalian fetuses the pituitary gland is removed, differentiation of the thyroid gland and the carbohydrate metabolism are disturbed. Growth retardation, however, has not been described.

## Telencephalon

The telencephalon, the most rostral of the brain vesicles, consists of two lateral outpocketings, the *cerebral hemispheres*, and a median portion, the *lamina terminalis* (figs. 15-4, 15-5, 15-20 and 15-21). The cavities of the hemispheres, the *lateral ventricles*, communicate widely with the lumen of the diencephalon through the *interventricular foramina of Monro*.

### Cerebral Hemispheres

The cerebral hemispheres arise at the beginning of the fifth week of development as bilateral evaginations of the lateral wall of the prosencephalon. As in other parts of the brain, cell proliferation

Special Embryology

occurs mainly in the neuroepithelial layer and large numbers of neuroblasts for the mantle layer are produced. By the middle of the second month the mantle layer in the basal part of the hemispheres (that is, the part which initially formed the forward extension of the thalamus) (fig. 15-20A) begins to increase in size. As a result this area bulges into the lumen of the lateral ventricle as well as into the floor of the foramen of Monro (figs. 15-20B and 15-21A, B). In transverse section, the rapidly growing region has a striated appearance and therefore is known as the *corpus striatum*.

The remainder of the wall of the hemisphere temporarily remains relatively thin and is known as the *pallium*, the primordium of the *cerebral cortex* (fig. 15-20B). In the region where the wall of the hemisphere is attached to the roof of the diencephalon, it fails to develop neuroblasts and remains very thin (fig. 15-20B). Here the hemisphere wall consists of a single layer of ependymal cells covered by vascular mesenchyme, and together they form the *choroid plexus*. Its position on the medial surface of the hemisphere is the result of the disproportionate growth of the various parts of the hemisphere. The choroid plexus should have formed the roof of the hemisphere, but now it protrudes into the lateral ventricle along a line known as the *choroidal fissure* (figs. 15-20B, 15-21B and 15-23B). Immediately above the choroidal fissure the wall of the pallium is thickened, thus forming the *hippocampus* (fig. 15-20B and 15-21B). This structure, which has an olfactory function, bulges out into the lateral ventricle.

With further expansion the hemispheres gradually cover the lateral aspect of the diencephalon, mesencephalon and the cephalic portion of the metencephalon (figs. 15-20 to 15-25). The corpus striatum, being a part of the wall of the hemisphere, likewise expands posteriorly and forms a longitudinal ridge in the floor of the lateral ventricle (fig. 15-23B). During this growth the corpus striatum is divided into two parts: (1) a dorsomedial portion which forms the *caudate nucleus*; and (2) a ventrolateral portion which develops into the *lentiform nucleus* (fig. 15-23B). This division is accomplished by an ever-increasing number of afferent and efferent axons passing to and from the cortex of the hemisphere and breaking through the nuclear mass of the corpus striatum. The fiber bundle so formed is known as the *internal capsule* (fig. 15-23B).[17] The lentiform nucleus is later divided into a lateral portion, the *putamen*, and a medial, lightly staining portion, the *globus pallidus*.

As a result of the posterior expansion of the hemisphere, its medial surface approaches the lateral surface of the diencephalon (fig. 15-21C). When the medial wall of the hemisphere and the lateral wall of the diencephalon subsequently fuse, the caudate nucleus and the thalamus come in close contact, while the nerve fibers descending from the cortex of the hemisphere pass through the plane of fusion to enter the peduncles of the mesencephalon (fig. 15-23B).[18]

Continuous growth of the cerebral hemispheres in anterior, dorsal and inferior directions results in the formation of the frontal, temporal and occipital lobes. As the region overlying the corpus striatum lags in growth, however, the area between the frontal and temporal lobes becomes depressed and is known as the *insula* (fig. 15-24A). This region is later overgrown by the adjacent lobes and at the time of birth is almost completely covered. During the final part of fetal life the surface of the cerebral hemispheres grows so rapidly that a great many convolutions (*gyri*) separated by fissures and sulci appear on its surface (fig. 15-24B).

## Cortex Development

The cerebral cortex develops from the pallium, which may be divided into two regions: (1) the *palaeo*- or *archipallium*, an area located immediately lateral to the corpus striatum; and (2) the *neopallium*, which occupies the rest of the surface of the hemisphere between the hippocampus and the palaeopallium (figs. 15-21B and 15-23B).

The palaeopallium appears in the seventh week of development and is formed by a conglomeration of cells migrating from the striated mantle layer into the marginal zone. Here, the cells establish a thin nuclear layer close to the surface that acts as a relay station for olfactory impulses.

Shortly after the appearance of the palaeopallium, the cells of the mantle layer of the neopallium likewise begin to migrate into the marginal zone, where they establish a superficial cortical layer (fig. 15-23B). At birth, this layer has a stratified appearance due to successive waves of cells from the mantle layer and to differentiation of the cells in the cortex itself.[19] Different areas of the cortex acquire specific cell types; for example, the motor cortex contains a large number of *pyramidal cells*, whereas the sensory areas are characterized by *granular cells*.

## Commissures

In the adult the right and left halves of the hemispheres are connected by a number of fiber bundles, the *commissures*, which cross the midline. The most important of these fiber bundles make use of the *lamina terminalis*, the midportion of the telencephalon which extends from the roof plate of the diencephalon to the optic chiasma

Special Embryology

(figs. 15-20 and 15-25). The first of the crossing bundles to appear is the *anterior commissure*. It becomes visible by the third month of development and consists of fibers connecting the olfactory bulb and related brain areas of one hemisphere to those of the opposite side (figs. 15-23 and 15-25).

The second commissure to appear is the *hippocampal* or *fornix commissure*. Its fibers arise in the hippocampus and converge on the lamina terminalis close to the roof plate of the diencephalon. From here the fibers continue, forming an arching system immediately outside the choroid fissure, to the mammillary body and the hypothalamus. Under influence of the enormous growth of the corpus callosum, which appears a short time later, the hippocampal or fornix commissure regresses greatly.

The most important commissure is the *corpus callosum*. It appears by the 10th week of development and connects the non-olfactory areas of the right and left cerebral cortex. Initially it forms a small bundle in the lamina terminalis immediately rostral to the hippocampal commissure. However, as a result of the continuous expansion of the neopallium, it rapidly extends first anteriorly and then posteriorly, thereby arching over the thin roof of the diencephalon (fig. 15-25).

The growth of the corpus callosum in anterior direction pulls the area of the lamina terminalis away from the fornix commissure and the lamina terminalis becomes locally very thin, thus forming the *septum pellucidum*. Frequently this septum contains a small cavity which has no relation to the brain ventricles. It has been suggested that the bilaminar structure of the septum consists of the apposed walls of the two hemispheres anterior to the lamina terminalis.

In addition to the three above-mentioned commissures developing in the lamina terminalis, three more appear. Two of these, the *posterior* and *habenular commissures*, are found just below and rostral to the stalk of the pineal gland. The third, the *optic chiasma*, appears in the rostral wall of the diencephalon and contains fibers from the medial halves of the retinae which cross the midline on their way to the lateral geniculate body and the anterior colliculus.

# Congenital Malformations

## Meningocele, Meningo-encephalocele, Meningohydro-encephalocele

The primary cause of all these malformations is an ossification defect in the bones of the skull. The most frequently affected bone is the squamous part of the occipital bone, which may be partially or totally lacking. The thus formed foramen is often confluent with the foramen magnum. If the opening of the occipital bone is small, only the meninges bulge through it (*meningocele*), but if the defect is large, part of the brain and even part of the ventricle may penetrate through the opening into the meningeal sac (fig. 15-26). The latter two malformations are known as *meningo-encephalocele* and *meningo-hydro-encephalocele*, respectively.[20]

### Anencephalus

Anencephalus is characterized by failure of the cephalic part of the neural tube to close and at birth the brain is represented by a mass of degenerated tissue exposed to the surface. The defect is almost always continuous with an open cord in the cervical region. The vault of the skull is absent, giving the head a characteristic appearance: the eyes bulge forward, the neck is absent, and the surfaces of the face and chest form a continuous plane. Since the fetus lacks the control mechanism for swallowing, the last two months of pregnancy are characterized by *hydramnios*. On an x-ray of the fetus, the abnormality can easily be recognized, since the vault of the skull is absent.

### Hydrocephalus

Hydrocephalus is characterized by an abnormal accumulation of cerebrospinal fluid within the ventricular system or, as in the case of external hydrocephalus, between the brain and dura mater. In the majority of cases, hydrocephalus in the newborn is thought to be due to an obstruction of the aqueduct of Sylvius. This prevents the

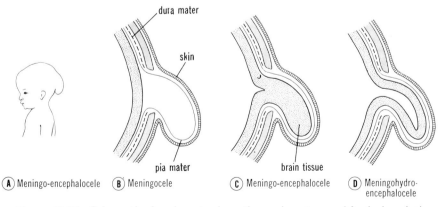

Figure 15-26. *Schematic drawings to show the various types of brain herniation due to abnormal ossification of the skull.*

Special Embryology

cerebrospinal fluid of the lateral and third ventricles from passing into the fourth ventricle and from there into the subarachnoidal space.[21] The malformation is often accompanied by a widening of the sutures of the skull, while the bones themselves gradually become thin. In extreme cases the skull may be three times the normal size.

It is obvious that the above-mentioned abnormalities are only the most serious ones and usually incompatible with life. A great many other defects of the central nervous system, however, may occur without much external manifestation. For example, the corpus callosum may be partially or completely absent without much functional disturbance. Likewise, partial or complete absence of the cerebellum may show only a little disturbance of coordination. On the other hand, cases of severe imbecility or idiocy may show hardly any morphological brain abnormalities.

## Environmental and Chromosomal Factors

To establish the teratogenicity of an environmental factor, one must show that the malformed children have a history of prenatal exposure to a teratogenic agent more often than non-malformed children. For this reason, only a few environmental teratogens have so far been identified in human beings.

It is now well established that abnormalities of the central nervous system can occur as the result of fetal infection by the *toxoplasma* organism. The affected child may then suffer from cerebral calcification, mental retardation, hydrocephalus, or microcephalus.[22] Likewise, radiation during the early stages of development may account for microcephalus.[23-25] Whether virus diseases affecting the fetus during the first trimester of development cause brain abnormalities awaits more information. Some authors have suggested that maternal infection with Asian influenza in the early stages of pregnancy may occasionally result in anencephalus, but that the risk is low;[26, 27] others, however, have reported no significant increase in the malformation rate following maternal influenza.[28, 29] Although the rubella virus can cause abnormalities of the heart, eye, and ear, abnormalities of the central nervous system have been reported only sporadically.[30]

The discovery that congenital malformations may be caused by chromosomal abnormalities has had important implications with regard to mental retardation. That a human defect could be caused by a chromosomal imbalance was first demonstrated by the discovery that children with mongolism had 47 chromosomes, chromosome number 21 being represented three times instead of twice (trisomy).[31, 32] Likewise, 47 chromosomes were found in patients with Klinefelter's syndrome, the extra chromosome being an X. This syndrome accounts for about 1 per cent of mentally defective children.[33] In addition to Klinefelter's syndrome, it has recently been discovered that many sex chromosome abnormalities are associated with mental retardation.[34] Likewise, many of the recently discovered congenital metabolic defects such as phenylketonuria cause or are accompanied by mental retardation.

Although little is known about the etiology of malformations of the central nervous system in man, over the past years many environmental teratogens have been detected as causing malformations of the central nervous system in the offspring of experimental animals. Anencephalus, hydrocephalus, spina bifida, cranium bifidum, exencephalus, meningocele, microcephalus, and cerebellar defects have been produced by a variety of teratogenic factors (vitamin A, riboflavin, folic acid, pantothenic acid, vitamin E, and nicotinamide deficiencies; maternal fasting; hypervitaminosis A; trypan blue; hypoxia; x-irradiation; and antibody treatment).[35-49] In the chick embryo it has been possible to produce a variety of abnormalities of the neural tube by virus inoculation and antibody treatment.[50-53] An excellent review of the factors causing congenital malformations of the central nervous system in experimental animals has recently been published by Kalter.[54]

Although the great majority of malformations of the central nervous system have been produced by treating pregnant animals during early stages of gestation, it was recently found that excess vitamin A when given to mice during the later stages of pregnancy may also cause abnormalities of the cerebral cortex.[55] These abnormalities were only detectable with the microscope and concerned degeneration or abnormal differentiation of the neuroblasts in certain areas of the cortex.

## References—Brain

1. WILSON, J. T. On the nature and mode of origin of the foramen of Magendie. J. Anat., 71: 423, 1937.
2. LARSELL, O. Development of cerebellum in man in relation to its comparative anatomy. J. Comp. Neurol., 87: 85, 1947.
3. DOW, R. S. The evolution and anatomy of the cerebellum. Biol. Rev., 17: 170, 1942.
4. JANSEN, J., AND BRODAL, A. Das Kleinhirn. In Handbuch des Mikroskopischen Anatomie des Menschen. Springer-Verlag, Berlin, 1958.
5. MIALE, I., AND SIDMAN, R. An autoradiographic study of histogenesis in the mouse cerebellum. Exp. Neurol., 4: 277, 1961.
6. UZMAN, L. The histogenesis of the mouse cerebellum as studied by tritiated thymidine uptake. J. Comp. Neurol., 114: 137, 1960.
7. FUJITA, S. Analysis of neuron differentiation in the central nervous system by tritiated thymidine autoradiography. J. Comp. Neurol., 112: 311, 1964.

8. HANAWAY, J. Formation and differentiation of the external granular layer of the chick cerebellum. J. Comp. Neurol., **131:** 1, 1967.
9. SHANER, R. F. Development of nuclei and tracts of mid-brain. J. Comp. Neurol., **55:** 493, 1932.
10. KINGSBURY, B. F. The fundamental plan of the vertebrate brain. J. Comp. Neurol., **34:** 461, 1922.
11. GLADSTONE, R. J., AND WAKELAY, C. P. G. *The Pineal Organ.* Baillière, Tindall & Cox, Ltd., London, 1940.
12. KITAY, J. L., AND ALTSCHULE, M.D. *The Pineal Gland.* Harvard University Press, Cambridge, Mass., 1954.
13. ARIENS KAPPERS, J. Development of the human paraphysis. J. Comp. Neurol., **102:** 425, 1955.
14. BULL, J. W. D., AND SUTTON, D. The diagnosis of paraphysial cysts. Brain, **72:** 487, 1949.
15. BOYD, J. D. Observations on the human pharyngeal hypophysis. J. Endocr., **14:** 66, 1956.
16. SHANKLIN, W. M. Differentiation of pituicytes in the human fetus. J. Anat., **74:** 459, 1940.
17. HEWITT, W. The development of the human internal capsule and lentiform nucleus. J. Anat., **95:** 191, 1961.
18. SHARP, J. A. The junctional region of the cerebral hemisphere and the third ventricle in mammalian embryos. J. Anat., **93:** 159, 1959.
19. CONEL, J. L. *Postnatal Development of the Human Cerebral Cortex.* Harvard University Press, Cambridge, Mass., 1959.
20. INGRAHAM, F. D., AND SCOTT, H. W. Spina bifida and cranium bifidum. New Engl. J. Med., **229:** 108, 1943.
21. RUSSELL, D. S. *Observations on the Pathology of Hydrocephalus* (Medical Research Council Special Report No. 265). His Majesty's Stationery Office, London, 1949.
22. FELDMAN, H. A. Toxoplasmosis. Pediatrics, **22:** 559, 1958.
23. MURPHY, D. F. Ovarian irradiation and the health of the subsequent child; a review of more than 200 previously unreported pregnancies in women subjected to pelvic irradiation. Surg. Gynec. Obstet., **48:** 766, 1929.
24. PLUMMER, G. Anomalies occurring in children exposed *in utero* to the atomic bomb in Hiroshima. Pediatrics, **10:** 687, 1952.
25. YAMAZAKI, J. N., WRIGHT, S. W., AND WRIGHT, P. M. Outcome of pregnancy in women exposed to the atomic bomb in Nagasaki. A. M. A. J. Dis. Child., **87:** 448, 1954.
26. COFFEY, V. P., AND JESSOP, N. J. Rubella and incidence of congenital abnormalities. Irish J. Med. Sci., **397:** 1, 1959.
27. DOLL, R., AND HILL, A. B. Asian influenza in pregnancy and congenital defects. Brit. J. Prev. Soc. Med., **14:** 167, 1960.
28. WALKER, W. M., AND MCKEE, A. P. Asian influenza in pregnancy. Obstet. Gynec. (N. Y.), **13:** 394, 1959.
29. WILSON, M. G., HEINS, H. L., IMAGAWA, D. T., AND ADAMS, J. M. Teratogenic effects of Asian influenza. J. A. M. A., **171:** 638, 1959.
30. ARIENS KAPPERS, J. Les malformations cérébrales consécutives à l'embryopathie rubéoleuse. In *Colloque sur les malformations congénitales de l'encéphalie*, edited by Heyer, Feld, and Gruner. Masson & Cie., Paris, 1959.
31. LEJEUNE, J., GAUTIER, M., AND TURPIN, R. Etudes des chromosomes somatiques de neuf enfants mongoliens. C. R. Acad. Sci. (Par.), **248:** 1921, 1959.
32. JACOBS, P. A., BAILIE, A. G., BROWN, W. M. C., AND STRONG, J. A. The somatic chromosomes in mongolism. Lancet, **1:** 710, 1959.
33. MACLEAN, N., *et al.* A survey of sex chromosome abnormalities among 4514 mental defectives. Lancet, **1:** 293, 1962.

34. HARNDEN, D. G., AND JACOBS, P. A. Cytogenetics of abnormal sexual development in man. Brit. Med. Bull., **17:** 206, 1961.

35. KALTER, H., AND WARKANY, J. Experimental production of congenital malformations in mammals by metabolic procedure. Physiol. Rev., **39:** 69, 1959.

36. GIROUD, A. Anencéphalie, encéphalôcèles, méningocèles par hypervitaminose A. Arch. Franc. Pediat., **15:** 835, 1958.

37. GIROUD, A., GOUNELLE, H., AND MARTINET, M. Données quantitatives sue le taux de la vitamine A chez le rat lors d'expériences de tératogénèse par hypervitaminose A. Bull. Soc. Chim. Biol., **39:** 331, 1957.

38. GIROUD, A. Méningocèles rachidiennes et fermeture imparfaite du tube médullaire. Arch. Anat. (Strasb.), **44:** 107, 1961.

39. GIROUD, A. Encéphalocèle, méningocèle par hypervitamonose A et considerations cliniques. Rev. Neurol. (Par.), **98:** 181, 1958.

40. WARKANY, J., WILSON, J. G., AND GEIGER, J. Myeloschisis and myelomeningocele produced experimentally in the rat. J. Comp. Neurol., **109:** 35, 1958.

41. RUNNER, M. N., AND MILLER, J. R. Congenital deformity in the mouse as a consequence of fasting. Anat. Rec., **124:** 437, 1956.

42. MILLER, J. R. Clinical and experimental studies on the etiology of skull, vertebra, rib and palate malformations. Ph.D. Thesis, McGill University, 1959.

43. RUSSELL, L. B. X-ray induced developmental abnormalities in the mouse and their use in the analysis of embryological patterns. II. Abnormalities of the vertebral column and thorax. J. Exp. Zool., **131:** 329, 1956.

44. HICKS, S. P., et al. Migrating cells in the developing nervous system studied by their radiosensitivity and tritiated thymidine uptake. Brookhaven Symposia Biol., **14:** 246, 1961.

45. INGALLS, T. H., AVIS, F. R., CURLEY, F. J., AND TEMIN, H. M. Genetic determinants of hypoxia induced congenital anomalies. J. Hered., **44:** 185, 1953.

46. PINSKY, H., AND FRASER, F. C. Congenital malformations following a two-hour inactivation of nicotinamide by its analogue, 6-aminonicotinamide in pregnant mice. Brit. Med. J., **2:** 195, 1960.

47. RUNNER, M. N., AND DAGG, C. P. Metabolic mechanisms of teratogenic agents during morphogenesis (symposium on normal and abnormal differentiation and development). Nat. Cancer Inst. Monogr., **2:** 41, 1960.

48. GLUECKSOHN-WAELSCH, S. The effect of maternal immunization against organ tissues on embryonic differentiation in the mouse. J. Embryol. Exp. Morph., **5:** 83, 1957.

49. BRENT, R. L., AVERICH, E., AND DRAPIEWSKI, V. A. Production of congenital malformations using tissue antibodies. Proc. Soc. Exp. Biol. Med., **106:** 523, 1961.

50. ROBERTSON, G. G., WILLIAMSON, A. P., AND BLATTNER, R. J. Origin of myeloschisis in chick embryos infected with influenza-A virus. Yale J. Biol. Med., **32:** 449, 1960.

51. ROBERTSON, G. G., WILLIAMSON, A. P., AND BLATTNER, R. J. Abnormal formation of neural tube in chick embryos inoculated with influenza-A virus. Anat. Rec., **127:** 479, 1957.

52. ROBERTSON, G. G., WILLIAMSON, A. P., AND BLATTNER, R. J. A study of abnormalities in early chick embryos inoculated with Newcastle disease virus. J. Exp. Zool., **129:** 5, 1955.

53. McCALLION, D. J., AND LANGMAN, J. An immunological study on the effect of brain extract on the developing nervous tissue in the chick embryo. J. Emb. Exp. Morph., **12:** 77, 1964.

54. KALTER, H. *Teratology of the Central Nervous System*. The University of Chicago Press, Chicago, 1968.

55. LANGMAN, J., AND WELCH, G. W. Excess vitamin A and development of the cerebral cortex. J. Comp. Neurol., **131:** 15, 1967.

Special Embryology

# AUTONOMIC NERVOUS SYSTEM

---

•SYMPATHETIC NERVOUS SYSTEM: *sympathetic chains; white and gray communicating rami*
  *Suprarenal gland:* fetal and definitive cortex; medulla
•PARASYMPATHETIC NERVOUS SYSTEM
  *Carotid bodies*

---

Functionally, the autonomic nervous system can be divided into two parts: a *sympathetic* portion which is localized in the thoracolumbar region, and a *parasympathetic* portion, found in the cephalic and sacral regions.

## Sympathetic Nervous System

In the fifth week of development cells, originating in the neural crest of the thoracic region and known as the *sympathetic neuroblasts*, migrate on each side of the spinal cord toward the region immediately behind the dorsal aorta (fig. 15-27). Here they form a bilateral chain of segmentally arranged sympathetic ganglia interconnected by longitudinal nerve fibers. Together they form the *sympathetic chains.* From their position in the thorax, the neuroblasts migrate toward the cervical and lumbosacral regions, thus extending the sympathetic chains to their full length. Although initially the ganglia are arranged segmentally, this arrangement is

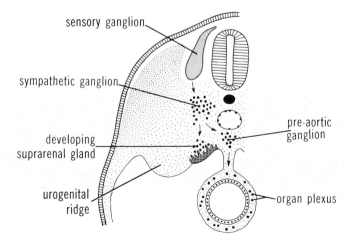

Figure 15-27. *Schematic drawing to show the formation of the sympathetic ganglia. A portion of the sympathetic neuroblasts migrates toward the proliferating mesothelium to form the medulla of the suprarenal gland (modified after Giroud).*

Central Nervous System                                                     329

later obscured, particularly in the cervical region, by the fusion of ganglia.

Some of the sympathetic neuroblasts migrate in front of the aorta to form the *pre-aortic ganglia*, such as the *coeliac* and *mesenteric ganglia*, located at the roots of the main aortic branches. Still other sympathetic cells migrate to the heart, lungs and gastrointestinal tract, where they give rise to the *sympathetic organ plexuses* (fig. 15-27).

Once the sympathetic chains have been established, nerve fibers originating in the viscero-efferent column of the thoracolumbar segments of the spinal cord penetrate the ganglia of the chain and form synapses around the developing neuroblasts (fig. 15-28). Some

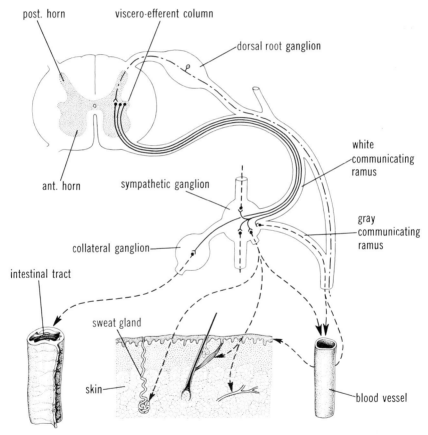

Figure 15-28. *Schematic drawing to show the relationship of the pre-ganglionic and post-ganglionic nerve fibers of the sympathetic nervous system to the spinal nerves. Note the origin of the pre-ganglionic fibers in the viscero-efferent motor column of the spinal cord.*

Special Embryology

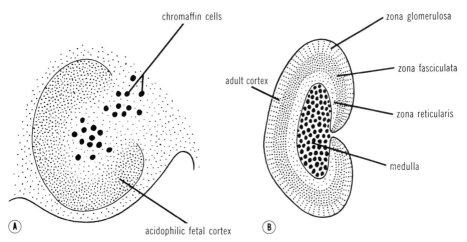

chromaffin cells

adult cortex

zona glomerulosa

zona fasciculata

zona reticularis

medulla

(A)

acidophilic fetal cortex

(B)

Figure 15-29. *A, Drawing showing the chromaffin (sympathetic) cells penetrating the fetal cortex of the suprarenal gland. B, At a later stage of development, the definitive cortex surrounds the medulla almost completely.*

of these nerve fibers either extend to higher or lower levels in the sympathetic chains or to the *pre-aortic* or *collateral ganglia* before synapsing. They are known as *pre-ganglionic fibers*, have a myelin sheath, and stimulate the sympathetic ganglion cells into action. Passing from the spinal nerves to the sympathetic ganglia, they form the so-called *white communicating rami*. Since the viscero-efferent column extends only from the first thoracic to the second lumbar segment of the spinal cord, the white rami are found only between these levels.

The axons of the sympathetic ganglion cells are called *post-ganglionic fibers* and have no myelin sheath. They pass either to other levels of the sympathetic chain or extend to the heart, lungs, and intestinal tract (fig. 15-28). Other fibers known as the *gray communicating rami* pass from the sympathetic chain to the spinal nerves and from there to the peripheral blood vessels, hair, and sweat glands. The gray communicating rami are found at all levels of the spinal cord.

*Suprarenal Gland*

The suprarenal gland develops from two components: (1) a mesodermal portion which forms the *cortex* of the gland; and (2) an ectodermal portion which forms the *medulla*.

During the fifth week of development, mesothelial cells located between the root of the mesentery and the developing gonad begin to proliferate and penetrate the underlying mesenchyme (fig. 15-27).

Here they differentiate into large acidophilic organs which form the *fetal* or *primitive cortex* of the suprarenal gland (fig. 15-29A). Shortly afterward a second wave of cells from the mesothelium penetrates the mesenchyme and surrounds the original acidophilic cell mass. These cells, smaller than those of the first wave, later form the *definitive cortex* of the gland (fig. 15-29A, B). After birth the fetal cortex regresses rapidly, except for its outermost layer, which differentiates into the reticular zone. The adult structure of the cortex is not achieved until the approach of puberty.

While the fetal cortex is being formed, cells originating in the sympathetic system invade its medial aspect, where they become arranged in cords and clusters. These cells, which give rise to the medulla of the suprarenal gland, do not form nerve processes, but stain yellow-brown with chrome salts and hence are called *chromaffin cells* (fig. 15-27 and 15-29). The staining is probably caused by epinephrine and norepinephrine in the cells. During embryonic life the chromaffin cells are widely scattered throughout the embryo, but in the adult the only persisting group is found in the medulla of the adrenal glands.

## Parasympathetic Nervous System

The origin of the parasympathetic ganglia found along the oculomotor, facial, glossopharyngeal, and vagus nerves is rather controversial. Some believe that the cells of these ganglia migrate out of the central nervous system along the pre-ganglionic fibers of the above-mentioned nerves, whereas others feel that they arise from neuroblasts originating in the sensory ganglia of the fifth, seventh and ninth nerves.

The post-ganglionic fibers of the parasympathetic ganglia pass to the branchial arches and to the cardiac, pulmonary, and intestinal plexuses. The action of these fibers is thought to be antagonistic to those of the sympathetic nervous system.

### Carotid Bodies

These bodies are formed by a mesodermal condensation around the origin of the internal carotid arteries and are supplied by branches of the glossopharyngeal nerve. They are invaded by cells from nearby autonomic ganglia and then develop into chemoreceptor organs, which serve as a reflex system in the regulation of blood pressure.

# CHAPTER 16

# Eye

NORMAL DEVELOPMENT
•OPTIC CUP AND LENS VESICLE
•RETINA, IRIS, AND CILIARY BODY
•LENS; CHOROID, SCLERA, AND CORNEA
•OPTIC NERVE

CONGENITAL MALFORMATIONS
•COLOBOMA IRIDIS
•PERSISTENT IRIDOPUPILLARY MEMBRANE
•MICROPHTHALMIA
•ANOPHTHALMIA
•CYCLOPIA
•CONGENITAL CATARACT
•EXPERIMENTAL DATA

## *Normal Development*

### Optic Cup and Lens Vesicle

The first sign of the developing eye appears in the 22-day embryo as a pair of shallow grooves on each side of the invaginating fore-brain (fig. 16-1A). With closure of the neural tube, these grooves form outpocketings of the forebrain, the *optic vesicles*, which are in contact with surface ectoderm (fig. 16-1B). During the following period of intimate contact between the two cell layers, the optic vesicle probably causes chemical changes in the surface ectoderm cells, necessary for lens formation.[1] Shortly thereafter the optic vesicle begins to invaginate and forms the double-walled *optic cup* (figs. 16-1C and 16-2A). The inner and outer layers of this cup are initially separated by a lumen, the *intra-retinal space*, but with further development this lumen disappears and the two layers are then apposed to each other (fig. 16-6). The invagination is not restricted to the central portion of the cup but also involves its ventral rim (fig. 16-2A). Here it forms the *choroid fissure*, which extends along the undersurface of the optic stalk, where it tapers off. During the

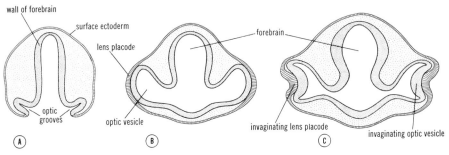

Figure 16-1. *A, Transverse section through the forebrain of a 22-day embryo (approximately 14 somites), showing the optic grooves. The neural tube is wide open to the surface (after Heuser). B, Transverse section through the forebrain of a 4-week embryo, showing the optic vesicles in contact with the surface ectoderm. Note the slight thickening of the ectoderm (lens placode). C, Transverse section through the forebrain of a 5-mm. embryo, showing the invagination of the optic vesicle and the lens placode (after Mann).*

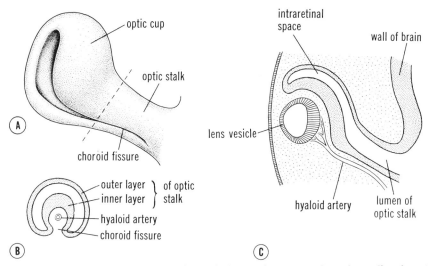

Figure 16-2. *A, Ventrolateral view of the optic cup and optic stalk of a 6-week embryo. The choroid fissure located on the undersurface of the optic stalk gradually tapers off. B, Transverse section through the optic stalk indicated as in A, showing the hyaloid artery in the choroid fissure. C, Section through the lens vesicle, the optic cup, and optic stalk at the plane of the choroid fissure (after Mann).*

Special Embryology

seventh week the lips of the choroid fissure fuse, and the mouth of the optic cup then becomes a round opening, the future *pupil*.[2, 3]

While these events occur, the cells of the surface ectoderm, initially in contact with the optic vesicle, begin to elongate and form the *lens placode* (fig. 16-1*B*, *C*). This placode subsequently invaginates and develops into the *lens vesicle*. During the fifth week the lens vesicle loses contact with the surface ectoderm and is then located in the mouth of the optic cup (fig. 16-2*C*).

## Retina, Iris, and Ciliary Body

The development of the outer layer of the optic cup is characterized by the appearance of small pigment granules which appear in the cells during the fifth week of development. The outer layer is then known as the *pigment layer of the retina* (figs. 16-3 and 16-6).

The development of the inner layer of the optic cup is more complicated. Its posterior four-fifths, known as the *pars optica retinae*, thickens considerably and undergoes a series of changes somewhat similar to those occurring in the wall of the brain vesicle. Bordering the intra-retinal space is the ependymal layer which, in the eye, differentiates into the light-receptive elements, the *rods* and *cones* (fig. 16-4). Adjacent to the photoreceptive layer is the mantle layer, which, as in the brain, gives rise to the neurons and supporting cells. In the adult the *outer nuclear layer*, the *inner nuclear layer*, and the *ganglion cell layer* can be distinguished (fig. 16-4). On the surface of the mantle layer is found the marginal zone which contains the axons of the nerve cells of the deeper layers. The nerve

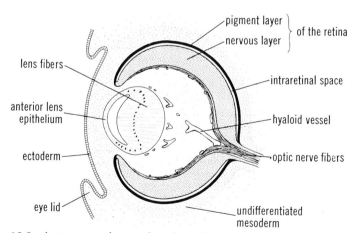

Figure 16-3. *Anteroposterior section through the eye of a 7-week embryo. The eye primordium is completely embedded in mesenchyme. The fibers of the nervous retina converge toward the optic nerve (modified after Mann).*

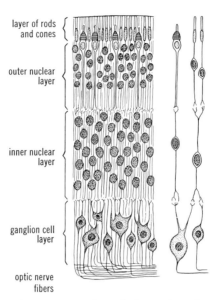

layer of rods
and cones

outer nuclear
layer

inner nuclear
layer

ganglion cell
layer

optic nerve
fibers

Figure 16-4. *Schematic representation of the various layers of the pars optica retinae in a fetus of approximately 25 weeks (modified after Mann).*

fibers in this zone converge toward the optic stalk, which develops gradually into the optic nerve (figs. 16-3 and 16-6).

The anterior one-fifth of the inner layer of the optic cup, the *pars caeca retinae*, does not change much and remains one cell layer thick. It is later divided into the *pars iridica retinae*, which forms the inner layer of the iris, and the *pars ciliaris retinae*, which participates in the formation of the ciliary body (fig. 16-5).

Meanwhile, the region between the optic cup and the overlying surface epithelium is filled with loose mesenchyme in which the *sphincter* and *dilator pupillae* develop (figs. 16-3 and 16-5). Whether in the human embryo these muscle fibers develop from the mesenchymal cells or from the underlying ectodermal cells of the optic cup, as has been shown for lower animals, is still not known.[4, 5] In the adult, the iris is formed by the pigment-containing internal and external layers of the optic cup as well as by a layer of richly vascularized connective tissue, which contains the pupillary muscles (fig. 16-5).

The *pars ciliaris retinae* is easily recognized by its marked folding (figs. 16-5B and 16-6). Externally it is covered by a layer of mesenchyme which forms the *ciliary muscle;* on the inside, it is connected to the lens by loose mesenchyme which forms the *suspensory ligament*. Contraction of the ciliary muscle changes the tension in the ligament and controls the curvature of the lens.

Special Embryology

## Lens

Shortly after the formation of the lens vesicle (fig. 16-2C), the cells of the posterior wall begin to elongate in an anterior direction and form long fibers which gradually fill the lumen of the vesicle (fig. 16-3). By the end of the seventh week these *primary lens fibers* reach the epithelium of the anterior wall of the lens vesicle and form the so-called *nucleus of the lens* (fig. 16-6). Growth of the lens, however, is not finished at this stage, but new (secondary) lens fibers are continuously added to the central core. These new fibers arise from the cells in the equatorial zone and it is believed that this process continues until the 20th year of life.

## Choroid, Sclera, and Cornea

At the end of the fifth week, when the optic cup and the lens vesicle have been formed, the eye primordium is completely surrounded by loose mesenchyme (fig. 16-3). This tissue soon differentiates into an inner layer comparable to the pia mater of the brain and an outer layer comparable to the dura mater. While the inner layer later forms a highly vascularized pigmented layer, known as

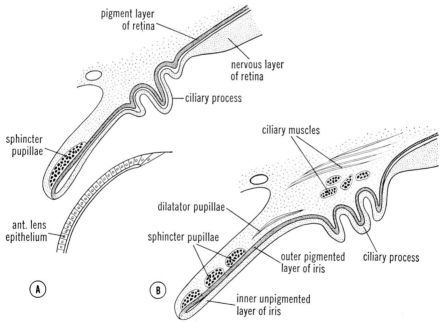

Figure 16-5. *Development of the iris and the ciliary body. The rim of the optic cup is covered by mesenchyme, in which the sphincter and dilatator pupillae develop.*

Eye

the *choroid*,[6] the outer layer develops into the sclera and is continuous with the dura mater around the optic nerve (fig. 16-6).

The differentiation of the mesenchymal layers overlying the anterior aspect of the eye is slightly different. Here, the cells arrange themselves in such a manner that a space, known as the *anterior chamber*, splits the mesenchyme into a thin inner layer immediately in front of the lens and iris, the *iridopupillary membrane*, and a thick outer layer continuous with the sclera. The anterior chamber itself is lined by flattened mesenchymal cells, which form the posterior lining of the cornea as well as the anterior covering of the iridopupillary membrane (fig. 16-6). Hence, the cornea from outside in is formed by: (1) an epithelial layer derived from the surface ectoderm; (2) a layer of dense connective tissue, the *substantia propria*, which is continuous with the sclera and is transparent; and (3) an epithelial layer which borders the anterior chamber. The iridopupillary membrane in front of the lens normally disappears completely.

Mesenchyme not only surrounds the eye primordium from the outside, but also invades the inside of the optic cup by way of the choroid fissure. Here, it participates in the formation of the hyaloid vessels, which during intra-uterine life supply the lens and form the vascular layer located on the inner surface of the retina (fig. 16-6). In addition, it forms a delicate network of fibers between the lens and the retina. The interstitial spaces of this network are later filled with a transparent gelatinous substance, thus forming the *vitreous body* (fig. 16-6).

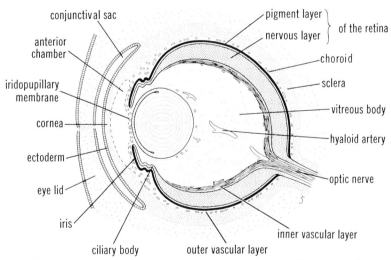

Figure 16-6. *Anteroposterior section through the eye of a 15-week embryo. Note the anterior chamber, the iridopupillary membrane, the inner and outer vascular layers, the choroid and the sclera.*

338                                                    Special Embryology

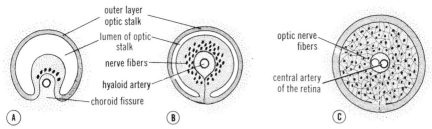

Figure 16-7. *Diagrams showing the transformation of the optic stalk into the optic nerve. A, At sixth week (9 mm.); B, seventh week (15 mm.); C, ninth week. Note the central artery of the retina in the optic nerve (adapted from several sources).*

## Optic Nerve

Initially the optic cup is connected to the brain by the optic stalk, which on its ventral surface has a groove, the *choroid fissure* (fig. 16-2). In this groove are found the hyaloid vessels. The nerve fibers of the retina returning to the brain are found among the cells of the inner wall of the stalk (fig. 16-7A). During the seventh week the choroid fissure closes and a narrow tunnel is formed inside the optic stalk (fig. 16-7B). As a result of the continuously increasing number of nerve fibers growing toward the brain, the inner wall of the stalk increases in size and the inside and outside walls of the stalk fuse (fig. 16-7C). The cells of the inner layer provide a network of neuroglia cells which support the optic nerve fibers.

The optic stalk is thus transformed into the *optic nerve*. In its center it contains the hyaloid artery, which is later called the *central artery of the retina*.

# Congenital Malformations

## Coloboma Iridis

Under normal conditions the choroid fissure closes during the seventh week of development (fig. 16-7). When this fails to occur, a cleft persists. Although such a cleft is usually located in the iris only and is known as *coloboma iridis* (fig. 16-8A), it may extend into the ciliary body, the retina, the choroid, and the optic nerve.[7] This malformation is frequently seen in combination with other eye abnormalities.[8]

## Persistent Iridopupillary Membrane

Usually the iridopupillary membrane disappears entirely during intra-uterine life. Sometimes, however, resorption is not complete

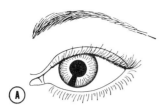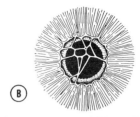

Figure 16-8. *A, Coloboma iridis. B, Partially persistent iridopupillary membrane.*

and a network of connective tissue is then suspended in front of the pupil (fig. 16-8*B*). This abnormality usually causes little disturbance of vision.

## Microphthalmia

In such a condition the over-all size of the eye is too small, and the eyeball may be reduced to two-thirds of its normal volume. Usually it is not associated with any other ocular abnormalities.

## Anophthalmia

Sometimes the eye is grossly absent and it is impossible to detect any trace of the eyeball except by histological means.[9] It is usually accompanied by other serious craniocerebral abnormalities.

## Cyclopia

In such an abnormality, both orbits are joined and there is only one median eye. This rare malformation is frequently accompanied by a *proboscis* and other craniocerebral abnormalities.[10]

## Congenital Cataract

This is a condition in which the lens has become opaque during intra-uterine life. Although this anomaly is usually genetically determined,[11] it may be caused by environmental factors. In 1941, Gregg[12] observed that children of mothers who suffered from German measles between the fourth and seventh weeks of pregnancy often showed congenital malformations of which cataract was one of the most common. If, however, the mother was infected after the seventh week of pregnancy, then the lens escaped damage, but the child might be deaf as a result of imperfect differentiation of the cochlea.[13] This seems to indicate that the most actively differentiating parts of the embryo are the most sensitive ones. Indeed, the lens goes through one of its most active stages of development during

Special Embryology

the sixth week of development, when the primary lens fibers fill the lumen of the lens vesicle.

## Experimental Data

In experimental work the primordium of the eye has been proved to be one of the most sensitive organs in the developing embryo, and a great number of eye abnormalities comparable to those in man have been produced.[14] It has been possible to show that a virus may produce eye abnormalities, but just as in the case of the German measles virus in man, it was found that the eye is sensitive only during certain stages of development.[15] Other teratogenic agents successfully used in the production of eye abnormalities are hypoxia,[16, 17] vitamin deficiency,[18-20] hypervitaminosis A,[21, 22] thyroid deficiency,[23] and x-irradiation.[24, 25] It was surprising to find that certain compounds (cysteamine) diminish, whereas others (cortisone) increase the sensitivity to x-irradiation.[26]

## References

1. LANGMAN, J. The first appearance of specific antigens during induction of the lens. J. Embryol. Exp. Morph., 7: 193, 1959.
2. MANN, I. C. The Development of the Human Eye. Grune & Stratton, Inc., New York, 1949.
3. BARBER, A. N. Embryology of the Human Eye. C. V. Mosby Co., St. Louis, 1955.
4. COLLIN, R. Recherches sur le développement du muscle sphincter de l'iris. Bibliographie anat., 11: 183, 1902.
5. NUSSBAUM, M. Die Entwicklung der Binnenmuskeln des Auges der Wirbeltiere. Arch. Mikroskopische Anat. Entwicklungsmech., 58B: 199, 1901.
6. BARTELMEZ, G. W. The formation of neural crest from the primary optic vesicle in man. Contrib. Embryol., 35: 55, 1954.
7. MANN, I. C. Developmental Abnormalities of the Eye. J. B. Lippincott Co., Philadelphia, 1957.
8. FRANCOIS, J., KLUYSKENS, J., AND PHILIPS, A. Colobomes iriens compliqués atypique et unilatéral dans un cas, typique et bilatéral dans un autre. Bull. Soc. Belg. Ophtal., 92: 188, 1949.
9. REDSLOB, E. Anophtalmie vraie et anophtalmie apparente chez un nouveau- né. Ann. Oculist. (Par.), 169: 433, 1932.
10. PAPOLCZY, F. Congenital cyclopia and orbital cyst together with other developmental anomalies on the same side of the face. Brit. J. Ophthal., 32: 439, 1948.
11. FRANCOIS, J. Heredity in Ophthalmology. C. V. Mosby Co., St. Louis, 1961.
12. GREGG, N. M. Congenital cataract following german measles in the mother. Trans. Ophthal. Soc. Aust., 3: 35, 1941.
13. TÖNDURY, G. Zur Kenntnis der Embryopathica rubeolica, nebst Bemerkungen über die Wirkung anderer Viren auf den Keimling. Geburtsh. Frauenheilk., 12: 865, 1952.
14. TUCHMANN-DUPLESSIS, H., AND MERCIER-PAROT, L. Production of congenital eye malformations particularly in rat fetuses. In The Structure of the Eye, edited by G. K. Smelser, p. 507. Academic Press, Inc., New York, 1961.
15. ROBERTSON, G. G., WILLIAMSON, A. P., AND BLATTNER, R. J. A study of abnor-

malities in early chick embryos inoculated with Newcastle disease virus. J. Exp. Zool., **129:** 5, 1955.

16. WERTHEMANN, A., AND REINIGER, M. Über Augenentwicklungsstörungen bei Rattenembryonen durch Sauerstoffmangel in der Frühschwangerschaft. Acta Anat. (Basel), **11:** 329, 1950.

17. INGALLS, T. H., CURLEY, F. J., AND PRINDLE, R. A. Experimental production of congenital anomalies. New Engl. J. Med., **247:** 758, 1952.

18. GIROUD, A. Phénomènes d'induction et leurs perturbations chez les mammifères. Acta Anat. (Basel), **30:** 297, 1957.

19. NELSON, M. M., BAIRD, C. D. C., WRIGHT, H. V., AND EVANS, H. M. Multiple congenital abnormalities in the rat resulting from riboflavin deficiency induced by the antimetabolite galactoflavin. J. Nutr., **58:** 125, 1956.

20. KALTER, H., AND WARKANY, J. Congenital malformations in inbred strains of mice induced by riboflavin-deficient, galactoflavin-containing diets. J. Exp. Zool., **136:** 531, 1957.

21. COHLAN, S. Q. Excessive intake of vitamin A as a cause of congenital anomalies in the rat. Science, **117:** 535, 1953.

22. GIROUD, A., AND MARTINET, M. Malformations oculaires avec fibrose du vitré chez des embryons de lapin soumis à l'hypervitaminose A. Bull. Soc. Ophtal. Franc., **3:** 191, 1959.

23. LANGMAN, J., AND VAN FAASSEN, F. Congenital defects in the rat embryo. Amer. J. Ophthal., **40:** 65, 1957.

24. WILSON, J. G., JORDAN, H. C., AND BRENT, R. L. Effects of irradiation on embryonic development. II. X-rays on the ninth day of gestation in the rat. Amer. J. Anat., **92:** 153, 1953.

25. HICKS, S. P. Developmental malformations produced by radiation. Amer. J. Roentgenol., **69:** 272, 1953.

26. WOOLLAM, D. H. M., MILLEN, J. W., AND FOZZARD, J. A. F. The influence of cortisone on the teratogenic activity of x-radiation. Brit. J. Radiol., **32:** 47, 1959.

CHAPTER **17**

# Ear

---

NORMAL DEVELOPMENT
- •INTERNAL EAR: *otic vesicle; saccule, cochlea, and organ of Corti; utricle and semicircular canals*
- •MIDDLE EAR: *tympanic cavity and Eustachian tube; ossicles*
- •EXTERNAL EAR: *external auditory meatus; eardrum; auricle*

CONGENITAL MALFORMATIONS
- •*Congenital deafness*

---

## *Normal Development*

Whereas in the adult the ear forms one anatomical unit serving both hearing and equilibrium, in the embryo it develops from three distinctly different parts: (1) the *external ear*, which serves as the sound-collecting organ, develops from the dorsal portion of the first pharyngeal cleft and six surrounding mesenchymal swellings; (2) the *middle ear*, which functions as a sound conductor from the external to the internal ear, arises from the first pharyngeal pouch; and (3) the *internal ear*, which converts the sound waves into nerve impulses and registers changes in equilibrium, is formed by the ectodermal otic vesicle.

### Internal ear

*Otic Vesicle*

The first indication of the developing ear can be found in embryos of approximately 22 days as a thickening of the surface ectoderm on each side of the rhombencephalon (figs. 17-1A and 5-4B).[1] These thickenings, the *otic placodes*, invaginate rapidly and form the *otic* or *auditory vesicles* (otocysts) (fig. 17-1B, C, D). During later development each vesicle divides into (1) a ventral component which gives rise to the *saccule* and the *cochlear duct*, and (2) a dorsal component which forms the *utricle, semicircular canals,* and *endolymphatic duct* (figs. 17-2 to 17-5). The epithelial structures so formed are known collectively as the *membranous labyrinth.* Initially, this intricate tubular structure is embedded in mesenchyme. With time, however, the surrounding mesenchyme is converted into a cartilaginous shell, which in turn ossifies to form the *bony labyrinth.* The membranous labyrinth is then entirely encased in the bony labyrinth, with only narrow perilymphatic spaces separating the two.[2]

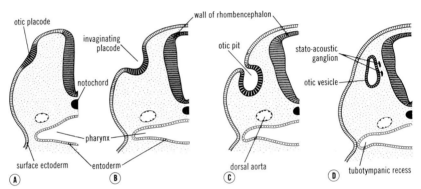

Figure 17-1. *Schematic transverse sections through the region of the rhombencephalon at various stages of development, showing the formation of the otic vesicles. A, At 22 days; B, 24 days; C, 27 days; D, 4½ weeks. Note the appearance of the stato-acoustic ganglion.*

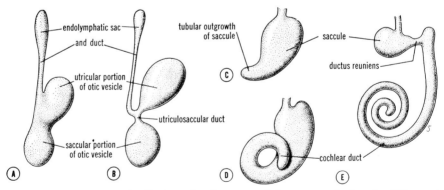

Figure 17-2. *A and B, Further development of the otocyst during the fifth week of development, showing a dorsal utricular portion with the endolymphatic duct, and a ventral saccular portion. C, D, and E, Development of the cochlear duct shown at 6, 7 and 8 weeks, respectively. Note the formation of the ductus reuniens and the utriculosaccular duct.*

Special Embryology

During formation of the otic vesicle a small group of cells breaks away from its wall and forms the *stato-acoustic ganglion* (fig. 17-1 D).[3, 4] Other cells of this ganglion probably are derived from the neural crest. The ganglion subsequently splits into cochlear and vestibular portions which supply the sensory cells of the organ of Corti (hearing) and those of the saccule, utricle, and semicircular canals (equilibrium), respectively.

*Saccule, Cochlea, and Organ of Corti*

In the sixth week of development the saccular portion of the otic vesicle forms a tubular-shaped out-pocketing at its lower pole (fig. 17-2C). This outgrowth, the *cochlear duct*, penetrates the sur-

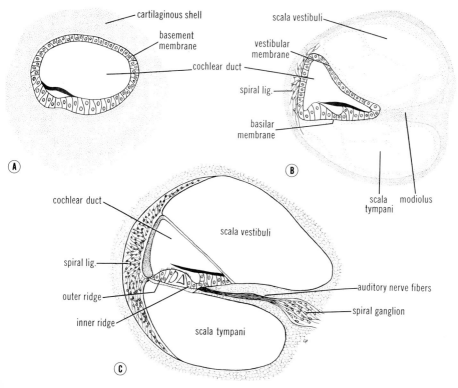

Figure 17-3. *Schematic representation of the development of the scala tympani and scala vestibuli. A, The cochlear duct is surrounded by a fibrous basement membrane and a cartilaginous shell. B, During the 10th week, large perilymphatic spaces appear in the cartilaginous shell. C, The cochlear duct (scala media) is separated from the scala tympani and the scala vestibuli by the basilar and vestibular membranes, respectively. On its lateral aspect it is connected to the bony cochlea by the spiral ligament. Note the auditory nerve fibers and the spiral ganglion.*

Ear                                                                    345

rounding mesenchyme in spiral fashion until, at the end of the eighth month, it has completed two and one-half turns (fig. 17-2 D, E). Its connection with the remaining portion of the saccule is then confined to a narrow pathway, the *ductus reuniens* (fig. 17-2 E).

The mesenchyme surrounding the cochlear duct soon differentiates into a thin, fibrous basement membrane lining the outside of the duct, and a large shell of cartilage (fig. 17-3A). In the 10th week this cartilaginous shell undergoes vacuolization and two perilymphatic spaces, the *scala vestibuli* and *scala tympani*, are formed (figs. 17-3B, C).[5] The cochlear duct is then separated from the scala vestibuli by the *vestibular* or *Reissner's membrane*, and from the scala tympani by the *basilar membrane* (fig. 17-3C). The lateral wall of the cochlear duct, however, remains attached to the surrounding cartilage by the *spiral ligament*, whereas its median angle is connected to, and partly supported by, a long cartilaginous process, the *modiolus*, the future axis of the bony cochlea (fig. 17-3B).

The epithelial cells of the cochlear duct are initially alike. With further development, however, they form two ridges (fig. 17-3C). The larger of the two, located close to the center of the cochlea, is known as the *inner ridge* (the future *spiral limbus*), while the other is known as the *outer ridge* (fig. 17-4A). The latter forms one row of inner and three or four rows of outer *hair cells*, the sensory cells of

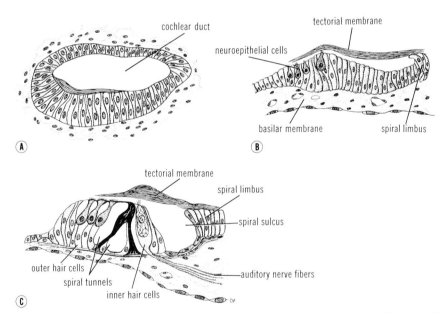

Figure 17-4. *Development of the organ of Corti. A, At 10 weeks; B, approximately 5 months; C, full term. Note the appearance of the spiral tunnels in the organ of Corti.*

Special Embryology

the auditory system (fig. 17-4*B*, *C*). They are covered by the *tectorial membrane*, initially a fibrillar gelatinous substance, which is carried by the spiral limbus and rests with its tip on the hair cells (fig. 17-4).[6,7] The neuroepithelial cells and the covering tectorial membrane together are known as the *organ of Corti*, the true organ of hearing. The impulses received by this organ are transmitted to the spiral ganglion and then to the nervous system by the auditory fibers of the eighth cranial nerve (figs. 17-3 and 17-4).

### Utricle and Semicircular Canals

During the sixth week of development the semicircular canals appear as flattened outpocketings of the utricular part of the otic vesicle (fig. 17-5*A*, *B*). The central portions of the walls of these outpocketings eventually become apposed to each other and disappear, thus giving rise to the three semicircular canals (fig. 17-5*E*, *F*). While one end of each canal dilates to form the *crus ampullare*, the other does not widen and is known as the *crus nonampullare* (fig. 17-5*E*). However, since two of the latter type fuse, only five crura enter the utricle—three with an ampulla and two without.

In the seventh week the cells in the crus ampullare of each semicircular canal form a crest, the *crista ampullaris*, containing the sensory cells for the maintenance of equilibrium. Similar sensory areas

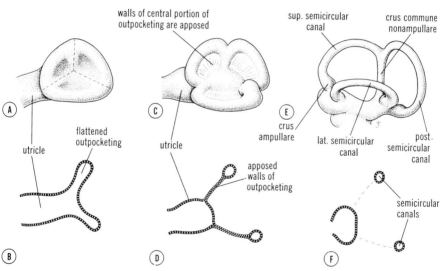

Figure 17-5. *Schematic representation of the development of the semicircular canals at the distal end of the utricle. A, At 5 weeks; C, 6 weeks; E, 8 weeks. B, D, and F show diagrammatically the apposition, fusion and disappearance of the central portions of the walls of the semicircular outpocketings. Note the ampullae in the semicircular canals.*

develop in the walls of the utricle and saccule, where they are known as *maculae acousticae*. Impulses generated in the sensory cells of the cristae and maculae as a result of a change in position of the body are carried to the brain by the vestibular fibers of the eighth cranial nerve.

## Middle Ear

### Tympanic Cavity and Eustachian Tube

Contrary to the ectodermal origin of the membranous part of the internal ear, the tympanic cavity is of entodermal origin. It is derived mainly from the first pharyngeal pouch, an outpocketing of the pharynx (figs. 17-1 and 17-6). This pouch, lined with epithelium of entodermal origin, appears in embryos of approximately 4 weeks, grows rapidly in lateral direction, and temporarily comes in contact with the floor of the first ectodermal cleft. The distal part of the pouch, the *tubotympanic recess*, widens and gives rise to the *primitive tympanic cavity*, while the proximal part remains narrow and forms the *auditory* or *Eustachian tube* (fig. 17-6B). The latter is the channel through which the tympanic cavity communicates with the nasopharynx. Its pharyngeal orifice is surrounded by a considerable amount of lymphoid tissue, the *tubal tonsil*. Particularly in young children, nasal inflammations associated with swelling of the tubal tonsil frequently result in occlusion of the tube and inflammation of the tympanic cavity (*otitis media*).

### Ossicles

By the end of the seventh week the mesenchyme directly above the primitive tympanic cavity shows a number of condensations caused by proliferation of the dorsal tips of the first and second pharyngeal arches (fig. 17-6B). With time, these condensations become the cartilaginous precursors of the *auditory ossicles*, the *malleus*, *incus* and *stapes* (fig. 17-7B). The malleus and incus are thought to be derived from the cartilage of the first pharyngeal arch, and the stapes from that of the second arch (fig. 17-7A).[8-10] Although the ossicles appear during the first half of fetal life they remain embedded in mesenchyme until the eighth month, when the surrounding tissue dissolves (fig. 17-7B). The entodermal epithelial lining of the primitive tympanic cavity then gradually extends along the wall of the newly developing space and wraps itself around the ossicles. When the ossicles are entirely free of surrounding mesenchyme the entodermal epithelium not only forms the mucosa

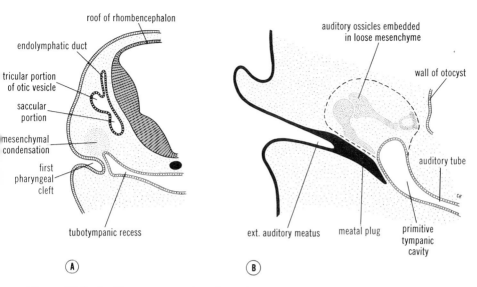

Figure 17-6. *A, Transverse section through the cephalic end of a 7-week embryo in the region of the rhombencephalon, showing the utricular and saccular portions of the otic vesicle, the tubotympanic recess, the first pharyngeal cleft, and the mesenchymal condensation between the otic vesicle and the primitive tympanic cavity, foreshadowing the development of the ossicles. B, Schematic representation of the middle ear, showing the cartilaginous precursors of the auditory ossicles embedded in loose connective tissue. Broken line indicates future expansion of the primitive tympanic cavity. Note the meatal plug extending from the primitive auditory meatus to the future tympanic cavity.*

around them, but also connects them in a mesentery-like fashion to the wall of the cavity (fig. 17-7B). The supporting ligaments of the ossicles later develop within these mesenteries.

Since the malleus is derived from the first pharyngeal arch, its muscle, the *tensor tympani*, is innervated by the mandibular branch of the trigeminal nerve. Similarly, the *stapedius muscle*, which is attached to the stapes, is innervated by the facial nerve.

## External Ear

### External Auditory Meatus

The external auditory meatus develops from the dorsal portion of the first pharyngeal cleft, which grows inward as a funnel-shaped tube until it reaches the entodermal lining of the tympanic cavity (fig. 17-6A). At the beginning of the third month the epithelial cells at the bottom of the meatus begin to proliferate, thereby forming

Ear

349

a solid epithelial plate, known as the *meatal plug* (fig. 17-6B). In the seventh month this plug dissolves and the epithelial lining in the floor of the enlarged meatus then participates in the formation of the definitive eardrum. Occasionally, the meatal plug persists until birth, resulting in congenital deafness.

### Eardrum or Tympanic Membrane

The eardrum is made up of (1) the ectodermal epithelial lining at the bottom of the auditory meatus; (2) the entodermal epithelial lining of the expanded tympanic cavity; and (3) an intermediate layer of loose connective tissue (fig. 17-7B). The major part of the eardrum is firmly attached to the handle of the malleus and is formed only after dissolution of the mesenchyme surrounding the ossicles (figs. 17-6B and 17-7B). The remaining, much smaller, portion of the eardrum forms the separation between the external auditory meatus and the original tubotympanic recess.

### Auricle

The auricle develops from a number of mesenchymal proliferations located at the dorsal ends of the first and second pharyngeal arches and surrounding the first pharyngeal cleft (fig. 17-8A). These swellings, three on each side of the external meatus, appear during

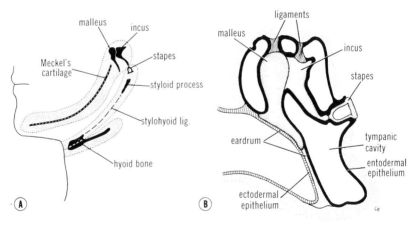

Figure 17-7. *A, Schematic representation of the derivatives of the cartilaginous components of the first three branchial arches. Note the malleus and incus at the dorsal tip of the first arch and the stapes at that of the second arch. B, Schematic representation of the middle ear, showing the handle of the malleus in contact with the eardrum. The stapes will establish contact with the membrane in the oval window.*

Special Embryology

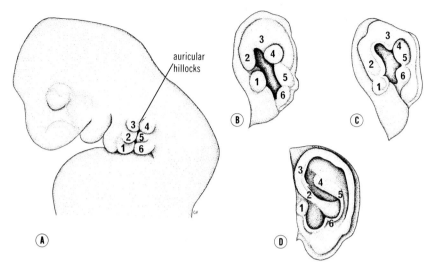

Figure 17-8. *A, Lateral view of the head of an embryo showing the six auricular hillocks surrounding the dorsal end of the first pharyngeal cleft. B, C and D show the fusion and progressive development of the hillocks into the adult auricle.*

the sixth week of development. The hillocks later fuse and are gradually transformed into the definitive auricle.[11] As the fusion of the auricular hillocks is rather complicated, developmental abnormalities of the auricle are not uncommon.

# Congenital Malformations

### Congenital Deafness

Congenital deafness, usually associated with deaf-mutism, may be caused by abnormal development of the membranous and bony labyrinths, as well as by malformations of the auditory ossicles and eardrum.[12] In the most extreme cases the tympanic cavity and external meatus are completely absent.

Although congenital deafness was believed to be mainly hereditary,[13, 14] during the last few years it has become evident that environmental factors affecting the mother early in pregnancy may likewise interfere with normal development of the internal and middle ear of the embryo. At present, it is generally accepted that the rubella virus, affecting the embryo in the seventh to eighth week of development, may cause severe damage to the organ of Corti.[15-17] Although it has been suggested that poliomyelitis, erythroblastosis fetalis, diabetes and toxoplasmosis may likewise cause congenital deafness, these observations await more evidence.[18-21]

Recently it has been possible, by means of x-irradiation, to produce in the rat anomalies of the ear leading to deafness.[22] On the other hand, a disturbance of locomotion and posture has been produced by feeding the animals a manganese-deficient diet during pregnancy.[23]

## References

1. O'RAHILLY, R. The early development of the otic vesicle in staged human embryos. J. Embryol. Exp. Morph., 11: 741, 1963.
2. BAST, T. H., AND ANSON, B. J. *The Temporal Bone and the Ear*. Charles C Thomas, Springfield, Ill., 1949.
3. POLITZER, G. Die Entstehung des Ganglion Acusticum beim Menschen. Acta Anat. (Basel), 26: 1, 1956.
4. BATTEN, E. H. The origin of the acoustic ganglion in the sheep. J. Embryol. Exp. Morph., 6: 597, 1958.
5. STREETER, J. L. The histogenesis and growth of the otic capsule and its contained periodic tissue spaces in the human embryo. Contrib. Embryol., 7: 5, 1918.
6. VAN DER STRICHT, O. The genesis and structure of the membrana tectoria and the crista spiralis of the cochlea. Contrib. Embryol., 7: 55, 1918.
7. VAN DER STRICHT, O. The arrangement and structure of sustentacular cells and hair cells in the developing organ of Corti. Contrib. Embryol., 9: 109, 1920.
8. HANSON, J. R., ANSON, B. J., AND BAST, T. H. The early embryology of the auditory ossicles in man. Quart. Bull. Northw. Univ. Med. Sch., 33: 358, 1959.
9. ANSON, B. J., AND BAST, T. H. Development of the stapes of the human ear. Quart. Bull. Northw. Univ. Med. Sch., 33: 44, 1959.
10. ANSON, B. J., AND BAST, T. H. Development of the incus of the human ear. Quart. Bull. Northw. Univ. Med. Sch., 33: 110, 1959.
11. WOOD-JONES, F., AND WEN., J. C. The development of the external ear. J. Anat., 68: 525, 1934.
12. ALTMANN, F. Malformations, anomalies and vestigial structures of the inner ear. A. M. A. Arch. Otolaryng., 57: 591, 1953.
13. STEVENSON, A. C., AND CHEESEMAN, E. A. Hereditary deaf-mutism with particular reference to Northern Ireland. Ann. Hum. Genet., 20: 177, 1956.
14. STERN, C. *Principles of Human Genetics*, Ed. 2, p. 107. W. H. Freeman and Co., San Francisco, 1960.
15. TÖNDURY, J. Zur Kenntnis der Embryopathia rubeolica, nebst Bemerkungen über die Wirkung anderer Viren auf den Keimling. Geburtsh. Frauenheilk., 10: 865, 1952.
16. GRAY, J. E. Rubella in pregnancy; fetal pathology in the internal ear. Ann. Otol., 68: 170, 1959.
17. LANCASTER, H. O. The epidemiology of deafness due to maternal rubella. Acta Genet. (Basel), 5: 12, 1954.
18. KELEMAN, J. Acute poliomyelitis of the mother with aural lesions of the premature infant. A. M. A. Arch. Otolaryng., 62: 602, 1955.
19. KELEMAN, J. Erythroblastosis fetalis. Pathologic report on the hearing organs of a newborn infant. A. M. A. Arch. Otolaryng., 63: 392, 1956.
20. KELEMAN, J. Aural changes in the embryo of a diabetic mother. A. M. A. Arch. Otolaryng., 62: 357, 1955.

21. JØRGENSEN, M. B. The influence of maternal diabetes on the inner ear of the fetus. Acta Otolaryng. (Stockh.), **53:** 49, 1961.
22. KELEMAN, J. Experimental defects in the ear and the upper airways induced by radiation. A. M. A. Arch. Otolaryng., **61:** 405, 1955.
23. HURLEY, L. S., WOOTEN, E., EVERSON, G. L., AND ASLING, C. W. Anomalous development of ossification in the inner ear of offspring of manganese-deficient rats. J. Nutr., **71:** 15, 1960.

CHAPTER **18**

# Face, Nose, and Palate

NORMAL DEVELOPMENT
- FACIAL SWELLINGS AND UPPER LIP
- INTERMAXILLARY SEGMENT
- SECONDARY PALATE
- NASAL CHAMBERS

CONGENITAL MALFORMATIONS
- CLEFT LIP AND CLEFT PALATE
- MEDIAN CLEFT LIP
- OBLIQUE FACIAL CLEFT
- MACROSTOMIA AND MICROSTOMIA
- HEREDITARY FACTORS
- ENVIRONMENTAL FACTORS
- EXPERIMENTAL DATA

## *Normal Development*

### Facial Swellings and Upper Lip

The center of the developing facial structures is initially formed by an ectodermal depression, known as the *stomodeum* (fig. 13-2). By the time the embryo is 4½ weeks old the stomodeum is surrounded by a series of elevations formed by proliferation of the mesenchyme. The *mandibular swellings* can be distinguished caudally to the stomodeum, the *maxillary swellings* laterally, and the *frontal prominence*, a slightly rounded elevation, cranially (fig. 18-1A). On each side of the frontal prominence and just above the stomodeum is a local thickening of the surface ectoderm, the *nasal placode* (fig. 18-1A).

During the fifth week, two fast-growing ridges, the *lateral* and *medial nasal swellings*, surround the nasal placode which then forms the floor of a depression, the *nasal pit* (fig. 18-1B). The lateral swell-

Special Embryology

ings will form the alae of the nose; the medial swellings will give rise to the middle portion of the nose, the middle portion of the upper lip, and the middle portion of the maxilla as well as to the entire *primary palate*. In the meantime, the maxillary swellings approach the medial as well as the lateral nasal swellings but remain separated from them by well marked grooves or furrows (fig. 18-1*B*).[1]

During the following 2 weeks the appearance of the face changes considerably. The maxillary swellings continue to grow in a medial direction and compress the medial nasal swellings toward the midline. Subsequently, these swellings merge with each other—that is, the groove separating them is smoothed out by the migration of mesoderm from the surrounding swellings—and at the same time with the maxillary swellings laterally. Hence, the upper lip is formed by the two medial nasal swellings and the two maxillary swellings (fig. 18-2*A*). In normal development the upper lip is never characterized by the presence of clefts.

In addition to their role in the formation of the upper lip, the maxillary swellings also merge over a short distance with the mandibular swellings. This results in the formation of the cheeks and determines the width of the mouth. The manner in which the maxillary swellings unite with the lateral nasal swellings is slightly more complicated. Initially these structures are separated by a deep furrow, the *nasolacrimal groove* (fig. 18-2*A*). Fusion of the swellings is established only when this groove is bridged over to form a portion of the *nasolacrimal duct*.

## Intermaxillary Segment

The two medial nasal swellings merge not only at the surface but also at the deeper level. The structures formed by the two merged

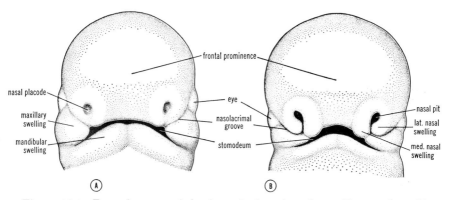

Figure 18-1. *Frontal aspect of the face. A, 5-week embryo. The nasal swellings are gradually separated from the maxillary swelling by deep furrows. At no time during normal development does the tissue in the furrows break down.*

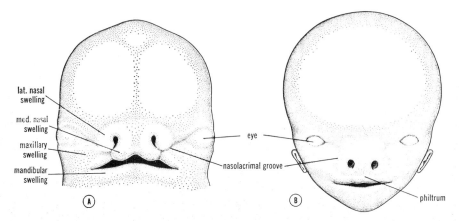

Figure 18-2. *Frontal aspect of the face. A, 7-week embryo; B, 10-week embryo. The maxillary swellings gradually merge with the nasal folds and the furrows are gradually filled up with mesenchyme.*

swellings are together known as the *intermaxillary segment.*[2] It is comprised of: (1) a *labial component*, which forms the philtrum of the upper lip; (2) an *upper jaw component*, which carries the four incisor teeth; and (3) a *palatal component*, which forms the triangular *primary palate* (figs. 18-3B and 18-7). Cranially the intermaxillary segment is continuous with the rostral portion of the nasal septum, which is formed by the frontal prominence.

## Secondary Palate

As pointed out above, the primary palate is derived from the intermaxillary segment (fig. 18-3B). The main part of the definitive palate, however, is formed by two shelf-like outgrowths of the deeper parts of the maxillary swellings. These outgrowths, the *palatine shelves*, appear in the sixth week of development and are directed obliquely downward on either side of the tongue (fig. 18-3 A). In the seventh week, however, the tongue moves downward and the palatine shelves ascend and attain a horizontal position (fig. 18-4A, B).

During the eighth week the palatine shelves approach each other in the midline, fuse, and form the *secondary palate* (fig. 18-5A, B). Anteriorly, the shelves fuse with the triangular primary palate, and the incisive foramen may be considered as the midline landmark between the primary and secondary palates. At the same time as the palatine shelves fuse, the nasal septum grows down and joins with the cephalic aspect of the newly formed palate (fig. 18-5A).

Special Embryology

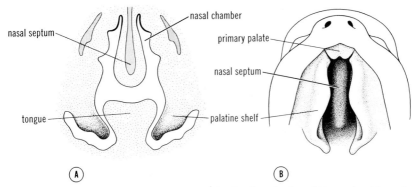

Figure 18-3. *A, Frontal section through the head of a 6½-week old embryo. The palatine shelves are located in the vertical position on each side of the tongue. B, Ventral view of the palatine shelves after removal of the lower jaw and the tongue. Note the clefts between the primary triangular palate and the palatine shelves, which are still in a vertical position.*

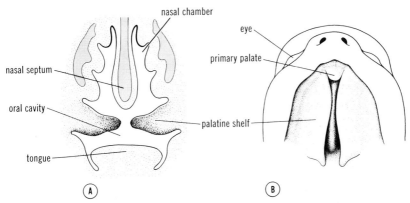

Figure 18-4. *Frontal section through the head of a 7½-week embryo. The tongue has moved downward and the palatine shelves have reached a horizontal position. B, Ventral view of the palatine shelves after removal of the lower jaw and tongue. The shelves are in a horizontal position.*

## Nasal Chambers

During the sixth week the nasal pits deepen considerably, partly because of the growth of the surrounding nasal swellings and partly because of their penetration into the underlying mesenchyme (fig. 18-6A). At first, the *oronasal membrane* separates the pits from the primitive oral cavity, but after its rupture the primitive nasal chambers open into the oral cavity by way of the newly formed foramina, the *primitive choanae* (figs. 18-3B and 18-6C). These choanae are located on each side of the midline and immediately behind

Face, Nose, and Palate                                                357

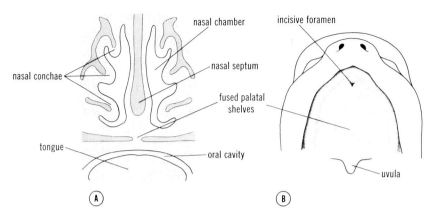

Figure 18-5. *A, Frontal section through the head of a 10-week embryo. The two palatine shelves have fused with each other and with the nasal septum. B, Ventral view of the palate. The incisive foramen forms the midline landmark between the primary and secondary palate.*

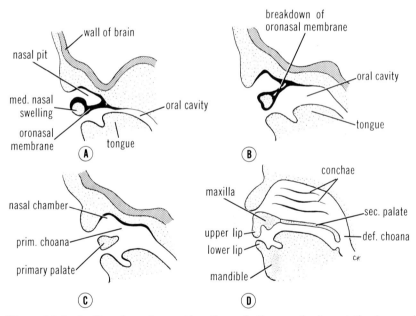

Figure 18-6. *A, Drawing of a section through the nasal pit and the lower rim of the medial nasal fold of a 6-week embryo. The primitive nasal cavity is separated from the oral cavity by the oronasal membrane. B, Similar section as in A, showing the oronasal membrane breaking down. C, In a 7-week embryo the primitive nasal cavity is in open connection with the oral cavity. D, Sagittal section through the face of a 9-week embryo, showing the intermaxillary segment, comprised of a labial component, a maxillary component, and the primary palate (modified from Clara).*

Special Embryology

the primary palate. Later, with the formation of the secondary palate and further development of the primitive nasal chambers (fig. 18-8D), the *definitive choanae* are located at the junction of the nasal cavity and the pharynx.

# Congenital Malformations

### Cleft Lip and Cleft Palate

According to Stark[1, 3] the *incisive foramen* should be considered as the dividing landmark between the anterior and posterior cleft deformities. Those anterior to the incisive foramen are based on the failure of proper mesodermal penetration and the actual breakdown of tissue in the furrows between the medial nasal and maxillary swellings and include the *lateral cleft lip*, the *cleft upper jaw*, and the *cleft* between the *primary and secondary palates* (fig. 18-7B, C, D). Those which lie posterior to the incisive foramen are caused by failure of the palatine shelves to fuse and include the *cleft (secondary) palate* and the *cleft uvula* (fig. 18-7E). The third category is formed by a combination of clefts lying anterior as well as posterior to the incisive foramen (fig. 18-7F). Since the palatine shelves fuse approximately 1 week after completion of the upper lip, and since

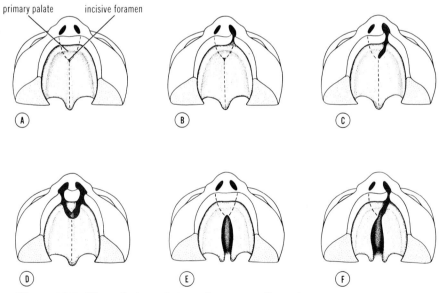

Figure 18-7. *Ventral view of the palate, gum, lip and nose. A, Normal; B, unilateral cleft lip extending into the nose; C, unilateral cleft involving lip and jaw, and extending to incisive foramen; D, bilateral cleft involving lip and jaw; E, isolated cleft palate; F, cleft palate combined with unilateral anterior cleft.*

Face, Nose, and Palate

the closing mechanisms of the lip and secondary palate differ greatly (merging and fusion, respectively), the anterior and posterior clefts must be considered as separate entities.

The anterior clefts may vary in severity from barely visible defects in the vermilion of the lip to clefts extending into the nose (fig. 18-7B). In more severe cases, the cleft extends to a deeper level, thereby forming a cleft of the upper jaw. The maxilla is then split between the lateral incisor and the canine tooth. Frequently, such a cleft extends to the incisive foramen (fig. 18-7C, D).

The posterior clefts likewise may vary in severity from clefts involving the entire secondary palate to clefts of the uvula only.

## Median Cleft Lip

The median cleft lip, a rare abnormality, is thought to be caused by the incomplete merging of the two medial nasal swellings in the midline. This anomaly is usually accompanied by a deep groove between the right and left sides of the nose (fig. 18-8D).

## Oblique Facial Cleft

Failure of the maxillary swelling to merge with its corresponding lateral nasal swelling results in an oblique facial cleft. When this occurs the nasolacrimal duct is usually exposed to the surface (fig. 18-8A).

## Macrostomia and Microstomia

The maxillary and mandibular swellings may fail to merge, resulting in *macrostomia* (fig. 18-8C), or they may merge to such an extent that the opening of the mouth is too small, a condition known as *microstomia*.

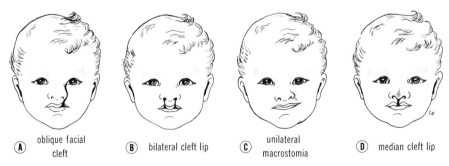

(A) oblique facial cleft    (B) bilateral cleft lip    (C) unilateral macrostomia    (D) median cleft lip

Figure 18-8. *A, Oblique facial cleft; B, bilateral cleft lip; C, unilateral macrostomia; D, median cleft lip with partially cleft nose.*

## Hereditary Factors

It is now generally accepted that the main etiological factor of the cleft lip and the cleft palate is genetic in nature. There is, however, no genetic correlation between a cleft lip and an isolated cleft palate.[4-6] The cleft lip (approximately 1:1000 births) is seen more in males than females; its incidence is slightly higher with increasing maternal age and varies in different population groups.[7-8]

With reference to the recurrence of the cleft lip, it is known that if the parents are normal and have had one child with a cleft lip, the chance that the next baby will have the same defect is 4 per cent.[9-11] If two siblings are affected the risk for the next child increases to 9 per cent. If, however, one of the parents has a cleft lip, and they have one child with the same defect, the probability that the next baby will be affected rises to 17 per cent.

With regard to the cleft palate, the frequency of this defect is much lower than that of the cleft lip (1:2500 births); it is seen more frequently in females than in males and is not related to maternal age. If the parents are normal and have one child with a cleft palate, the probability of the next child being affected is about 2 per cent. If, however, there is a similarly affected relative or a parent and child with a cleft palate, the probability increases to 7 and 15 per cent, respectively.

## Environmental Factors

Although it has been suggested that cortisone during the first trimester of pregnancy may cause a cleft palate, evidence for this suggestion is insufficient.[12] In fact, a number of cases have recently been reported in which the mother received cortisone during early pregnancy and the baby was normal.[13, 14] So far, it has been impossible to implicate any one environmental factor as a cause of cleft palate in man. Nothing is known regarding the etiology of the cleft lip.

## Experimental Data

In experimental work, it has been possible to cause cleft palates in the offspring of the rat and mouse by a variety of teratogenic agents.[15] In particular, three experimental procedures have been highly successful in producing this defect in almost 100 per cent of the offspring. These are cortisone injections into susceptible strains of mice,[16, 17] hypervitaminosis A in rats,[18] and pteroylglutamic acid deficiency in rats.[19, 20] From these studies it has become evident that congenital clefts of the palate can be produced in several different ways, each influenced by multiple genetic and environmental factors.[15] In addition, these studies have been valuable in analyzing the mechanisms of palate closure,[21] and the possible role of the tongue, the growth of the mandible and the head, and the inherent movements of the palatine shelves in palate closure.[22-25]

In recent work, Johnston showed that the neural crest cells, which migrate above and below the optic cup into the area of the face, greatly contribute to the formation of the facial swellings.[26] Extirpation of neural crest on one side of the forebrain frequently resulted in clefts of the primary palate on the same side. Hence, it may be that interference with the migration of neural crest cells at a stage long before the formation of the facial swellings may result in a cleft lip at a much later stage of development.

## References

1. STARK, R. B., AND EHRMANN, N. A. The development of the center of the face with particular reference to surgical correction of bilateral cleft lip. Plast. Reconstr. Surg., **21:** 177, 1958.

2. PATTEN, B. M. The normal development of the facial region. In *Congenital Anomalies of the Face and Associated Structures*, edited by S. Pruzansky, p. 11. Charles C Thomas, Springfield, Ill., 1961.

3. STARK, R. B. The pathogenesis of harelip and cleft palate. Plast. Reconstr. Surg., **13:** 20, 1954.

4. FOGH-ANDERSON, P. Inheritance patterns for cleft lip and cleft palate. In *Congenital Anomalies of the Face and Associated Structures*, edited by S. Pruzansky, p. 123. Charles C Thomas, Springfield, Ill., 1961.

5. FOGH-ANDERSON, P. *Inheritance of Harelip and Cleft Palate.* Arnold Busck, Copenhagen, 1942.

6. FRASER, F. C. Thoughts on the etiology of clefts of the palate and lip. Acta Genet. (Basel), **5:** 358, 1955.

7. MACMAHON, B., AND McKEOWN, T. The incidence of harelip and cleft palate related to birth rank and maternal age. Amer. J. Hum. Genet., **5:** 176, 1953.

8. NEEL, J. R. A study of major congenital defects in Japanese infants. Amer. J. Hum. Genet., **10:** 398, 1958.

9. CURTIS, E. J., FRASER, F. C., AND WARBURTON, D. Congenital cleft lip and palate. Amer. J. Dis. Child., **102:** 853, 1961.

10. FRASER, F. C. Genetic counseling in some common paediatric diseases. Pediat. Clin. N. Amer., **5:** 475, 1958.

11. FRASER, F. C. Genetics and congenital malformations. In *Progress in Medical Genetics*, edited by A. G. Steinberg, p. 38. Grune & Stratton, Inc., New York, 1961.

12. HARRIS, J. W. S., AND ROSS, J. P. Cortisone therapy in early pregnancy; relation to cleft palate. Lancet, **1:** 1045, 1956.

13. PREISLER, O. Is prolonged cortisone treatment in pregnancy damaging to the infant? Zbl. Gynaek., **18:** 675, 1960.

14. BONGIOVANNI, A. M., AND McPADDEN, A. J. Steroids during pregnancy and possible fetal consequences. Fertil. Steril., **11:** 181, 1960.

15. FRASER, F. C. Experimental induction of cleft palate. In *Congenital Anomalies of the Face and Associated Structures*, edited by S. Pruzansky, p. 188. Charles C Thomas, Springfield, Ill., 1961.

Special Embryology

16. FRASER, F. C., WALKER, B. E., AND TRASLER, D. G. Experimental production of congenital cleft palate; genetic and environmental factors. Pediatrics, **19:** 782, 1957.

17. KALTER, H. The inheritance of susceptibility to the teratogenic action of cortisone in mice. Genetics, **39:** 185, 1954.

18. GIROUD, A., AND MARTINET, M. Tératogénèse par hautes doses de vitamine A en fonction des stades du développement. Arch. Micro. Morph. Exp., **45:** 577, 1956.

19. NELSON M. M., ASLING, C. W., AND EVANS, H. M. Production of multiple abnormalities in young by PGA deficiency during gestation. J. Nutr., **48:** 61, 1952.

20. ASLING, C. W., NELSON, M. M., DOUGHERTY, H. D., WRIGHT, H. V., AND EVANS, H. M. The development of cleft palate resulting from maternal pteroylglutamic acid deficiency during the latter half of gestation in rats. Surg. Gynec. Obstet., **111:** 19, 1960.

21. WALKER, B. E., AND FRASER, F. C. The embryology of cortisone-induced cleft palate. J. Embryol. Exp. Morph., **5:** 201, 1957.

22. ASLING, C. W. Congenital defects of face and palate in rats following maternal deficiency of pteroylglutamic acid. In *Congenital Anomalies of the Face and Associated Structures*, edited by S. Pruzansky, p. 173, Charles C Thomas, Springfield, Ill., 1961.

23. TRASLER, D. G. Influence of uterine site on occurrence of spontaneous cleft lip in mice. Science, **132:** 420, 1960.

24. TRASLER, D. G., WALKER, B. E., AND FRASER, F. C. Congenital malformations produced by amniotic sac puncture. Science., **124:** 439, 1956.

25. FRASER, F. C. Cleft lip and cleft palate. Science, **158:** 1603, 1967.

26. JOHNSTON, M. C. A radioautographic study of the migration and fate of cranial neural crest cells in the chick embryo. Anat. Rec., **156:** 143, 1966.

CHAPTER **19**

# Integumentary System

---

- SKIN: *epidermis; dermis*
- HAIR
- MAMMARY GLAND: *mammary line; polythelia; polymastia*
- TEETH: *cap and bell stage; odontoblasts and dentine; ameloblasts and enamel; cementoblasts and cementum; periodontal ligament*

---

## Skin

The skin has a twofold origin: a superficial layer, the *epidermis*, which develops from the surface ectoderm, and a deep layer, the *dermis*, developing from the underlying mesoderm.

*Epidermis*

Initially the surface of the embryo is covered by a single layer of ectodermal cells (fig. 19-1*A*). In the beginning of the second month this epithelium divides and a layer of flattened cells, the *periderm* or *epitrichium*, is laid down on the surface (fig. 19-1*B*). With further proliferation of the cells in the basal layer, a third, so-called intermediate zone is formed (fig. 19-1*C*). Finally at the end of the fourth month the epithelial layers constituting the epidermis of the skin acquire their definitive arrangement and four layers can then be distinguished (fig. 19-1*D*). The basal layer, responsible for a continuous stream of new cells toward the periphery, is known as the *germinative layer* or *prickle-cell layer*. This layer later forms ridges and hollows which are filled by the underlying mesoderm, and the pattern so formed is reflected on the surface of the skin in the fingerprint.[1, 2] On top of the germinative layer is a thick *spinous layer* consisting of large polyhedral cells connected by fine tonofibrils. This layer is followed by a *granular layer*, the cells of

Special Embryology

which contain small keratohyaline granules, the first sign of keratinization. An outermost layer, the *horny layer*, forming the tough, scale-like surface of the epidermis, is made up of several layers of closely packed dead cells, loaded with keratin. The flattened cells of the periderm layer are usually cast off during the second part of intra-uterine life.

During the first 3 months of development the epidermis is invaded by cells believed to be of neural crest origin.[3] These cells, known as *dendritic cells*, synthesize *melanin* pigment, which can be transferred to other cells of the epidermis by way of the dendritic processes. These cells are later known as *melanoblasts*, and after birth cause pigmentation of the skin.[4, 5]

*Dermis*

The dermis, or deeper layer of the skin, arises from mesoderm. During the third and fourth months this tissue forms many collagenous and elastic fibers. Simultaneously, the superficial layer of the dermis, the *corium*, forms irregular papillary structures, the *dermal papillae*, which project upward into the epidermis. These papillae usually contain a small capillary and a sensory nerve end organ. The deeper layer of the dermis, the *subcorium*, is characterized by the presence of large amounts of fatty tissue.

At birth, the skin is covered by a whitish paste, the *vernix caseosa*, formed by secretion of the sebaceous glands and degenerated

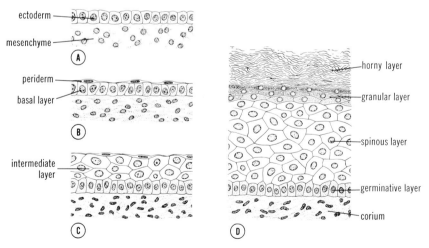

Figure 19-1. *Schematic drawing showing the formation of the skin at various stages of development. A, At 5 weeks; B, 7 weeks; C, 4 months; D, at birth.*

epidermal cells and hairs. It is believed to protect the skin against the macerating action of amniotic fluid.

The skin of the newborn may show varying degrees of keratinization. Sometimes, however, the superficial layers show excessive cornification, giving the skin a scale-like appearance. Such a condition is known as *ichthyosis*.

## Hair

The hairs appear as solid epidermal proliferations penetrating the underlying mesenchyme (fig. 19-2A). At their terminal ends the hair buds invaginate. The invaginations are rapidly filled with mesoderm in which vessels and nerve endings develop (fig. 19-2B, C).[6]

Soon, the cells in the center of the hair follicles become spindle-shaped and keratinized, forming the *hair shaft*, while the peripheral cells become cuboidal, giving rise to the outer *hair sheath*. Continuous proliferation of the epithelial cells at the base of the shaft pushes the hair upward, and by the end of the third month

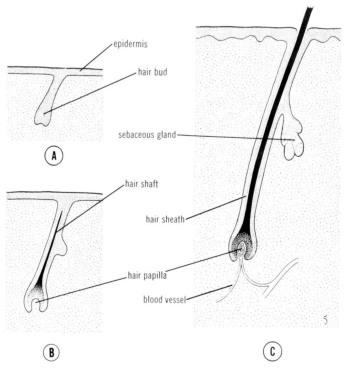

Figure 19-2. *Schematic representation of the development of a hair and a sebaceous gland. A, At 4 months; B, 6 months; C, newborn.*

Special Embryology

the first hairs appear on the surface in the region of the eyebrow and upper lip. These hairs, *lanugo hairs,* are shed at about the time of birth and are later replaced by coarser hairs arising from new hair follicles.

The epithelial wall of the hair follicle usually shows a small outbudding penetrating the surface mesoderm (fig. 19-2C). The cells in the center of these outbuddings, the *sebaceous glands,* degenerate, thereby forming a fat-like substance which is secreted into the hair follicle.

Excessive hairiness, known as *hypertrichosis,* caused by the increased formation of hair follicles, may be localized in certain areas of the body (dorsal midline region) or may be general over the whole body. *Atrichia,* the congenital absence of hair, is usually associated with abnormalities of other ectodermal derivatives as teeth and nails.

## Mammary Glands

The first indication of the mammary glands is found in the form of a band-like thickening of epidermis, the *mammary line* or *ridge.* In a 7-week embryo, this line extends on each side of the body from the base of the forelimb to the region of the hindlimb (fig. 19-3C). Although the major part of the mammary line disappears shortly after its formation, a small portion in the thoracic region persists

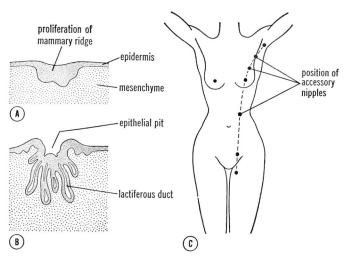

Figure 19-3. *A and B, Sections through the developing mammary gland at the third and eighth months, respectively. C, Diagram showing the positions of accessory nipples (broken line indicates position of mammary line).*

and penetrates the underlying mesenchyme (fig. 19-3A). Here it forms 16 to 24 sprouts, which in turn give rise to small, solid outbuddings. By the end of prenatal life the epithelial sprouts are canalized, forming the *lactiferous ducts*, while the outbuddings form the small ducts and alveoli of the gland. The *lactiferous ducts* at first open into a small epithelial pit (fig. 19-3B). Shortly after birth this pit is transformed into the nipple by proliferation of the underlying mesenchyme.

Normally only a small part of the mammary line persists in the midthoracic region. Occasionally other fragments persist which then give rise to accessory nipples. Such a condition is known as *polythelia*. Accessory nipples may develop anywhere along the original mammary line, but are most frequently seen in the axillary region (fig. 19-3C). Sometimes an abnormally located remnant of the mammary line may develop into a complete mammary gland, an abnormality known as *polymastia*.

Occasionally the lactiferous ducts open into the original epithelial pit, which has failed to evert as a nipple. Such a condition, known as *inverted nipple*, is usually of congenital origin, but may be caused by retraction of the nipple as a result of the presence of a fast-growing tumor in the gland.

## Teeth

By the sixth week of development the basal layer of the epithelial lining of the oral cavity proliferates rapidly and forms a band-like structure, the *dental lamina*, over the region of the upper and lower jaw. This lamina subsequently gives rise to a number of outbuddings which penetrate the underlying mesenchyme (fig. 19-4A). These buds, 10 in each jaw, form the primordia of the ectodermal components of the teeth. Soon the deep surface of the buds invaginates, resulting in the so-called *cap stage of tooth development* (fig. 19-4B). Such a cap consists of an outer layer, the *outer dental epithelium*, an inner layer, the *inner dental epithelium*, and a central core of loosely woven tissue, the *stellate reticulum*. The mesenchyme located in the indentation lined by the inner dental epithelium proliferates and condenses to form the *dental papilla* (fig. 19-4B).

As the dental cap grows and the indentation deepens, the tooth takes on the appearance of a bell (*bell stage*) (fig. 19-4C). The mesenchyme cells of the papilla adjacent to the inner dental layer then differentiate into *odontoblasts*. These cells produce the *predentine*, which is laid down immediately below the inner dental layer. With time the predentine calcifies and is transformed into the definitive

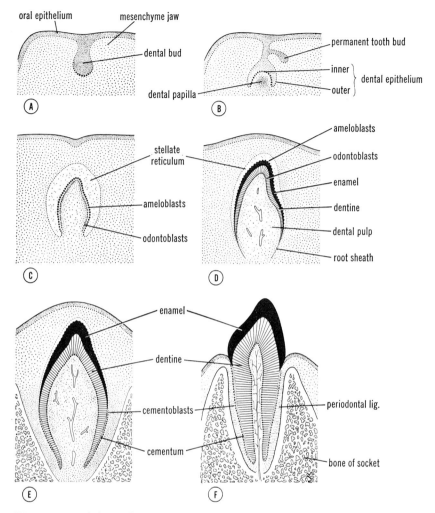

Figure 19-4. *Schematic representation of the formation of the tooth at successive stages of development. A, At 8 weeks; B, 10 weeks; C, 3 months; D, 6 months; E, 8 months, F, after eruption.*

*dentine*. With the continuous thickening of the dentine layer, the odontoblasts retreat into the dental papilla, thereby leaving a thin cytoplasmic process (*dental process*) behind in the dentine (fig. 19-4D). The odontoblast layer persists throughout the life of the tooth and continuously provides predentine, which is subsequently transformed into dentine. The remaining cells of the dental papilla form the *pulp* of the tooth (fig. 19-4D).

In the meantime the epithelial cells of the inner dental layer differentiate into the *ameloblasts* (enamel formers). These cells produce long enamel prisms which are deposited over the dentine (fig. 19-4D). The contact layer between the enamel and dentine layers is known as the *enamel dentine junction.*[7]

The enamel is first laid down at the apex of the tooth and from here spreads gradually toward the neck, thus forming the enamel covering on the crown of the tooth. When, by apposition of new layers, the enamel th; ;kens, the ameloblasts retreat into the stellate reticulum until they finally reach the outer dental epithelial layer. Here they regress, temporarily leaving a thin membrane (the *dental cuticle*) on the surface of the enamel. After eruption of the tooth this membrane gradually sloughs off.

The formation of the root of the tooth begins shortly before eruption of the crown. The inner and outer dental epithelial layers, which are apposed to each other in the region of the neck of the tooth, penetrate deeper into the underlying mesenchyme and form the *epithelial root sheath* (fig. 19-4D).[7] The cells of the dental papilla in contact with this sheath differentiate into odontoblasts, which lay down a layer of dentine continuous with that of the crown (fig. 19-4E, F). As more and more dentine is deposited on the inside of the existing layer, the pulp chamber narrows and finally forms a canal containing the blood vessels and nerves of the tooth.

The mesenchymal cells located on the outside of the tooth and in contact with the dentine of the root differentiate into *cementoblasts* (fig. 19-4E). These cells produce a thin layer of specialized bone, the *cementum*, which is deposited over the dentine of the root. Outside the cement layer, the mesenchyme gives rise to the *periodontal ligament* (fig. 19-4E, F). The fibers of this ligament are embedded in the cementum at one end and in the bony wall of the alveolar socket at the other. Hence, the ligament holds the tooth firmly in position and simultaneously functions as a shock absorber.

With further lengthening of the root, the crown is gradually pushed through the overlying tissue layers into the oral cavity (fig. 19-4E). The eruption of the *deciduous* or *milk teeth* occurs 6 to 24 months after birth.

The buds for the permanent teeth are located on the lingual aspect of the milk teeth and are formed during the third month of development (fig. 19-4B). These buds, which develop in a manner similar to that of the milk teeth, remain dormant until approximately the sixth year of postnatal life. Then they begin to grow, thereby pushing against the underside of the corresponding milk teeth and aiding in their shedding.

Occasionally the two lower central incisors have already erupted at birth. They are then usually abnormally formed and have little enamel and no roots. Although abnormalities of the teeth are mainly hereditary in nature, environmental factors such as rubella, syphilis, and irradiation have been described as causes for tooth anomalies.[8, 9]

## References

1. CUMMINGS, H., AND MIDLO, C. *Fingerprints, Palms and Soles*. Blakiston Co., Division of McGraw-Hill Book Co., Inc., New York, 1943.
2. HALE, A. R. Morphogenesis of volar skin in the human fetus. Amer. J. Anat., **91:** 147, 1952.
3. RAWLES, M. E. Origin of melanophores and their role in development of color patterns in vertebrates. Physiol. Rev., **28:** 383, 1948.
4. BOYD, J. D. The embryology and comparative anatomy of the melanocyte. In *Progress in the Biological Sciences in Relation to Dermatology*, edited by A. Rook. Cambridge University Press, London, 1960.
5. BILLINGHAM, R. E., AND SILVERS, W. K. Melanocytes of mammals. Quart. Rev. Biol., **35:** 1, 1960.
6. PINKUS, H. The embryology of hair. In *Biology of Hairgrowth*, edited by W. Montague and R. A. Ellis. Academic Press, Inc., New York, 1958.
7. ORBAN, B. *Oral Histology and Embryology*, Ed. 4, C. V. Mosby Co., St. Louis, 1957.
8. MILES, A. E. W. Malformations of the teeth. Proc. Roy. Soc. Med., **47:** 817, 1954.
9. TÖNDURY, G. Zur Wirkung des Erregers der Rubeolen auf den Menschlichen Keimling. Helv. Paediat. Acta, **1:** 105, 1952.

# Index

A

Achondroplasia, 96
Acrocephalus, 138
Acrosomic granule, 18, 19
Ala orbitalis, 137
  temporalis, 137
Alar plate, 297, 311, 314
Alisphenoid bone, 137
Alkaline phosphatase, 113
Allantois, 50, 65, 156, 237
Alveoli, 250, 251
Amelia, 89, 138
Ameloblast, 369
Aminopterin, 90
Amnioblast, 39
Amnio-ectodermal junction, 39, 78
Amnion, 78, 80
Amniotic cavity, 39
  fluid, 80
Anal fold, 173, 274
  membrane, 64, 156
Anencephaly, 80, 88, 90, 303, 324
Angioblast, 61
Angiogenetic cell cluster, 61, 183
Annular pancreas, 264, 265
Annulus fibrosis, 134
Anophthalmia, 94, 340
Anorectal canal, 156, 157, 273
Anterior chamber, 338
Antibodies, 91
  transmission of, 77
Antigen-antibody reaction, 113
Antihistamines, 90
Antrum, follicular, 14, 15
Aorta
  coarctation of, 218
  dorsal, 185, 214
  overriding, 208
Aortic arch, 214
  double, 220
  fifth, 215
  first, 214
  fourth, 215
  interrupted, 220
  right, 222
  sixth, 215
Aortic valvular atresia, 210
  stenosis, 210
Aorticopulmonary septum, 199
Aplasia of thyroid gland, 253

Appendicular skeleton, 138
Appendix epididymis, 169
  testis, 169
Appendix, primitive, 269
Aqueduct of Sylvius, 293
Archipallium, 322
Artery
  basal, 32
  carotid
    common, 215
    external, 215
    internal, 215
  coeliac, 218
  hyoid, 214
  iliac
    common, 218
    internal, 218, 275
  intersegmental, 134
  maxillary, 214
  mesenteric
    inferior, 159, 218, 275
    superior, 218, 267
  pulmonary, 214
  spiral, 75
  stapedial, 214
  subclavian, 219
  umbilical, 218
  vesical, superior, 218, 234
  vitelline, 218
Arytenoid swelling, 247
Asian influenza, 88
Astrocyte
  fibrillar, 299
  protoplasmic, 299
Atresia of aorta, 210
  of bile duct, 263
  of cervix, 180
  of esophagus, 80, 253, 254
  of the gut, 89, 271
  of rectum, 275
  of tricuspid valve, 206
  of uterovaginal canal, 179, 180
  of vagina, 180
Atrial septum, abnormalities, 205
Atrichia, 367
Atrioventricular canal, 189, 196
  abnormalities, 206
  persistent, 206
Atrioventricular cushions, 196, 197
Atrium, common, 205

Atrophy, testicular, 95
Auditory meatus, 247, 349, 350
Auricle, 350, 351
Autoimmunization, 91
Autonomic nervous system, 329–332
Autosome, 4
Axial filament, 19
Axon, primitive, 298

B

Basal plate, 136, 297, 307–311, 313, 314
Basilar membrane, 345
Basis pedunculi, 314
Bicornuate uterus, 179
Bilaminar germ disc, 37, 39
Bile duct, 260
  atresia of, 263
Bivalent, 7
Bladder, 156–158
  exstrophy of, 178, 179
Blastocele, 29
Blastocyst, 29
  abnormal, 44
Blastomere, 28
  multinucleated, 33
Blastopore, 111
Blindness, 88
Blood island, 61, 183
  vessel, extra-embryonic, 183
    formation, 183–186
Bone cell, 131
  formation, 130–134
    inhibition of, 90
  hyoid, greater horn, 243
    lesser horn, 242
  periosteal, 131
  spicule, 131
Bowman's capsule, 152, 155
Brain, 290, 306–326
  abnormalities, 323–326
  vesicles, 57, 290
Branchial cyst, 251
  fistula, 253
Bronchus, 250
Buccopharyngeal membrane, 64, 239
Bulboventricular flange, 196
  fold, 189
  sulcus, 189
Bulbus cordis, 189

C

Caecal swelling, 268
Calyx, major, 154
  minor, 154
Cap stage of tooth development, 368
Cardiac abnormalities, 89
Cardiac jelly, 187

Cardiogenic plate, 186
Cardiovascular abnormalities, causes, 211
Carotid body, 323
Carotid duct, 218
Carrier, of trisomy 21, 93
Cartilage, 129
  arytenoid, 243
  cricoid, 243
  elastic, 130
  fibrous, 129
  hyaline, 129
  hypophyseal, 136
  matrix, 129
  Meckel's, 138, 241
  parachordal, 136
  Reichert's, 138, 242
  thyroid, 243
Cataract, congenital, 340, 341
Cauda equina, 302
Caudate nucleus, 321
Cell
  population
    expanding, 122
    renewing, 122
    static, 122
  proliferation, 118, 119, 121
  size, 117, 119, 120
Cementoblast, 370
Cementum, 370
Central canal, 293, 297
Central nervous system, 55, 290
Centriole, 27
Centromere, 7–9, 28
Cephalic flexure, 290
Cerebellar nucleus, 313
  plate, 312
Cerebellum, 293, 310, 312, 313
Cerebral calcification, 87, 88
Cerebral cortex, 321
  hemisphere, 320–322
Chemodifferentiation, 114
Chiasma, 9
Chickenpox, 88
Choanae
  primitive, 357
  definitive, 359
Chondroblast, 59, 129
Chondrocranium, 135
Chondromucoprotein, 120
Chorda-mesoderm tissue, 111
Chordae tendineae, 203
Chorioallantoic membrane, 121
Chorionepithelioma, 44
Chorion frondosum, 74
  laeve, 74
Chorionic cavity, 43
Chorioretinitis, 87, 88
Choroid, 337, 338
  fissure, 334, 339

plexus, 309, 314, 321
Chromaffin cell, 323
Chromatin
  -negative, 94
  -positive, 94
Chromosomal DNA, 115
  pattern, 92
Chromosome, sex, 4
  abnormalities, 94
Ciliary body, 335, 336
Circulatory changes at birth, 232–236
Cleavage, 28, 29
Cleft, facial, oblique, 360
  jaw, upper, 359
  lip, 90, 93, 359, 360
  lateral, 359
  median, 360
  palate, 88, 90, 359, 360
  uvula, 359
  vertebra, 138
Cleidocranial dysostosis, 96
Clitoris, 175
Cloacal fold, 173
  membrane, 64, 273
Cochlea, 345
Cochlear duct, 344, 345
Coelom
  extra-embryonic, 42
  intra-embryonic, 276
Coelomic cavity, 276
Collecting tubule, 153, 154
Colliculus, mesencephalic, 314
Coloboma iridis, 339
Colon, ascending, 269
  mobile, 289
Commissure
  anterior, 322, 323
  habenular, 315, 323
  hippocampal, 323
  posterior, 315, 323
Connecting stalk, 53
Conoventricular flange, 196
Contraceptive, 25
Conus, abnormalities, 208, 209
  cordis, 190, 199
Copula, 247
Cor trilocular biventriculare, 205
Cord, sex, cortical, 166
Corium, 365
Cornea, 337, 338
Corona radiata, 26
Corpus albicans, 25
  atreticum, 24
  graviditatis, 25
Corpus callosum, 323
  striatum, 321
Corpus luteum, 25
Corti, organ of, 86, 345
Corticobulbar tract, 314

Corticopontine tract, 314
Corticospinal tract, 314
Cortisone, 90, 99
Cretinism, 91
Crista ampullaris, 347
Crista dividens, 232
Crossing over, 9
Cross-striated muscle, 141–146
Crown
  -heel length, 69
  -rump length, 66, 69
Crus ampullare, 346
  nonampullare, 346
Cryptorchism, 179
Cumulus oophorus, 14, 15, 23
Cyclopia, 340
Cystic kidney, 158, 159
Cytomegalovirus, 87, 88
Cytotrophoblast, 37, 38, 53, 72

D

Deafness, congenital, 86, 88, 90, 93, 351
Decidua basalis, 74
  capsularis, 74
  parietalis, 74
Decidual plate, 74, 75
  septum, 75
Dendrite
  primitive, 298
  transient, 298
Dental cuticle, 370
  epithelium
    inner, 368
    outer, 368
  lamina, 368
Dentine, 369
Dermis, 61, 364–366
Derepression, 116
Dermatome, 59, 141
Dermis, 61
Dextrocardia, 210
Diabetes, 91
Diakenesis, 9
Diapedesis, 31
Diaphragm, 278
Diaphragmatic hernia, 288
Diaphysis, 132
Dictyotene stage, 13
Diencephalon, 291, 314–320
Differentiation, 110, 112
  gene action in, 116, 117
Digastric, anterior belly of, 242
Digestive tube, 237–275
Dilator pupillae, 146, 336
Diplotene stage, 8
Diverticulum, Meckel's, 266, 269, 270
DNA, chromosomal, 115
  duplication, 4–6

DNA synthesis, 118
Double monster, 82
Douglas' pouch, 33, 34
Down's syndrome, 92
Duct
    endolymphatic, 344
    genital, 167
    lactiferous, 368
    mesonephric, 152, 166, 167
    Müllerian, 167
    nasolacrimal, 355
    omphalomesenteric, 64, 237, 266
    pancreatic, 262, 263
    paramesonephric, 167
    pronephric, longitudinal, 151
    of Santorini, 263
    of Wirsung, 262
Ductuli efferentes, 168
Ductus arteriosus, 216, 232
    closure of, 234
    deferens, 153, 166, 168, 169
    reuniens, 345
    venosus, 226
Duodenum, 258, 259
Dysostosis, cleidocranial, 96

E

Ear, 343
    external, 343, 349–351
    internal, 343–347
    middle, 343, 347–349
Eardrum, 245, 247, 350
ECHO virus, 88
Ectodermal germ layer, 37, 39, 54–57
Ectopia cordis, 211
Ectopic pregnancy, 34
Edinger-Westphal, nucleus of, 314
Embryoblast, 29, 37
Embryology, experimental, 107
Enamel-dentine junction, 370
Enamel layer of teeth, 57
Endbrain, 291
Endocardium, 188
Endochondral ossification, 131–134
Endolymphatic duct, 344
Endometrium, 31, 38, 52
Enterocystoma, 269, 270
Entodermal germ layer, 37, 39, 62–65
Ependymal zone, 294
Epicardial ridge, 247
Epicardium, 188
Epidermis, 364, 365
Epididymis, 169
Epigenesis, 108
Epigenital tubule, 168
Epiglottis, 247

Epimere, 141
Epiphyseal plate, 133
Epiploic foramen of Winslow, 281
Epispadia, 178
Epithalamus, 315
Epitrichium, 364
Epoophoron, 173
Erythrocyte mosaism, 81
Erythropoiesis, 121
Esophagus, 250, 257
    atresia of, 253–254
Estrogenic hormone, 25, 78
Ethmoid, bone, 136
Eustachian tube, 245, 347, 348
Eventration, abdominal viscera, 271
Excretory system, 155, 156
    formation of, 149, 150
Exocoelomic cavity, 39
    cyst, 43
Extra-embryonic coelom, 42
    vascular system, 73
Extra-uterine pregnancy, 34
Extremities, defects of, 88
Eye, 333
    abnormalities, 339–341

F

Face, development, 354–359
    abnormalities, 359–362
Facial cleft, oblique, 360
    swelling, 354, 355
Fallopian tube, 26, 29, 170
    abdominal ostium, 170
Fertility, 20
Fertilization, 26–28
Fetal membranes, 72–76
    period, 69, 98
    portion of placenta, 74
    weight, 71
Fibrinoid, 78
Filum terminale internum, 302
Fistula
    branchial, 252
    esophagotracheal, 253, 254
    pre-auricular, 252, 253
    thyroglossal, 253
    umbilical, 269
    vitelline, 269, 270
Flagellum, 19
Flocculonodular lobe, 312
Flocculus, 312
Floor plate, 297
Follicle, Graafian, 13–15
    primordial, 13, 24
Follicular antrum, 14, 15
    cell, 13–15, 116

Fontanelle, 138
Foramen caecum, 248
    epiploic, of Winslow, 281
    interventricular, primary, 190, 198
    of Luschka, 309
    of Magendie, 309
    magnum, 137
    of Monro, 314
Forebrain, 290
Foregut, 64, 237
Forelimb, 66
Fornix, vaginal, 172
Frontal prominence, 354

G

Galactosemia, 96
Gall bladder, 259-262
    atresia, 263
Gamete, abnormal, 19
Gametogenesis, 3
Gamma-globulin, 77
Ganglion cell layer, 335
    coeliac, 330
    mesenteric, 330
    pre-aortic, 330, 331
Gargoylism, 97
Gärtner's cyst, 173
Gastrointestinal tract, duplication, 271
Gastrula stage, 109
Gene abnormalities, 96
    action in protein synthesis, 115, 144
        in differentiation, 116, 117
    recessive, 97
    regulator, 116
Genital ridge, 163
    swelling, 174
    system, 163-181
        congenital malformations, 177-181
    tubercle, 173
Genitalia
    in female, 175
    in male, 174, 175
    masculinization, 90
Germ disc, bilaminar, 37, 39
    germ layer
        ectodermal, 37, 39, 54-57
        entodermal, 37, 39, 62-65
        mesodermal, 47, 58-62
German measles, 86, 87
Gland
    parathyroid
        inferior, 245
        superior, 245, 246
    para-urethral, 158
    parotid, 309
    suprarenal, 331

Glans penis, 175
Glia cell, 297, 299
Gliablast, 299
Globus pallidus, 321
Glomerulus, 150, 164
Glycoprotein, 13
Golgi II neuron, 313
Gonad, 163
Gonadal dysgenesis, 95
    ridge, 163
Gonadotropic hormone, 25
Gonadotropins, 78
Graafian follicle, 13, 15, 23
Gray matter of spinal cord, 296
Ground substance, 129
Growth regulation, 117-123
Gubernaculum testis, 176
Gut
    abnormalities, 251-255
    atresia, 271
    stenosis, 271
Gynecomastia, 95
Gyrus, 322

H

Habenular commissure, 315, 323
Habenular nucleus, 315
Hair, 366, 367
    lanugo, 367
    shaft, 366
    sheath, 366
Haploid number, 6, 9
Head cap, 18, 19
    fold, 63
    process, 49
Heart
    development, abnormal, 205-211
    loop, 188
    tube, bulboventricular portion of, 188
Hematopoietic function, 261
Hemisphere, 320-322, 312
    primitive, 291
Hemochorial placenta, 77
Henle, loop of, 156
Hensen's node, 46, 290
Hepatic diverticulum, 259
    flexure, 269
    sinusoid, 224
Hepatitis, 88
Hepatocardiac channel, 224
Hepato-splenomegaly, 87
Hepato-subcardinal anastomosis, 226
Hermaphrodite, 180
Hernia
    esophageal, 289
    inguinal, 179
    parasternal, 288

Hernia—*continued*
  retrocolic, 289
  umbilical cord, 270, 271
Heterozygous, 96
Heuser's membrane, 29
Hindbrain, 290
Hindgut, 64, 237, 273–275
  abnormalities, 275
Hindlimbs, 66
Hippocampus, 321
Histone, 116
Homocystinuria, 96
Homologous pair, 4
Homozygous, 96
Hormones, 90
Hyaluronidase, 26
Hydatidiform mole, 44
Hydramnios, 80, 324
Hydrocele, 179
Hydrocephalus, 88, 90, 97, 324, 325
Hymen, 173
Hyoid arch, 242
  bone, body, 242
  greater horn, 243
Hypertrichosis, 367
Hypobranchial eminence, 247
Hypoglossal canal, 136
Hypomere, 141
Hypophyseal cartilage, 136
Hypophysis, 57, 319, 320
  anterior lobe, 319
  posterior lobe, 320
Hypoplasia
  of ovary, 180
  of thyroid, 253
Hypospadia, 177
Hypothalamic sulcus, 317
Hypothalamus 317
Hypoxia, 92

I

Ichthyosis, 366
Implantation, 28
  abnormal, 33
Incisive foramen, 359
Incus, 138, 242, 348
Induction, 107–112
Inductive agents, 110
Inductor, 109
Infracardiac bursa, 283
Infrahyoid musculature, 142
Infundibular stenosis, 208
Infundibulum, 319
Inheritance
  autosomal dominant, 96
    recessive, 97
  sex-linked, 96, 97
Insula, 322

Insulin, 100
Integumentary system, 364
Intercellular material, 120
Intermaxillary segment, 355, 356
Intermediate mesoderm, 59, 61
Intermuscular septum, 141
Interseptovalvular space, 195
Intersexuality, 180
Interstitial cell of Leydig, 166
Interthalamic connexus, 317
Interventricular foramen of Monro, 293, 320
Interventricular septum
  abnormalities, 206–208
  membranous part, 201
Intestinal loop
  abnormal rotation, 271
  reversed rotation, 271
  primitive, mesentery, 285–287
Intracardiac shunting, 205
Intraretinal space, 333
Intervertebral disc, 134
Intervillous space, 73
Intestinal atresia, 89
Intra-embryonic coelomic cavity, 58
Invagination, 47
Iodine deficiency, 91
Iridopupillary membrane, 338
  persistent, 339, 340
Iris, 335, 336

J

Jaw, upper, cleft, 359
Jelly
  cardiac, 187
  of Wharton, 80
Junction
  amnio-ectodermal, 78
  atrioventricular, 189
  enamel-dentine, 370

K

Kernicterus, 87, 90
Kidney
  ascent of, 156
  horseshoe, 159
  pelvic, 159
Klinefelter's syndrome, 95

L

Labia majora, 174, 175
  minora, 175
Labyrinth
  bony, 344
  membranous, 344
Lactiferous duct, 368

Lamina terminalis, 320, 322
Lanugo hair, 367
Laryngeal orifice, 247, 250
Lateral plate, 58
Lens, 109, 337
  fibers, primary, 337
  nucleus, 337
  placode, 57, 113, 114, 335
  vesicle, 57, 333–335
Lentiform nucleus, 321
Leptotene stage, 7, 13
Leydig, interstitial cell of, 166
Ligament
  coronary, 281
  falciform, 260, 261, 281
  gastrolienal, 284
  genital, caudal, 176
  periodontal, 370
  sphenomandibular, 242
  spiral, 345
  stylohyoid, 242
  suspensory, ovary, 177
  umbilical, medial, 157
    broad, of the uterus, 171
    round, 177
  vesico-umbilical, lateral, 218, 234
Ligamentum arteriosum, 234
  teres hepatis, 226, 234, 281
  venosum, 226, 234
Limb bud, 143, 144
Lingual swelling, lateral, 247
Lip, cleft, 90, 93, 359, 360
  upper, 354, 355
Liver, 259–262
  bare area of, 261, 281
Lobster claw, 96, 139
Loop of Henle, 156
Lung, 250
  abnormalities, 254, 255
  buds, 250
  congenital cyst, 254
  lobe, ectopic, 254
Luteal cell, 25

M

Macrostomia, 360
Maculae acousticae, 347
Malformations, congenital, 84
  chromosomal factors, 92–98
  environmental factors, 86–92
    antibodies, 91
    chemical agents, 89, 90
    drugs, 89, 90
    hormones, 90, 91
    infectious agents, 86–89
    nutritional deficiencies, 91, 92
  etiology, 85–98

genetic factors, 92–98
incidence, 84, 85
  race, 85
Malleus, 138, 242, 348
Mammary gland, 367, 368
  ridge, 367
Mammillary body, 317
Mandible, 242
Mandibular arch, 241
  process, 241
  swelling, 354
Massa intermedia, 317
Maturation division, 3, 6, 16, 18
Maternal portion of placenta, 74
Maxillary process, 138, 241
  swelling, 354
Measles, 88
  German, 86, 87
Meatus, auditory, 247, 349, 350
Meckel's cartilage, 138, 241
  diverticulum, 266, 269, 270
Medulla oblongata, 293
Medullary velum
  anterior, 313
  posterior, 313
Melanin, 365
Melanoblast, 365
Membrane
  basilar, 345
  buccopharyngeal, 64, 239
  chorioallantoic, 121
  cloacal, 64, 273
  Heuser's 39
  oronasal, 357
  pleuropericardial, 278, 280
  pleuroperitoneal, 280
  Reissner's, 345
  tectorial, 345
  tympanic, 245, 350
  urogenital, 64, 156, 274
  vestibular, 345
Membranous ossification, 130, 131, 136
Meningocele, 90, 303, 323, 324
Meningo-encephalitis, 87
Meningo-encephalocele, 323, 324
Meningohydro-encephalocele, 323, 324
Meningomyelocele, 303
Menstrual bleeding, 24, 25
Mental retardation, 86, 88, 93, 95
Meprobamate, 90
Mesencephalon, 290, 313, 314
Mesentery, 276, 281–288
  abnormalities, 288, 289
  dorsal, 281, 282
  proper, 282, 285–287
  ventral, 281
Mesocolon, 282
Mesoderm
  intermediate, 59, 61, 149

Mesoderm—*continued*
  intra-embryonic, 145
  layer
    somatic, 276
    splanchnic, 276
  paraxial, 58
  somatopleuric, 42
  splanchnopleuric, 42
Mesoduodenum, dorsal, 282, 285
Mesogastrium
  dorsal, 282
  ventral, 261
Mesonephric duct, 152, 166, 167
Mesonephros, 150–153
Metabolism, inborn errors, 96
Metanephric blastema, 153
Metanephros, 150, 153–156
Metencephalon, 293, 310–313
Microcephaly, 87, 88, 138
Microglia cell, 299
Micrognathia, 93
Micromelia, 139
Microphthalmia, 86, 88, 94, 340
Microstomia, 360
Microvilli, 76
Midbrain, 290
Middle ear cavity, 245
Midgut, 64, 237, 266–271
  abnormalities, 269–271
Miotic division, 3, 6
  abnormal, 9–11
  first, 6–9
  second, 9
Mitosis, 4, 5
Mitotic phase, 118
Mixed bone spicule, 131
Modiolus, 345
Mole, hydatidiform, 44
Monosomy, 10, 92
Morula, 28
Mosaicism, 95
  erythrocyte, 81
Motor column
  somatic efferent, 308
  special visceral efferent, 307, 308, 310
Müllerian duct, 167
  tubercle, 168
Muscle
  abdominis, rectus, 142
  ciliary, 336
  constrictor of the pharynx, 243
  cricothyroid, 243
  digastric, posterior belly of, 243
  dilator pupillae, 146, 336
  facial expression, 243
  intercostal, 141, 142
  mastication, 242
  papillary, 203
  pupillary, 336

regeneration, 146
sphincter pupillae, 146, 336
stapedius, 243, 349
sternalis, 142
stylohyoid, 243
stylopharyngeal, 243
Musculature
  infrahyoid, 144
  limb, 143–146
  pharyngeal arch, 146
Mutation, 97
Myelencephalon, 293, 306–309
Myelination, 301
Myelocele, 303
Myoblast, 141
Myocardium, 188
Myoepicardial mantle, 187
Myometrium, 173
Myotome, 60, 141, 142
  occipital, 142, 143
  preotic, 142, 143

N

Nasal chambers, 357–359
  pit, 354
  placode, 354
  swellings, 354
Nasolacrimal duct, 355
Neopallium, 322
Nephric tubule, 149
Nephrogenic cord, 61, 149, 150
Nephron, 155, 156
Nephrotome, 61, 149
Nerve,
  abducens, 310
  accessory, 308
  facial, 243, 310
  glossopharyngeal, 243, 248
  hypoglossal, 308
  laryngeal, 243, 244, 248
  medial, 145
  oculomotor, 313
  optic, 339
  phrenic, 280
  radial, 144
  spinal, 298, 300
  trigeminal, 310
  trochlear, 313
  ulnar, 145
  vagus, 309, 311
Nervous system
  autonomic, 329–332
  central, 55, 290
  parasympathetic, 329, 332
Neural crest, 300
  groove, 55, 290
  plate, 55, 290
  tube, 55, 290

Neurenteric canal, 50
Neurilemma cell, 301
Neuroblast, 295, 298
  apolar, 298
  bipolar, 298
  multipolar, 298
  sympathetic, 329
Neurocranium, 135–138
Neuroepithelial cell, 294
Neuron, 298
  association, 298
  Golgi II, 313
Neuropore
  anterior, 55, 290
  posterior, 55, 290
Nicotinamide, 100
Nipple, inverted, 368
Node of Hensen, 46, 290
Nodule, 312
Nondisjunction, 10, 93
Nose, 354
  abnormalities, 359–362
Notocord, 50, 134
Notochordal process, 49
Nucleoprotein, 110
Nucleus
  ambiguus, 308
  caudate, 321
  cerebellar, deep, 313
  Edinger-Westphal, 314
  lentiform, 321
  pontine, 311
  pulposus, 134
  ruber, 314
  salivatory, 309, 310

O

Occipital somite, 136
  tectum, 136
Odontoblast, 368
Oligodendroglia cell, 299
Olivary nuclear complex, 309
Omental bursa, 258, 282
Omentum
  greater, 284
  lesser, 261, 281
Omphalocele, 270, 271
Omphalomesenteric duct, 64, 237, 266
Oocyte, 3
  mature, 9
  primary, 13
  secondary, 15
Oogenesis, 12–16
Oogonia, 12
Optic chiasma, 323
  cup, 333–335
  vesicle, 57, 109, 333
Orbitosphenoid bone, 137

Organ of Corti, 86, 345
Organizer, primary, 109
Oronasal membrane, 357
Ossicle, 348, 349
Ossification
  endochondral, 131–134
  membranous, 130, 131, 136
Osteoblast, 59, 130, 131
Osteoclast, 131
Osteocyte, 131
Osteogenesis, imperfecta, 96
Osteoid, 130
Ostium
  primum, 194
    defect, 206
  secundum, 195
    defect 195, 205
Otic pit, 57
  placode, 57
  vesicle, 57, 137
Otitis media, 348
Oval foramen, 196
  closure of, 234
    premature, 205
  probe patency of, 196, 205
Ovarian cycle, 24
  hyplasia, 180
  medulla, 166
Ovary, 166, 167
Oviduct, 168, 170
Ovulation, 23

P

Pachytene stage, miosis, 7, 8
Palaeopallium, 322
Palate, 354
  cleft, 88, 90, 359, 360
  primary, 355, 356
  secondary, 356
Pallium, 321
Pancreatic bladder, 265
  bud
    dorsal, 262
    ventral, 262
  duct
    accessory, 263
    common, 262
  islets, 263
  tissue, heterotopic, 265
Papilla
  dental, 368
  dermal, 365
Paradidymis, 169
Paragenital tubule, 169
Paramesonephric duct, 167
Paraphysis, 315
Parasympathetic nervous system, 329, 332
Parathyroid gland, 245, 246

Para-urethral gland, 158
Paraxial mesoderm, 58
Parietal mesoderm layer, 58, 61
Paroophoron, 173
Parotid gland, 309
Parthenogenesis, 32
Parturition, 78
Patent ductus arteriosus, 218
Peduncle, middle cerebellar, 311
Penis, divided, 178
Pericardial cavity, 61, 184, 278, 280
Pericardioperitoneal canal, 278
Pericardium, 187, 188, 280
Perichondrium, 131
Periderm, 364
Perineal body, 156
Perineum, 274
Periosteum, 131
Periotic capsule, 137
Peritoneal cavity, 61
    sac, lesser, 282
Perivitelline space, 27
Phallus, 174
Pharyngeal arches, 239, 241–244
    clefts, 239, 247
    pouches, 239, 244–247
    musculature, 146
Pharyngotympanic tube, 245
Pharynx, 237, 239
Phenocopies, 97
Phenylketonuria, 96
Phocomelia, 89, 139
Physiological umbilical hernia, 79, 266
Pia mater, 309
Pigment layer of retina, 335
Pineal body, 315
Pinocytosis, 77
Pituicyte, 320
Placenta, 29, 72–78
    praevia, 34
Placental barrier, 77
Placode, lens 57
    otic, 57
Pleural cavity, 61, 278, 280
Pleuropericardial membrane, 278, 280
    ridge, 279
Pleuroperitoneal fold, 279
    membrane, 280
Pneumato-enteric recess, 282
Polar body, 9, 15
Poliomyelitis, 88
Polymastia, 368
Polythelia, 368
Pons, 293, 310, 311
Pontine flexure, 293
Post-ganglionic fiber, 331
Potassium iodide, 90
Prebone, 130
Precartilage, 129

Predentine, 368
Preformation, 108
Pregnancy
    ectopic, 34
    extra-uterine, 34
    ovarian, 34
    tubal, 34
Primordial follicle, 13, 24
    germ cell, 11, 163, 164
Probe patency, oval foramen, 196, 205
Proboscis, 340
Process, head, 49
    notochordal, 49
Prochordal plate, 44, 49, 185
Proctodeum, 274
Progestational compounds, 25
Progesterone, 25, 30, 78
Progestin, 90
Proliferative phase, endometrium, 32
Prometaphase, 5
Pronephric duct, longitudinal, 151
Pronephros, 150, 151
Pronucleus
    female, 27
    male, 27
Prophase, 5
Prosencephalon, 290
Prostate gland, 158
Protein synthesis, 115, 144
Proteolytic enzyme, 30
Pseudohermaphroditism, 180
Pteroylglutamic acid deficiency, 99
Pulmonary channel, 198
Pulp of tooth, 269
Pupil, 335
Purine group, 5
Purkinje cell, 313
Putamen, 321
Pyloric part, stomach. 258
    stenosis, 263
Pyramidal cell, 322
Pyrimidine group, 5
Pyruvic acid, 100

Q

Quinine, 90

R

Rachischisis, 303
Radiation, 88, 89
Ramus, communicating
    gray, 331
    white, 331
Rathke's pouch, 319
Rectal atresia, 275
    fistula, 275

Reduced penetrance of gene, 97
Regeneration, muscle, 146
Regulator gene, 116
Reichert's cartilage, 138, 242
Reissner's membrane, 345
Renal agensis, 159, 160
    pyramid, 154
Repressor, 116
Resorption, osteoclastic, 134
Respiratory diverticulum, 249
    system, 249–251
Retardation, mental, 86, 88, 93, 95
Rete testis, 164
Retina, 335, 336
Rh-incompatibility, 77
Rhombencephalic isthmus, 293
Rhombencephalon, 290
Rhombic lip, 311
Ribonuclease, 112
Ribonucleic acid, 115
Ridge
    epicardial, 247
    genital, 163
    gonadal, 163
Ring, umbilical, primitive, 78
RNA, 112
    messenger, 115
    transfer, 115
Rods, 335
Roof plate, 297, 309, 314, 315
Rubella, 86, 87
    antibody, 87
    vaccine, 87

S

Saccule, 344, 345
Salivatory nucleus, 309, 310
Santorini, duct, 263
Scala tympani, 345
    vestibuli, 345
Schwann cell, 301
Sclera, 337, 338
Sclerotome, 59, 134
Scrotal swelling, 174
Sebaceous gland, 367
Sella turcica, 136
Semicircular canal, 344, 346, 347
Seminal vesicle, 169
Seminiferous tubule, 17
    hyalinization, 95
Septum
    cardiac, formation, 193–201
        in atrioventricular canal, 194–197
        in atrium, 194–197
        in conus cordis, 198–201
        in truncus arteriosus, 198–201
        in ventricles, 197, 198
    esophagotracheal, 249

interventricular, membranous part of,
    201
    pellucidum, 323
    scrotal, 175
    secundum, 195
    spurium, 193
    transversum, 259, 278
Sertoli cell, 17, 166
Sex chromatin, 181
    chromosome, 4
        abnormalities, 94
    cord, cortical, 166
        primitive, 17, 164
Sinovaginal bulb, 171
Sinu-atrial fold, 192
Sinus, coronary, 193
    horn, 192
    urogenital, 156, 273
    venosus, 192, 188
Sinusoid, hepatic, 224
Sirenomelia, 139
Situs inversus, 210
Skeletal system, 129
Skelton, appendicular, abnormalities, 138
Skin, 364–366
Skull, 135–138
    defects, 88, 138
Smoking, 90
Smooth musculature, 146
Solitary tract, 309, 311
Somatic mesoderm layer, 58, 61
Somite, 58, 59
    occipital, 136
Sperm, head cap, 18, 19
Spermatid, 18
Spermatocyte
    primary, 18
    secondary, 18
Spermatogenesis, 17, 18
Spermatogonia, 17, 18
Spermatozoon, 3, 19, 26, 179
Spermiogenesis, 18, 19
Sphenoid bone, 136, 137
Sphincter pupillae, 146, 336
Spina bifida, 88, 303, 304
Spinal cord, 55, 290, 294–304
    abnormalities, 302–304
    gray matter, 296
    mantle layer, 294–296
    marginal layer, 294–296
    neuroepithelial layer, 294–296
    positional changes, 301, 302
    white matter, 296
Spicule
    bone, 131
    mixed, 131
Spiral limbus, 345
Splanchnic mesoderm layer, 58, 61
Stapes, 138, 242, 348

Stato-acoustic ganglion, 345
Stellate reticulum, 368
Stenosis
    aortic valvular, 210
    of gut, 271
    infundibular, 208
    pyloric, 263
    subaortic, 210
Sterility, 95
Stomach, 257, 258
Stomodeum, 354
Streptomycin, 90
Subaortic stenosis, 210
Subarachnoidal space, 309
Substantia nigra, 314
Sulcus limitans, 297
Sulphonurea derivatives, 90
Sustentacular cell of Sertoli, 17, 166
Suture, 137
Sympathetic chain, 329
Sympodia, 139
Syncytial giant cell, 75
Syncytiotrophoblast, 37, 38
Syndactyly, 93, 139
Syphilis, 88

T

Tail fold, 63
Tectorial membrane, 345
Tela choroidea, 309
Telencephalon, 291, 320–323
Tensor tympani, 242, 349
Teratogens, susceptibility to, 98
Testicular atrophy, 95
Testis, 164–166
    cord, 164
    descent of, 175–177
Tetracycline, 90
Tetralogy of Fallot, 208
Thalamus, 317
Thalidomide, 89, 139
Theca externa, 15
    interna, 15
Thymus, 245
Thyroglossal duct, 248
Thyroid gland
    aberrant, 253
    aplasia, 249, 253
    lateral, 246
Tissue inductor, 108, 110–112
Tongue, 247–248
    musculature, 143
Tonsil, palatine, 245
Tooth, 368
    deciduous, 370
    enamel layer, 57
    milk, 370
Toxoplasmosis, 88, 325

Trachea, 250
Translocation, 93
Transplantation, 121
Tricuspid atresia, 206
Trigone of the bladder, 157
Trilaminar germ disc, 46–52
Triple-X syndrome, 95, 96
Trisomy, X, 92
    13-15, 92–94
    17-18, 92, 93
    21, 92, 93
Trophoblast, 29, 37, 51, 72
Tropocollagen, 120
Trunco-aortic sac, 199
Truncus
    abnormalities, 208, 209
    arteriosus, 190
        persistent, 209
    septum, 198
Tube
    Eustachian, 245, 347, 348
    Fallopian, 170
Tuberculum impar, 247
Tubotympanic recess, 244, 347
Tubule
    collecting, 154
    convoluted, 156
    epigenital, 168
    paragenital, 169
    seminiferous, 17, 166
Tubulus rectus, 166
    contortus, 166
Tunica albuginea testis, 165, 166
    vaginalis, 177
Turner's syndrome, 95, 180
Twins, 80–83
    conjoined, 82
    dizygotic, 80
    monozygotic, 81
Tympanic cavity, 245, 347, 348

U

Ultimobranchial body, 246
Umbilical cord, 53, 78–80
    congenital hernia into, 270, 271
    herniation, physiological, 266
Urachal cyst, 160, 161
    fistula, 160, 161
Urachus, 157
Ureter, double, 160
Ureteric bud, 153
Urethra, 156–158
    membranous, 157
    penile, 157
    prostatic, 157
Urethral fold, 173
    gland, 158
    plate, 174

384                                                                  Index

Urinary bladder, 156
Urogenital groove, 174
    membrane, 64, 156, 274
    mesentery, 152, 175
    ridge, 152
    sinus, 157, 171, 273
    system, 148
Urorectal septum, 156, 273
Uteroplacental circulation, 41
Uterovaginal canal, 167, 171
    atresia of, 179, 180
    duplication of, 179, 180
Uterus, 168
    arcuatus, 179
    bicornis unicollis, 180
    bicornuate, 179
    didelphys, 179
Utricle, 344, 346, 347
Utriculus prostaticus, 169

V

Vaccine, rubella, 87
Vagina, 168
    atresia, 180
Valve
    atrioventricular, 202, 203
    bicuspid, 203
    coronary sinus, 193
    inferior vena cava, 193
    mitral, 203
    semilunar, 203, 204
    tricuspid, 203
    venous, 193
Vasa efferentia, 166
Vascular abnormalities, 86
Vascular ring, 220
Vein,
    azygos, 227
    branchiocephalic, left, 227
    cardinal, 224, 226–228
        anterior, 224, 227
        common, 192, 224
        posterior, 224
    gonadal, left, 226
    hemiazygos, 227
    iliac, left common, 226
    intercostal, left superior, 227
    mesenteric, superior, 224
    oblique, of Marshall, 193
    omphalomesenteric, 192, 224
    portal, 224
    pulmonary, 228, 229
    renal, left, 226
    sacrocardinal, 226
    subcardinal, 226
    supracardinal, 227
    umbilical, 192, 224–226

    closure of, 234
    vitelline, 192, 224, 225
Vena cava
    inferior, 225
        absence of, 229, 230
        double, 229
    superior, 228
        double, 230
Venous drainage
    abnormal, 229–231
    pulmonary, abnormal, 230, 231
Ventral fissure, 297
Ventricle
    fourth, 293
    lateral, 293, 320
    left, 190, 197, 200
    right, definitive, 190, 197, 200
Ventricular septum, muscular, 198
Vermis, 312
Vernix caseosa, 72, 365
Vertebral body, 134
    column, 134, 135
        abnormalities, 138
Vesicle
    auditory, 343
    brain, 57
    lens, 57, 333–335
    optic, 57, 109, 333
    optic, 57, 137, 343–345
    seminal, 169
Vestibular membrane, 345
Vestibule, 157, 175
Vestibulocochlear complex, 311
Villus
    secondary, 72
    stem
        primary, 42, 52
        secondary, 53
Virus, ECHO, 88
Viscerocranium, 135, 138
Vitelline duct, 64, 78, 237, 266
    remnants of, 269, 270
Vitreous body, 338

W

Webbed neck, 95
Weight, fetal, 71
White matter, spinal cord, 296
Winslow, epiploic foramen of, 281
Wirsung, duct, 262
Wolffian duct, 152, 166, 167

X

X-chromosome, 4

Y

Y-chromosome, 4
Yolk sac, 237
  definitive, 43
  primary, 39
  secondary, 43

Z

Zona pellucida, 15, 26
  reaction, 26
Zygote, 3, 28, 29
  abnormal, 33
Zygotene stage, miosis, 7, 13